A WORLD OF CHANCE

OR

WHENCE, WHITHER, AND WHY?

BY

EDWARD GLEASON SPAULDING

MCCOSH PROFESSOR OF PHILOSOPHY, PRINCETON UNIVERSITY

NEW YORK

THE MACMILLAN COMPANY

1936

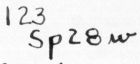

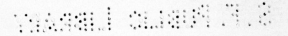

PREFACE

This book, as I would have the title suggest, is a defense of, or an argument for, a thorough-going Indeterministic position as regards the Structure of Reality, to include in the meaning of this term not only Nature, but also that realm of fact which is not part of Nature, but of which, conversely, Nature itself is an instance. By Indeterminism I mean the absence of Necessity, either causal or logical, or any other kind,—if there is any other than these two kinds,—and, positively, the presence of Chance or Contingency. Instances of Necessity, *i.e.*, limited "fields" or realms within which there are "connections" that are characterized by Necessity, I do find, but that the "occurrence" itself of such fields is necessitated, or that there are necessary connections between these "fields," I do not find. Accordingly, I discover that Contingency, or Chance, "runs," as it were, or is present, in this sense, throughout the whole of Reality, whatever this term may comprise and denote, and I find that it denotes much more than what is usually called Nature, *i.e.*, much more than what is contained within those realms of phenomena or of facts that are usually designated as Inorganic, Organic or Vital, Psychological and Social.

Chance, as I thus use the term, does not have quite its usual meaning, which is in connection with the term, Probability. According to this more frequent meaning, Chance *is* Probability. Thus, *e.g.*, to take a familiar example, that of the tossing of a coin, we say that there are equal *chances* both of heads and of tails, but no certainty, even in any finite number of throws, of either. *Chance*, as thus used, even though its "abstract principles" may be *a priori*, is, in its application, quite empirical, *i.e.*, the chance or probability of any particular "event" is determined in terms of the frequency with which, in a large number of "trials," that "event" occurs. On this basis, as is well known, there is empirically discoverable a certain regularity and uniformity in the behavior of groups of "individuals," whether, (1), these individuals are "connected" in accordance with some principle of necessity (*e.g.*, causation), of whose precise character we are, nevertheless, ignorant, or, (2), there is no such objective connection. It is such an application of the general Theory of Probability that is made, *e.g.*, in Modern Physics, when causal laws are identified with generalizations from empirical observations of the regularity and uniformity of the behavior of *groups* of "individuals" which *as individuals* may or may not "act" with regularity (causal), but with it impossible, for one reason or another, to ascertain empirically which of these two possibilities is realized.

Chance, then, may have three meanings. It may mean, (1), the presence of an objective Indeterminism, (2), the presence of an objective Determinism, with, however, no knowledge, *i.e.*, ignorance, of the precise nature of this, and, (3), the probability, as based on observed frequencies, of any particular phenomenon occurring or not occurring.

Now, in writing a book with the title, *A World of Chance*, I am primarily interested not in the second or third of these meanings, but in the first, although in a much broader or wider sense than, perhaps, my example would indicate. What I wish to establish is, that, whether or not there is an objective Indeterminism in Nature, especially in the sub-atomic realm, as this is accepted by most physicists today, not only is such an Indeterminism possible, but also, whether it is merely possible, or also actual, it is but a special case of a Principle that has a much wider application. And this is, indeed, what I find. Defining Chance or Contingency as the absence of both Necessity and Impossibility, I discover not only that there is Chance throughout Nature, here and there, but also throughout the whole Structure of Reality of which Nature itself is but an instance, and, at that, only a chance-instance. In other words, Nature itself, and all that it contains, is only "one deal of the cards." It *is*, but it need not be. It is one possibility out of many, but there is no necessity why this particular possibility should be realized. Indeed, one may go further, and say, that there is no necessity why there should be even that objective realm of possibilities, one of which, as realized, *is* nature. This realm also, quite as much as Nature, is contingent. Indeed, the whole of Reality, as including Nature, Logical Entities, Values, etc., etc., is this. In brief, there is no necessity for there being anything at all.

As the foregoing statements would, perhaps, indicate, the purpose of my book is not the negative one of engaging in controversy, but, rather, the positive one of developing a constructive position. My method is that of Rational Inquiry; the outcome of that inquiry, a thorough-going Realism as regards my Theory of Knowledge, and an equally thorough-going Indeterminism as regards the Structure of Reality. Discussing, as I do, problems as to the nature of Mind, of Society, of Evolution, as well as problems that concern Relativity and the Principle of Indeterminacy in Physics, I may also say that, in writing the book, I have had in mind not so much the college student as the general reader who is interested in the broader, or the philosophical, aspects of these subjects.

As concerns both my method and my results I, of course, do not expect universal agreement. Few books, if any, least of all those in the field of Philosophy, are so unfortunate as to receive this; so disagreement and criticism I shall not only anticipate, but also welcome, for I shall then feel that, if I have done nothing else, I have at least stimulated further Rational Inquiry in the special field of investigation with which my book is concerned.

Because of both the technical and, perhaps, also, the rather radical character of much of my material, I have asked some of my colleagues to read certain parts of my manuscript. Professor DeWitt Parker of the Department of Philosophy of the University of Michigan, and Dr. Paul Henle of Smith College, have read the Introduction and the first four chapters, Dr. J. B. Rosser, of the Department of Mathematics of Princeton University, has read the Introduction and the first eight chapters, and Professor Alonzo Church, of the same Department, has read Chapters II, III, IV, VI, and VII. Dr. Henle and Dr. Rosser have expressed themselves as being in essential agreement with the chapters they have read. Professor Parker, while agreeing in general with the detailed distinctions I have made, finds all of these to be within the realm of Experience,—a position, however, to which I have, in anticipation, as it were, given a reply in Chapter III. Professor Church's chief criticism concerns my violation, under certain circumstances, of the Theory of Types, but to his criticism there is a reply in Chapters III and IV.

To all of these colleagues I am indebted for a number of suggestions and criticisms.

I also wish to acknowledge the assistance which Dr. Owen N. Hillman, of Princeton University, has given me in the reading of the proofs.

In conclusion I wish to express my gratitude to both the Department of Philosophy and the President and Board of Trustees of Princeton University for having granted me a "half-year's" leave of absence in order that I might complete the writing of this book.

EDWARD GLEASON SPAULDING

PRINCETON, N. J.
January 15, 1936.

CONTENTS

INTRODUCTION

I offer this volume as the result of an endeavor to make a synthesis of some of the more important results of research in Modern Logic (Symbolic), in the Physical Sciences (Relativity and Indeterminacy), in Biology, and in certain aspects of the Theory of Knowledge and the Theory of Values. Since it has been my effort to make such a synthesis, the book makes no pretensions to completeness in any of these fields. It is not a Logic, it is not a Physics, nor is it a Biology, an Epistemology, or a Theory of Value. It could not possibly be all of these, and it has been my purpose not to make it any one of them. These sciences (if Epistemology and the Theory of Value may, by courtesy, be called sciences) have been drawn upon in order to construct a Philosophy, or, more specifically, in order to obtain an account of the Structure of Reality. Such an account I call a Metaphysics.

Each one of these sciences has been drawn upon, because each, I find, makes its contribution to Metaphysics, either by way of the special results obtained in its domain, or by way of its presuppositions, or both, and also by way of the relation of the subject-matter of each science to that of others.

The main thesis of the book is, as my title indicates, that this is "A World of Chance," by which I mean that Chance or Contingency runs through and through the entire universe. By "the universe" I mean, of course, *the entire realm of fact*, and this realm I find to be very extensive. It includes *facts of a great many different kinds*, or, of a great many orders. In using this term (fact), I intentionally disclaim the logical possibility, in Philosophy, of ultimately taking any other position than a Realistic one. It may be possible, and, indeed, I think it is possible, logically to develop positions, such as Pragmatism and Phenomenalism, that are opposed to Realism up to a certain point, but I shall maintain that, beyond that point, all these (opposed) positions rest in a larger frame of Realism. I shall, therefore, frankly accept and defend a Realistic, or Spectator Theory of Knowledge.

Facts are found, not made or constructed, and one fact which is found is that there is a *structure* of facts, this structure consisting of facts related (= another fact) in various ways (= still other facts). *Among* the facts which Logic, Physics, Biology, the Theory of Knowledge, and the Theory of Value find, or with which they deal,—and I herewith tentatively grant that there may be other kinds of fact,— are those facts that are called *properties* or *qualities*. Properties or Qualities are illustrated by,—to take examples at random from different fields,—Necessity, Impossibility, and Negation (Negativity) from Logic; Relativity, Indeterminacy, and Irreversibility from Physics; Reproductivity from Biology; and Relatedness from Epistemology. Some of these may seem strange; if they do, then one may add such possibly more familiar properties as Impenetrability, Redness, Spaciality, Temporality.

I shall carry out my program from the standpoint of Properties or Qualities or Functions, using these terms synonymously, and also in a very general, but still in a very specific sense. A *property* I shall define as that which something may have or possess, and, conversely, I shall say that, whatever is "something," *i.e.*, is a fact, is *a* "something" with *some* one or more specific qualities or properties that distinguish it from other "somethings." [1] Indeed I shall maintain that the prior fact about all facts is that they are instances of the common property of *factuality*, and that that alone which is the prior basis (fact) for distinguishing facts is their qualitative distinctness or their distinctness as qualities (which is itself another specific property or quality).[2] Accordingly I shall claim that certain rivals of *property* for priority, such as *substance*, *event*, and *relatedness*, can really be rivals, and also be *distinguished* from each other, only because of their *qualitative* distinctness. Substance, *a* substance, is but an instance of the property of *substantiality*, and an event is an instance of "*eventness*." These two, then, and *relatedness*, as distinct from each other, are distinct as *qualities* or *properties*.

I shall therefore proceed from the standpoint of regarding, because I find it to be the case (fact) on investigation, *property* as that term of which *substantiality*, *eventness*, and *relatedness* are but instances although not coördinate instances. I shall therefore regard *property* as the most general

[1] That is, a "something" *x*, *e.g.*, an atom of Hydrogen, may have certain qualities (some) in common with the other atoms of the Periodic Table, and it is a fact that a Hydrogen atom does have such common qualities; but the Hydrogen atom is distinct from the atoms of the other elements by virtue of being an instance of certain other qualities that are different and distinct from the qualities of which other elements are instances. The ground for the distinctness of instances in such a case is, then, that of certain qualities (of which these are the instances) that are themselves distinct. In other cases, *i.e.*, in all those cases in which the instances are themselves properties or qualities, *e.g.*, redness, blueness, greenness, yellowness, in Nature, and Negation (Negativity), Disjunction, and Conjunction, in Logic, *it is the properties themselves that are* distinct; they are not distinct by virtue of the possession of properties that are distinct. If this were not the case, there would be an infinite regress.

[2] Distinctness may be at least (a) qualitative, (b) quantitative, and there may be still other kinds. But *distinctness* is itself a property. What else is it?

term I can use, but in using it I find no necessity (another property) for there being anything by way of *substance* or *substances* to bear properties, or to be a substratum in which properties inhere. I shall offer, then, a *substanceless* metaphysics, or, if my (possible) reader prefer, "a world without substance." [3] But, although I shall maintain that *there are no substances* as bearers of qualities, or as the "somethings" which possess properties, I shall insist, because I again find it to be the case, *that properties belong to something, at least in a great many cases, if not in all.* That to which a property belongs is, perhaps in the majority of cases, merely one or more *other properties*. This means that, strange as it may seem—and yet it should not seem strange—properties have properties, and, perhaps, these properties have still other properties, and so on. For example, the three properties of which (1) the existential organic evolutionary series is an instance, namely, (2) Temporality, Divergency, as regards "more and more," or greater variety of, species, and Irreversibility,[4] have in common the property, (3) of "being serial," and, in turn, "being serial" has the property, (4) of "being ordered," and "being ordered" has the property, (5) of "being related." In other words, whatever *evolves* (I am selecting organic evolution) is *temporal;* whatever is temporal is a *series* of "temporal elements" (days, years, decades, etc.); a series is a *special kind of order* (linear), and there is no order without *relatedness.* But there can be relatedness without serial order, and serial order without time (*e.g.*, the cardinal numbers in

[3] The Metaphysics which I present is distinctly *adjectival.*

[4] I have in mind the irreversibility that is present in the cause and effect series that is involved in the lines of reproductive inheritance—and developmental processes which together constitute, in part, the organic evolutionary process. This will be dealt with later. However, Irreversibility as such is of higher order than Temporality and Divergency.

their "natural order," 1, 2, 3 . . .), and time without evolution (a purely mechanistic "world"—Newtonian—is "in
time," but it does not of necessity "evolve").

But properties are not the only "somethings" to which
properties belong, for both events and relations have properties. Thus, *e.g.*, an event may have the property of being,
relatively, "fast," or "slow," and a relation may have the
properties of *Asymmetry* and of *Transitivity* to distinguish
it from a relation that is Symmetrical and Intransitive.[5]

I shall accordingly proceed from the standpoint of what
I find to be the fact, namely, that at least some properties
have instances which are themselves other properties of the
next lower order, and so on "down" to something which is
no longer capable of being instanced, or realized, or exemplified, namely, the particulars of Nature, *e.g.*, atoms,
planets, organism, organic individuals, etc. When we reach
this point, we have struck bottom. I cannot maintain,
then, that a property is always instanced by *another* property, or by *other properties*. In fact, I find that I cannot
maintain that a property *is* "always" *instanced*. It may be
instanced, but, also, it may not be. Whether it is instanced
or not does not depend on the property itself. No property,
e.g., perfection, "generates" or *necessitates* its own instances.[6] A property merely is, and, *being, it is merely a
specific possibility-of-being-instanced, or realized, or exemplified*. This may be accepted as a definition, or as *a* property, *of all properties that can be exemplified*, but there are
certain properties to which this definition does not apply.

---

[5] There are also other properties of relations than the four thus indicated.
Relations will be discussed later.

[6] If Perfection, as a property, necessitated its own instances, then from
Perfection we could infer at least One Perfect Being. But this we cannot do.
Perfection, then, may *be*, but its instances *not be*.

They are those properties which are instances of Impossibility. These properties not only are not, but they cannot be, exemplified; they thus determine null classes, or *one null class*.

If, now, all properties other than those that are instances of Impossibility are *specific possibilities-of-being-instanced*, but if no such property necessitates its instances,—*e.g.*, if Perfection does not imply *a* perfect Being—, then the instances as neither necessitated nor impossible, but *simply as being*, as "occurring,"—may I say as "happening"—, are entirely, completely, and absolutely *contingent*.

It is for this reason, then, that, finding facts of various kinds and orders, and the specific relations among these facts just discussed, I discover that this is "A World of Chance." From "the top,"—from the ultimate Property or Properties, whatever they may be, but of which all other properties are directly or indirectly, instances— "down" to Nature, I find Contingency, through and through. Everything is an instance of this property. Nothing necessitates the ultimate properties themselves; they simply *are*, and, *being*, are not impossible; thus (1) they are quite contingent. Contingent, also, are (2) the instances of any property, (3) the whole of Nature as a manifold of particulars, (4) the specific products of the evolutionary process, such as living beings (Life), (5) the occurrence of Knowing and of Knowledge, (6) the truth and falsity of propositions, and (7) the fact of value. None of these *need* be at all. Of all of them one can only say that they *are*, and, that, *being*, they are not impossible. Indeed, of Contingency itself these same properties hold, so that Contingency is itself contingent.

In thus stressing Contingency, I do not, however, deny

Necessity and the instances of this—*necessities*. Necessities are found in certain specific realms—*perhaps* in the field of logic, *e.g.*, in all cases of (strict) implication (*p* necessitates *q*) and *possibly* also, in Nature, in all instances of causality. But, if there are these instances, in limited realms, they are, as *instances* of Necessity, *not* necessitated, any more than is Necessity itself, as will be found later.

This "situation" *seems* to create a paradox in the sense, on the one hand, that instances *of Necessity* are, as *having* this property, *necessary*, and yet that, on the other hand, *as instances*, they are *not necessary*. However, I think that this paradox is easily solved. To be *necessary* means to be necessitated, and to be necessitated is to be necessitated by something. Accordingly, it may be said, first, that each instance of necessity is *necessary* in the sense that, in agreement with the definition (of Necessity) which is subsequently accepted, it is implied (necessitated) by its own denial or its own negative. Thus, *e.g.*, to *deny* negation is to presuppose it; to deny alternation or disjunction (either—or) is to use this very principle itself in "setting up" an alternative,—the denial. In general, a property is necessary and so itself possesses the property of necessity, if it is implied [7] by its own negative. But, secondly, by this same definition or norm, no instance of Necessity is necessitated by this property, *i.e.*, the relation of the instance to the property is not that of the instance being implied by its denial or negative "in the form" of the assertion, *that the property is not, i.e., is something other than, the instance.* If this were the case, then both of any two positive terms, *x* and *y*, would be necessary, since, with *y* = *not-x*, *x* would

---

[7] Or "demanded by," or "presupposed by"; I shall discuss this in detail in Chapter IV.

be necessitated by y, and with $x = not\text{-}y$, y would be necessitated by x. Accordingly, everything would be necessary.

It is simply a question then, as to what is found to be *the case*. Are there x's which can be found that are independent of, *i.e.*, that are without y's, y's that are without x's? I think that such x's and such y's are found. For example, in Nature, physical entities are found without life, living things without consciousness or awareness, learning processes without reasoning; and in logical systems, such as geometrical systems, there are sets of specific propositions which are "without" certain other propositions that nevertheless have their "place" in other logical systems. So also,—and this is my main contention—there may be properties *without* instances, and, therefore, *empty classes*, either because those properties are impossibilities, or because—a very simple reason—no instances are found. In general it may be said that some properties (most)—*e.g.*, those that are not impossibilities—may have instances, but whether they do or not does not depend on these properties themselves. Accordingly, there may be and there are instances of Necessity that are *necessary* in the sense that they are necessitated by their own denial or negative, but not by the property, Necessity, itself. Thus, paradoxically, "one and the same thing" can be both *necessary* "in one relation" and *not necessary* in another. The seeming contradiction is "solved" by the fact of the *two* relations. Thus an instance of Necessity may be both necessary (as possessing this property) and contingent (as an instance of it).

In order to elucidate it, we may now return to the statement made in a preceding paragraph to the effect that ultimately one *must* grant a realistic position,[8] even though

[8] This is an instance of Necessity, on the ground of the definition, dis-

"this side" of that position, as regards certain situations, one need not accept this specific Theory of Knowledge, but may accept some other theory. It is now proposed to state briefly why this is the case.

Realism is that specific Theory of Knowledge in accordance with which, (1) that which is known is independent of being known. This is the condition of facts "really" being known.[9] If this situation or possibility is not realized, at least in some cases, then there are no known facts, and all so-called facts are really the product, in some way, of knowing, *i.e.*, are *constructs*—though, of course, if this itself were known to be *the case*, it would be a (known) fact (as to "constructs") and *not a construct*. (2) Realism is, further, the position, as a corollary of (1), that "there is no reason" why facts should not be *of many kinds*. There is "no reason" why they must be this, or, conversely, why they must not. Independent of being known, their character, *i.e.*, the specifically different properties which they are found to be, or to possess, is an entirely contingent matter. Facts are what they are found to be, and one of the facts found may be just this one, namely, that of the complete independence of fact of being found or known.[10] Realism, as identical with the position that this is *the fact about facts*, is quite "self-consistent" or "self-critical."

Realism is thus, (2), in its method, completely positivistic and radically empirical, and in its results "qualitatively pluralistic. It is, frankly, a "Spectator Theory of Knowl-

cussed later, of that property, as "the property of being presupposed by denial (or negative)."

[9] Whether by "a finite" or by "an absolute mind," if there be such.

[10] Realism as thus defined—Epistemological Realism—would be quite compatible with finding almost any *ontological* "state of affairs." Thus, *e.g.*, Realism would be quite compatible with an ontological Idealism, or an ontological Materialism.

edge," though this does not in the least preclude, as, *e.g.*, Professor Dewey seems to think it does,[11] Knowledge from being an "agency" in the production of change. Indeed, quite the contrary. The fact of such agency and change is itself simply *one* among *many* facts, different in kind, perhaps, from other facts, but, like them, both known and yet independent of being known. So the "Spectator Theory" applies to this fact as well as to others.

With Realism thus defined, let us consider the reasons for its acceptance. These reasons are so strong, in my opinion, that they amount to *necessity*. That is, *Knowledge is ipso facto realistic*. It is impossible for it to be anything else.

That this is the case is certainly difficult to *demonstrate*, and it may be impossible. But, if this is so, then, at least there may be elucidation. So I propose to elucidate, if not to demonstrate or prove.[12]

I shall begin my "elucidation" with a brief statement of a situation in Physics that is analogous to the situation in Philosophy as regards "Knowing" and Knowledge. Physics, as is well known, uses the method of measurement, accompanying experiment, in order to find or discover quantities in Nature. These quantities are found to be qualitatively different, as is illustrated simply by the *pressure*, *temperature*, and *volume* of a gas, and they are also found in some cases to be correlated with one another. Thus, *e.g.*, when the temperature of a gas is kept constant, the pressure varies inversely with the volume, and conversely. Now, with the beginnings of Physics in the work, *e.g.*, of such a pioneer as Galileo, the method of measurement, and what was involved in it, was not studied.

---

[11] Dewey, *The Quest for Certainty*, 1929, Chaps. IV, V, VI, VIII.
[12] Of course, if it is impossible to demonstrate this, this itself is a fact that is either capable or incapable of demonstration.

Indeed, there was no "awareness" that there was any problem here at all. There was no self-consciousness or self-criticism on the part of the physical scientist as to his method and its "implications."

In due time, however, such a consciousness and criticism developed. Measurement itself, the *process* of measuring, its conditions, etc., became the subject of investigation. The outcome, as is well known, is, on the one hand, Relativity, and on the other hand, (the Principle of) Indeterminacy. Relativity calls attention to the importance (even necessity) of "considering" the frame of reference in which the measurer and his instruments are situated *and* the frame of reference in which that which is measured "resides." The *two* frames may be *one*, but they may also be *two*, in motion with reference to one another, either with uniform rectilinear velocity or not. It is with the observation of this fact that the Special Theory of Relativity begins.

The Principle of Indeterminacy "arises" from an awareness of still other possibilities, which prove to be actualities. Does the process of measuring or the "instrument" used to measure (and both process and instrument are always physical), or both, have any "effect" on that which is to be measured? Up to recent times it was held that they did not, but it is now recognized that they do have. That is, it is now accepted as a *fact*, in Physics, that measurement cannot be indefinitely increased in its refinement, so that it can, theoretically, approach perfect measurement ever more and more closely, for the reason that *Nature itself sets the limits to such an approach*. These limits are set because, in certain cases, the very process of measuring, by virtue of becoming more and more accurate as regards one quantity, becomes less and less accurate as regards another quantity. Thus, *e.g.*, the measuring (ideally) of the *position* of an electron by means of light so disturbs the electron that its velocity cannot simultaneously be measured. It is for this reason that *prediction* in the field of the sub-atomic is impossible, and that Indeterminacy, at least in this sense, is held to reign, for prediction in such an instance demands the measurement of both position *and* velocity simultaneously, and this is impossible.[13]

Physics has thus become critical—aware of—its own methods, and has recently developed two very revolutionary theories on the basis of this criticism.

But Philosophy became self-critical long before Physics, although this criticism was not directed, I shall maintain, to the proper objective. I do not propose, in discussing this point, to write the History of Modern Philosophy, but only to point out that Philosophy thought that it was becoming critical of its own method when, *e.g.*, in the case of Kant, *criticism was directed to Knowing*, to Reason. Therefore, the *Critique of Pure Reason*.

This specific criticism seems, on the face of it, to be quite justified. Does not the philosopher think and reason and know? Indeed, does not the scientist do this, too? Then why not *criticize knowledge, i.e., investigate Knowing* in order to discover its nature and its possible limitations before one attempts to know in other fields? May not such prior criticism of Knowing possibly save one from entering upon a forlorn hope, whether one be philosopher or scientist?

It would seem that this would be the case, yet I shall try

---

[13] This is the epistemological aspect; there is also the ontological interpretation, which will be discussed in Chapter VII.

to show that it is not. In other words, I shall maintain that criticism in Epistemology should be pointed, not in the direction of Reason, of Understanding, of Knowing (as, *e.g.*, this was done by Kant) with the tacit assumption that these may have a structure or machinery which will limit or "color" our Knowing, but, rather, *in the direction of propositions* [14] as those "elements" which are present in any Knowing or Knowledge whatsoever, whether it be a Knowledge of or about Knowledge, or of or about something else, including propositions. In brief, I shall maintain that, paradoxical though it may seem, we know, not through Knowing, *but through propositions*,[15] whatever these may be, and that, therefore, if there is to be a genuine Epistemology, it is to be found through research in this direction, even as the physicist has found that, in order to investigate the problem as to the character and possible limitations of his Knowledge, he must study, not his own Knowing, but the means or methods of this Knowing, namely *measurement*. The carrying out of such a program leads, I find, to Realism, so it is for this reason that I maintain, throughout this volume, a realistic position. Let us see, then, why this is the case.

First, there is no situation that cannot be *investigated* in some way,—at least, if by no other means, then by reason; *i.e.*, *any situation* is open to investigation by rational if not by other means. For example, when the physicist investigates *measurement*, at a certain point, at least, he ceases to investigate measurement by measurement, and

[14] A proposition is not the words of a sentence, nor an "awareness" of any kind; rather it is an objective "state of affairs," a meaning, that is "made" true or false by something external to itself.

[15] Even Kant himself actually, in the *Critique of Pure Reason*, presented a body of *propositions* about Knowing. He thus knew Knowing, not directly, but through and by means of *propositions*.

begins to study this method rationally, *i.e.*, by means of propositions. It follows that those situations, those "states of affairs," that are themselves identical with propositions, can be investigated propositionally. The purpose of the investigation is to find what are the *facts* in the case.

Secondly, the method of rational investigation, which is the only method of investigating at least some situations, is that of "using" propositions that are *logically connected*. It is in this way that we *reason* about situations, in order to discover, if possible, the facts in the case. "Propositions that are logically connected" are propositions that are, *e.g.*, (1), *consistent* with another, and, (2), in some cases, *implicatively related*.[16]

Thirdly, this presupposes, of course, that the method of rational investigation can itself be investigated, but there is no way of doing this except, again, by means of propositions that are logically connected. The *results* of such an investigation will themselves be "stated" in a body of propositions which are disclosed by the investigation; these propositions are the "theorems" that are implied by the "earlier" propositions.

Fourthly, in reaching these propositions as a conclusion, we believe or regard them as *true*. These propositions are, however, not identical with the symbols (words or ideograms) for them, nor with specific conscious processes called judgments. Rather, the proposition is *a specific objective state of affairs* through or by means of which we judge. It is a possibility, but a specific one, namely, that of being *open to realization by something external to itself*. If the proposition is *realized*, it is *true*, if it is not, it is false. Truth and falsity, then, are characteristics (qualities) of propositions,

---

[16] There are other "logical connections," to be discussed later.

and not of judgments. Judgments are correct or incorrect. Judgments are identical with "holding" certain propositions to be true or certain propositions to be false. A judgment is *correct* if, (a), a proposition is held to be true, and, (b), the proposition *is* true, *i.e.*, if it is realized by a "state of affairs" external to itself; also, (c), if a proposition is held to be false, and the proposition *is* false; on the other hand, a judgment is incorrect if a proposition is held to be true when it is false, or false, when it is true.[17]

In asserting a certain position to be true, then, what we are really doing is to believe that certain *propositions* are true, so that, through them, we get at the *facts* which, not propositions themselves, (unless we are investigating propositions) "make" the propositions true "through" their "agreement"[18] with it. The point I wish to make is, then, that, in asserting any position to be true, we are presupposing, (1), that a certain set of propositions is disclosed, and, (2), that through the propositions which constitute this set, we are getting at facts which are independent of both the propositions and the judgments. This is Realism.

However, neither this *presupposition* nor the *definition* of a true proposition as that specific possibility with which an independent external state of affairs *agrees*, furnishes a criterion or test for the *factuality* of this agreement. Nor is the belief itself that a proposition is true, either a criterion of, or a guarantee for, its truth. Such a belief, which is *purely psychological*, may reach the degree of absolute, dogmatic certainty, but such certainty is no more of a criterion or guarantee than its weaker brethren.

---

[17] *Cf.* Lewis and Langford, *Symbolic Logic*, pp. 473–474.
[18] Agreement means "realizes," etc. I shall discuss this later, in detail.

However, this presupposition is not in every case merely psychological; it is also, in certain cases, logical as well. In such cases, it is the specific presupposition, that one position is or must be true, because *it* is presupposed by its denial (*i.e.*, by its negative) in another, opposed, position. This opposed position is, at least tacitly, assumed to state the facts by means of a set of logically connected propositions. Accordingly it presupposes logically, at least, (1), the *objectivity* of the propositions which constitute the position, and also, (2), the *objectivity* of the facts that would make these propositions true, if they are true. This is a proof of Realism.

To illustrate: I would claim that the position I have just outlined as regards judgments, propositions, truth and falsity, and, especially, the *independence* of both propositions and facts, (which, as a position, I have given in the form of propositions) is presupposed to be true by the denial of it, because this denial itself could be made only by presupposing, (1), not only the very *distinctions* I have made between judgments, propositions, and that which makes propositions true or false, namely, fact, but also, (2), the independence, as regards Knowing, of both the propositions and the facts. In other words, the denial is itself *an instance of what it denies, and therefore presupposes what it denies.*[19] This particular situation is itself an instance of the more general principle that anything, x, is presupposed by its denial, or its negative, if the denial is self-contradictory in the sense that, in explicitly denying x, it tacitly affirms x, in being an instance of x.

[19] I should even "go so far" as to claim that, if one "denied" the position I am defending, by denying the reality of propositions and facts, substituting "judgments" for them, this "denial" is itself *a proposition*, either true or false by reference to *facts* that are external to and independent of it.

Now I frankly grant, as concerns this "proof" of Realism, that in the last analysis it does not get beyond belief— belief, namely, in the proposition or principle of "presupposition by denial" as itself *true* because it is *realized* by facts. To escape this, one might try to prove this principle, *i.e.*, derive it from true propositions, but, if one did this, then, I would insist, one is taken only further back to these "earlier" propositions.

I am frank to admit, then, that neither through *this method*, nor through *the method* of "presupposing the *facts*" which may *"make true"* the propositions of any position which we *accept as true*, nor through *the definition* of truth as identical with the agreement of the facts with the proposition, do we "establish" this agreement. This seems to me to be the crux of the whole problem. If we can show the agreement, then we shall have established the truth of the proposition, but this agreement must be established independently. To derive it, *i.e.*, to derive fact, from the truth of the proposition, and then, conversely, to regard the proposition as true because it is realized by fact, is, obviously, squirrel-like, to indulge in a circular process.

All this is undoubtedly a very complicated way of "establishing" the Realistic position. Yet it may be the only way. One certainly does not get very far philosophically by dogmatically *asserting* Realism or any other position to be true; nor is bare belief itself—belief with no attempt at justification whatsoever—a better method. Some justification of some kind must be attempted.

Now I find only three possible ways of "establishing" Realism, namely, (1), by induction, (2), by deduction from certain propositions "further back"—*i.e.*, from assumptions—, and, (3), by "the method of presupposition by denial."

To attempt to establish Realism *inductively* involves a *Petitio Principii*, since the "typical cases" that might form the basis for the induction must themselves be interpreted realistically. Likewise, one cannot derive Realism from *assumed* premises unless in those premises themselves Realism is assumed. There remains only "the method of presupposition," albeit even this method ultimately may not get further than belief. I am willing to admit this, since, if I counter this by saying that this itself is the *factual situation* about Epistemology, I am but again getting at this fact through the realm of propositions which I *believe* to be true, but which I have not exhaustively proved to be such.

I am willing to admit, then, that I *believe* that every position which is opposed to Realism is itself realistic at a certain point, and so is identical with the presupposition of Realism at this point.

To illustrate: Suppose I develop a solipsistic position,[20] raising the question as to the status of the "external" world, and reach the conclusion that the independent existence of this "world" both as an entirety and as regards its details cannot be proved, and, therefore, that it is a "construct" of and from "ideas."[21]   Now at this point *Realism appears* in the form of the presuppositions, (1), that this account itself, as a set of propositions, is not a "construct," but an objective, independent "state of affairs," and, (2), that it is "made" true by something that is external to the propositions of the account itself, namely,

<hr />

[20] The position, namely, that everything, except myself, my "ego," is my idea; that my ideas are all that I am absolutely certain of, all that I directly experience. *Cf.* Berkeley, *Treatise concerning the Principles of Human Knowledge.*

[21] Stace, W. T., *Theory of Knowledge and Existence*, 1932; *passim.*

by *a fact—the fact of the "construct,"* or the fact of the "artificiality" of the external world. Both this fact and the propositions through which this fact is known are presupposed to be independent of the Knowledge of them.

Now what I maintain is that this example is typical. There are any number of other examples of the same situation. The example chosen illustrates the fact that, ultimately, in any position presented through propositions, even in one which interprets certain "entities" or "things" as being, not facts, but "constructs" (or appearances, or fictions, etc.), it is at least tacitly presupposed, (1), that there are facts or objective "states of affairs" which, on the one hand, are disclosed or got at through propositions, and which, on the other hand, make the propositions, through which we believe, true. Or, conversely, in believing the propositions to be true—and the adherent of any one position (*e.g.*, Pragmatism) believes, to a greater or lesser degree of conviction, his position to be true—there is the presupposition that the constituent propositions of the position are made true by facts which are independent both of the belief and the propositions. But there is also, (2), the methodological presupposition that, prior to the investigation by means of propositions (logically connected), one cannot tell what facts will be disclosed by the propositions that constitute the conclusion of the investigation. As regards the outcome, one should be entirely open-minded. Anything may be shown to be the case by the investigation. Facts may prove to be different in kind, or to be of only one kind; to be related in certain ways, and not in other ways, etc., etc. But the investigation cannot fail to find *something that is fact*—even, paradoxically, the fact that there are no facts.

This book is, however, an exposition and defense of the position, through propositions, that it is a fact that there are facts of a great many different kinds, and that these facts are so related that there is *a specific structure* of facts. Accordingly it will also be found that there is *a structure of propositions*, and then, since there are both propositions and facts, *a structure of truths*, in other words, that there is more than one kind, or one "level" of truth. These are all facts.

I may illustrate this position, that there are facts of many different kinds, by giving the following list of what I regard to be neither mere words, nor "constructs," nor "fictions," nor "ideas," but *facts, realities:* Functionality ("Propertiness") Possibility, Necessity, Contingency, Impossibility, Relatedness, Negation; Validity, Realization, Truth, Falsity; *the facts of and about* Propositions, Beliefs, Propositional Functions, Classes, Logic, Mathematics, Philosophical Systems, Values. But it is not my purpose to write a catalogue. These examples, taken at random, illustrate the point of view that the word-symbols of such a list stand not for "ideas" or "concepts" as mental processes, but for *something objective*, for facts or realities, *of which* there are "*ideas*," and *for which* there are *symbols*.

No better example of this pluralistic and realistic position can be found than is offered by the following quotation from one of the works of that eminent logician, Professor C. I. Lewis. This author, discussing logic and alternative logics, says: [22]

"Traditional logic is a highly selected body of truth within an immensely greater body of truth. . . . The same is true also of any logic. . . . Just as the weight of any grain of sand . . .

[22] Lewis and Langford, *opus cit.*, pp. 256–258. The italics are mine.

is a physical fact, . . . so the truths about the relations of propositions are all of them *logical facts*. . . . Logic represents a certain order or arrangement of facts—the order of our *chosen* ways of ordering in general. Nevertheless, . . . we could not arrange facts in a certain order *if the facts themselves did not have certain relations.*

"The *facts* summarized by a system, and the relations of these facts, *are not created* by the system, *nor dependent on the process of inference.* . . . Inference . . . makes a map of facts, but it does not create the geography of them. . . . Inference is something which we *do*, upon observation of *certain relationships amongst the facts* with which we are dealing. We make the inference of B from A when we observe that *a certain relation exists between A and B. But the relation exists whether it is observed or not.*"

In conclusion I may say that the account which I give in this book, consisting, as it does, of the presentation of certain facts which I have selected, of their relations to one another, *i.e.*, their structure, etc., I regard as a *true* account. I must perforce give this account in the form of propositions, and this I do; but these propositions I believe to be true. If they are true, then through them I am getting at facts, and my belief is correct. But I cannot, from the strength of my belief, derive the facts themselves which are the very condition both of the truth of my propositions, and of the correctness of my belief. These facts should, then, if possible, be got at in some other way. Whether or not there is "some other way" remains to be seen. I shall endeavor to find it. But, if there is no other way, then I must rest content with the belief that my account nevertheless is true.

A WORLD OF CHANCE

I

THE COMMUNICATION OF MINDS

The purpose of this book is to convey to the reader, if the author is so fortunate as to have readers, something about such intangibles as Chance and Possibility, Fact and Truth, Existence and Non-Existence, Good and Evil, not only in themselves, but also as regards their relationship to one another. The principle which is "in the author's mind,"—whatever a "mind" may be—, and which seems to connect these diverse intangibles, may be stated simply, and perhaps convincingly. It is, that *whatever is actual or real in any sense must also be possible*, although the converse does not follow, that whatever is possible must also be actual.[1] The realm of Possibility is thus, as it were, the womb out of which there is born the realm of the Actual. For example, Nature itself is only one case, one possibility out of many. Nature *is* what it is, but it might have been quite different; indeed, it need not be at all. Nature might now be, and have been, quite different, had the start been different, and that there should have been a different start is quite conceivable. Such a position suggests, however, the inquiry whether "the world"—Nature —is what it is, from its start to the present, for any such "reason" as that it is a good world, or the best of all possible worlds. In other words our principle that what is

---

[1] Possibilities are realities, but if they are "actualized" this is due to realities *at a different "level" from that of the possibility* that is "actualized."

actual must be, or have been, possible, and that the actual, in this case, the world—Nature—is just one possibility,— this principle must be supplemented by the inquiry: Did Goodness and Beauty, in any sense of their meaning or "application" whatsoever, in any way determine that Nature should be what it is, and not something different? In brief, Why this world rather than some other equally conceivable world? Is it because this world, as possible, would also be good and beautiful, perhaps the best of all possible worlds, or did goodness and beauty have nothing whatsoever to do with the matter? Indeed, must we go further and say that, just as stars and suns, planets and satellites, life and consciousness undoubtedly *are*, but need not either be or have been, so, also, goodness and beauty *are*, but need neither be nor have been, and that a world without them is quite conceivable.

From what Source, to what End, if any, and for what Reason, if any, is our inquiry? And in order that we find an answer to these questions, we critically examine our intangibles, Chance and Possibility, Fact and Truth, Good and Evil, and a host of others, and endeavor to convey to the reader the results of our investigation.

To do this we must communicate with the reader, we must convey to him our meanings, if possible, and to accomplish this purpose we write, the book is printed, and the reader reads the printed page.

This seems a simple process. It is one that is familiar and common, indeed obvious. Hardly, in it, would there seem to be ground for any philosophy, and yet I think that very far-reaching philosophical principles are as a matter of fact involved. These principles, with what they involve, might be called the Philosophy of Language or

the Philosophy of Communication of one mind with another.

Just what the character of the assurance is, to any one
mind, that there are *other* minds I shall not at this point
consider, but shall accept, for the time being at least, the
common-sense point of view that there are minds—persons,
consciousnesses, they may also be called—and that there
are facts, perhaps of various kinds, which these minds
know or of which they are aware in one way or another.
How, now, can or do these minds communicate these
facts to one another, or, concerning them, with one another *if* there really is any such thing as genuine communication?

Communication takes place normally by the use of
words, either spoken and heard, or written or printed and
read. Let us examine an instance of the first case, words
spoken by one person and heard by another. We have
such an instance if I say to you, "The earth moves around
the sun in an elliptical orbit." I speak and you hear. Let
us assume that you understand what I mean. What is
involved in this?

To answer this question the following distinctions must
be made:

The words as I speak them are physical events, sounds.
Psychologically they are the result of very specific motor
actions, and seemingly spring from my mind or consciousness. To me they have a meaning which I wish to convey
to you.

These specific physical events are sensuously perceived
both by me and by you; they are heard, as sounds, *but only
if they have the same meaning to you that they have to me,
have I really communicated with you.*

There are, then, to be distinguished in the situation thus far:

(1) The words as physical events—a succession of sounds.

(2) The sense-consciousness or awareness, by both of us, of these events.

(3) The consciousness, (a), in me, (b), in you, of the _meaning_. These two consciousnesses are distinct. In me and in you they constitute what is called a _judgment_. The judgment is not the words, nor the consciousness of the words, for there are many instances of words which are _heard_ but whose meanings are not understood.

(4) Distinct from, (a), the consciousness of the words, (b), the consciousness of the meaning, and, (c), the meaning itself, whatever this may be—and just what it is, is our special purpose in this chapter, to find out—, are (d), the _facts_ that "make" the meaning true or false.

In the example given these facts would be said to be _physical_, namely, the actual occurrence, again and again, of the motion of the earth around the sun in an elliptical orbit. Such an actual occurrence makes the meaning _true_. But meanings can also be false. This would be the case if I say, _e.g._, "The earth goes around the sun in a circular orbit." The meaning of the words in this case does not "correspond" to or is not "realized" by physical fact. Nevertheless, there _is_ the _meaning_. It _subsists_ or _is_, as the case may be, whether true or false. If it did not, there would be nothing to be true or false.

Now it is not my purpose at this point to consider all the varieties or kinds of fact that make meanings true or false. This topic is reserved for a later chapter. It need only be remarked at this juncture that, if two or more minds can genuinely communicate by the use of words, and if, as a condition for this, words must have meanings, and if meanings are made true or false by facts, then the range of fact must be as extensive as the range of communication, irrespective of whether what we communicate is true or false. In brief, if we can communicate *about anything whatsoever*, then the range of fact must be as extensive as what we can communicate about. And since I know of nothing that I cannot think about and examine rationally, I also know of nothing concerning which I cannot at least endeavor to communicate with another mind. The range of fact, then, or the kinds of fact, which make meanings true or false is perhaps without limit.

Now, the thesis which I wish at this point to emphasize is, that what I have called *the meaning* cannot, *if there is genuine communication* of one mind with another, be identical with, (a), the words, for these are purely physical events; (b), the consciousness of the words, for this is two-fold or n-fold,—in you,—in me, etc., and the meaning is *one;* (c), the consciousnesses of the meaning, for these are also n-fold; (d), facts, for these are, at least from a common-sense and a scientific and also, I hold, (Realism) a philosophical standpoint, independent of being communicated about. Facts simply are: they are neither true nor false. The meaning is, then, not a mental or conscious entity; it is also not a physical one; it is, therefore, neither conscious nor physical; still, it is either something or nothing. But it must be something, and *one, single something,* in any case of genuine communication between minds. I am not saying that there ever is such communication— there may be and there may not be—but only that, if there is, then this is possible on one and only one condition, and that is *that there is one and only one meaning of which two or more minds are aware.*[2]

This *meaning* is, in any particular instance, identical with what is usually called a *proposition*, and I shall use these two word-symbols to denote or designate the same fact or entity. According to this usage a *proposition* is an objective "state of affairs" that is to be distinguished, *because it is distinct*, (a), from the two or more *judgments* that are awarenesses of it; (b), from the word-symbols that formulate it; (c), from the specific consciousnesses of these symbols; (d), from the facts that make it true or false, and, (e) from the consciousnesses of these facts. It itself is, indeed, a special kind of fact that would make certain propositions, namely propositions about propositions, true or false.[3]

Now it is the virtue of this analysis (these distinctions) that it consistently allows me, in this chapter, to investigate the problem as to *what a proposition is*, and then to endeavor to convey to the mind of the reader the results of my investigations by means of propositions. This is exactly what I am doing. I am presenting, by the use of word-symbols, *propositions about propositions* (as well as about other "things"). These propositions (about propositions) are either true or false. They are true if a proposition really is what the propositions about it, as contained in this chapter, "assert" it to be. It is false, if this is not

[2] Of course I would grant that this is not a sufficient condition, for there must be, also, some "agency" on the part of one mind as it "attempts" to communicate with another mind. But this agency by itself is also not a sufficient condition.

[3] For example, the proposition that "a proposition is a specific objective 'state of affairs' that is capable of being either true or false." This proposition must itself be either true or false by virtue of something "external" to and distinct from itself.

the case. But, in any event, a proposition must be interpreted to be the kind of entity that consistently allows one to "make" or "discover" propositions about it. And that a proposition is the kind of entity that it is pointed out in the foregoing paragraphs to be, is, I maintain, the only interpretation that does consistently allow one to investigate the problem, and then endeavor to communicate to another mind the results of this investigation. The interpretation is thus self-critical.

This position—this "philosophy of communication"—is, I hold, presupposed by the attempt which is made, in one form or another, to deny it.[4] This denial really reduces to three forms, although it may seem to present a greater variety than this. These three forms are, (1), Behaviorism —the modern doctrine of many psychologists, (2), Mentalism, and (3), Nominalism. Each of these positions is, I maintain, self-contradictory in that each, as an attempted denial of the position taken in this chapter, presupposes that position.

Let us examine the Behavioristic position first. As is well known, for those who take the *extreme* behavioristic position [5] consciousness and mind do not, in what would be their particular instances, exist. So, for this reason, if for no other, communication between minds is impossible. But, though there are no minds, no consciousnesses, there

---

[4] Whether or not that which is presupposed by its denial (negative) is for that reason *true*, may be a question. (*Cf.* Lewis, C. I., *Mind and the World Order*, pp. 206–212.) I go no further than to say, (1), that there is the general situation of "being presupposed by denial," (2), that there are instances of this, and, (3), that this is one instance.

[5] I select the extreme form of this "theory," since, if one takes a less extreme form, consciousness and mind might be granted to exist, yet the claim also might be made that they are not needed in order to "explain" or describe behavior. But then it might be the case that, although behavior, at least of certain kinds, could be "explained" without mind, communication could not be.

are, for the behaviorist—and here he is an out and out
realist—organisms, physical stimuli of various kinds, re-
ceptors, sensory, central, and motor nerves, and organs of
response; there are also inherited reflexes, and "conditioned," and those combinations and integrations of these
which are called habits. Such a habit, now, is, *e.g.*, the
"use" of language in both its motor and sensory aspects;
one of the motor forms of this habit is *talking;* and the
sub-vocal form of this last is "thinking." Another motor
form is, of course, writing.

According to this view, then, when one organism would
communicate with another, *e.g.*, by talking, the motor
acts of the one organism produce physical events—sounds
—which are stimuli to a specific sense-organ, normally the
ear and auditory nerve, of the other. If thinking is identified with "sub-vocal talking," then, according to this
view, the sensory process in the recipient must produce in
him, in order that he may really understand, at least that
"incipient" motor process which is *identical* with "sub-
vocal talking." All that there is, then, in the process of
communication is, (1), a motor process in one organism,
(2), a series of "sound vibrations" (air-waves), (3), a sensory
response, and, (4), a motor response. The sounds *as sounds*,
although there is only one set of them, cannot be the meaning, for there can be sounds with no meaning. So that the
single meaning involved in the genuine communication,
if there is such, must somehow reside in the two sub-vocal
motor processes in the two organisms. But these are *two*
distinct processes—separate in both space and time. *The
single meaning* cannot, therefore, be identical with them,
as *two* processes. The only possibility of "finding" it in
them is by way of their similarity to, or identity in some

respect with, one another. But, if this argument is made, then, on the one hand, an appeal is made to a *relation*, and therefore, to a *non-physical* factor and fact, therewith to contradict the explicit tenet of Behaviorism, that everything is physical; and, on the other hand, the question may be raised as to what is the probability of the two sub-vocal motor processes being *exactly similar*, so that the *one single meaning* might be claimed to be identical with this "exact similarity." In the first case, the way is paved for the position, in support of which this chapter is written, that a meaning, a proposition, is an objective fact that is not only not physical, but also not mental, so that this interpretation of the behavioristic account of communication may be accused of presupposing what it denies. And, in the second case, the position must be taken, in accordance with all the evidence from biology and psychology as regards "individual differences," that it is most improbable that the two motor events in the two organisms are exactly similar. This improbability rests on the fact, as found by both the biologists and the behaviorists themselves, that no two individuals, either by heredity or by conditioning by the environment, or by both, are ever exactly alike in any respect. The Behavioristic argument reduces, therefore, to a Relativistic one. The character of the two spatially distinct motor acts that are involved when, *e.g.*, I *say* to you, "*Two plus two equals four*," and you hear and respond sub-vocally, (= *by definition, your thinking*), is *relative* to my and to your whole psychological make-up as determined by both heredity and environment. "*Two plus two equals four*" is, then, not one fact, but two physical occurrences, not exactly alike, but relative, and different to a greater or lesser degree.

For the behaviorist, then, according to his explicit theory and its implications, there is "no such thing" as genuine communication. Indeed, this is quite impossible.

The behaviorist may be correct. I am not saying that he is not. But I am saying that if he is correct, then he cannot, according to his own theory, genuinely communicate that theory to another mind.[6] But he does endeavor to communicate this theory. To this end he indeed talks vociferously and writes voluminously. And therewith he presupposes, or at least hopes, that what he says and writes has, or is, the same meaning for another human organism—possibly mind, that it has, or is, for himself. He thus, however, presupposes quite another theory than his own as regards the nature of meanings and propositions. His own theory is self-contradictory. It presupposes what it denies. Thus the opposed theory is presupposed by this denial. The opposed theory is, that a meaning or a proposition is an objective fact or state of affairs that is not identical, (1), with the distinct physiological processes in two or more organisms, nor, (2), with those specific sounds or graphs that are called words, nor, (3), with the facts—of whatever kind they may be—that make a specific proposition true or false. If this last distinction did not exist, one mind could not convey to another that specific meaning which is identical with a false proposition, as, *e.g.*, the proposition, "The moon is inhabited."

There remain two other forms which the denial of the theory that is supported in this chapter takes, and which,

[6] Perhaps the extreme behaviorist might reply that he is not trying to communicate with anyone, but that he is merely endeavoring to arouse certain vocal and sub-vocal reactions, but if he takes this position, he is granting that his theory has no place in it for communication. He could not even *communicate* this reply, but only produce, by it, as a stimulus, a reaction, or response.

as denials, presuppose what they deny. These two forms include, I think, what might seem to be more than two.

In contrast with Behaviorism (a subdivision of Materialism), which fallaciously identifies a proposition or meaning with a physiological process, according to *one* of these two other forms, a proposition or meaning is *mental* in character; according to the *other*, it is identical with the *mere words*, as sounds or marks, or, in the case of some scientific propositions (including symbolic logic), formulae, or equations, with special ideograms. Under the former, which I call the Mentalistic or psychological interpretation, I include Conceptualism and Solipsism; under the second, which I call Nominalism, I include Positivism and Instrumentalism. It is my purpose to discuss these views only very briefly.

The conceptualist, as distinct from the solipsist, (1), grants that there are other minds than his own, *i.e.*, that there is a plurality of minds and, then, (2) maintains that meanings or propositions are identical with *ideas* and with certain specific connections of "ideas" or mental events (judgments) in these minds. There are, then, two possibilities, (a) that all the ideas of any one mind should be at least a little bit different from all the ideas of any other mind; (b) that, while some, or, indeed, most ideas in any two minds should be different, a few should nevertheless be exactly similar or alike. This second position is illustrated in a general way by the well-known "doctrine" of the "categories" as contained, *e.g.*, in the *Critique of Pure Reason* of Kant.

Now as regards the former position, it is readily seen that, quite as in the case of Behaviorism, *genuine* communication in the sense of absolute singleness of meaning is quite impossible. At least the occurrence of such communication is a matter of mere chance, and is, therefore, most improbable. The position thus becomes merely one of *psychological relativism* rather than of physiological. Yet, to present the theory and *genuinely to communicate it* to another mind is possible only on the basis of the specific theory of communication which is presented in this chapter. This means that the theory can be presented only by propositions or meanings that are, (1), formulated by words, (2), distinct from the facts which "validate" them, and, (3), distinct from the awareness both of the propositions, the words, and, possibly also, the facts. *But the theory is presented.*[7] It thus explicitly denies what it tacitly presupposes.

The second form of Conceptualism escapes the complete relativism of the first. For it, there are a few concepts, albeit they are not many, and are regarded as not being derived from experience, but as *a priori*, that are exactly similar in two or more minds. For Kant, *e.g.*, the list of such concepts, called "pure," included, as is well known, *causation, substance, unity, plurality*, etc. But I find that for this position also it is impossible to give such an account of meaning as will allow it *consistently* to interpret the nature or status of itself as an account that can be communicated. According to this position, a meaning or proposition is mental in nature; and communication is possible only in so far as, and because, there is exact similarity (identity) between two or more mental processes. But this explanation fails to explain, first, the *similarity*, which according to the theory is "external" to the two or more mental processes or

---

[7] Of course, the theory could be presented with no hope of communicating it, but only of arousing, in some way, ideas in another mind.

entities which are the "end-terms," as it were, of the communication. *It* is, then, not identical with them nor they with it, and, therefore, there is as much ground for saying that the similarity is not mental in character as for saying that it is. The prior fact is that the similarity is distinct from the two "end-terms," even as the similarity, *e.g.*, between a man and a woman is not identical with either term, and is certainly not itself either male or female. But, secondly, the theory fails, because it does not specify *that respect* in which two mental processes must be similar in order to be in communication. *Bare similarity* is not enough, and *certain* specific similarities do not explain. One might as well maintain, *e.g.*, that the Earth and Mars are in communication because they are similar as planets, as maintain that I am in communication with you and you with me, because my ideas (some of them at least) are *like* yours, *as ideas*, in respect to, *e.g.*, their vividness, their duration, etc., etc. *There is only one specific similarity that does explain*, and that is the similarity which is present when two mental processes, be these ideas, or judgments, or series of judgments, are each an awareness of exactly the same meaning(s) or proposition(s). But there are, then, (a), the two or more awarenesses, (b), the fact of the specific similarity, and, (c), that which this specific similarity involves, namely, the *oneness of the meaning*.[8]

The Conceptualistic account of communication, then, does not explain. It is a set of false propositions. As such and *as* communicated, or with the endeavor made to com-

---

[8] *Cf.* Lewis, *Mind and the World Order*, p. 73: Lewis says, "We have language to convey thought: if language really conveys anything, then there must be something which is *identical* in your mind and mine when we understand each other." (Italics mine.)

This identical element is recognized by Lewis, p. 72, to be *the meaning*.

municate it, and on the assumption that this endeavor is successful, it presupposes the theory and the analysis supported in this chapter.

The "would-be" Solipsistic interpretation of the nature of meaning, or, of a proposition and of communication—the second form of "Mentalism"—must be, it is obvious, in accordance with the basic principle of the whole solipsistic position.   This principle is, as is perhaps well known, that "the whole world"—everything—is "my idea," *i.e.*, is a set of ideas "in my mind."   The solipsist thus grants "ideas"—many of them—and *a mind* (or soul or spirit)—but, consistently, *only his own.*   "I" am his "idea," or a special set of ideas, as is everything else, so that "I," strictly speaking, am not a mind.   To be a mind is a special privilege reserved for the Solipsist himself.   The theory may seem to the reader to be absurd,[9] yet it is sometimes regarded as the only logical outcome of the great historical principle in philosophy, that all that one can directly and certainly know is one's own "ideas." [10]

It is obvious, then, that, strictly speaking, for the Solipsist there is no communication between *minds*.   There cannot be, for there are no minds—in the plural.   There is seemingly, then, no occasion for him to ask, "What is a proposition, a meaning?" or, at least, "What is communication?"   At best a proposition can be for him only some relation between ideas within his own mind, and communication, whatever its nature might be, could be only with himself.

[9] The seemingly absurd sometimes is true.

[10] As a good example of a philosophical position (in certain fields) that is based on Solipsism, we have Mr. W. T. Stace's *Theory of Knowledge and Existence*, 1932.   This author says "The initial position of every mind must be Solipsistic," p. 66.   I remark: This itself is *a proposition*, that is "objective."

But the Solipsist is not consistent. He wishes to convince other minds of the correctness of his theory. To this end he writes—in order to communicate his position—and therewith formulates propositions, which he would have other minds aware of and accept. In doing this, he herewith tacitly accepts other minds, as well as his own. To these other minds he would communicate the, to him, basic proposition, *that each mind with its ideas, including all other minds, is everything.* But this proposition itself, this "state of affairs," as a meaning that is communicated, and by its own meaning cannot be an *idea* in the solipsist's own mind nor in any other mind with which he might succeed in communicating. *It is not an idea, but a proposition* (and a false one), a meaning, that is entirely objective as regards any one mind and, therefore, all minds, and that any one mind might be aware of without therewith making it identical with an "idea."

The Solipsist, accordingly, in communicating, or in attempting to communicate, his theory to other minds, contradicts himself, and deserts his solipsism. Consistently, as a Solipsist, he cannot communicate; but he does communicate, or endeavors to do so, and therewith he is no longer a Solipsist.

The behavioristic and the mentalistic theories of communication, of meaning, and of the nature of a proposition have each been examined and found wanting. Each as a denial presupposes the specific theory presented in this chapter. It remains to scrutinize the Nominalistic Theory.

According to this theory, which need be formulated only to the extent that it concerns the question with which we are interested, there is "no such thing" as a proposition or meaning in the sense that has been defended in this chapter, but there are, (1), words—sounds or marks—and the special symbols of science, especially of those sciences that use mathematics, and, (2), facts or data of some kind. These words and symbols in some cases designate or point to the facts, *while in other cases they are just symbols*. The words, *Gold is yellow*, illustrate the first class of cases. The ideograms, $2 + 3 = 5$, the second. These symbols are useful (—to human beings—) in computing, predicting, and expressing themselves, but "between" them and the facts, where there are facts, there is nothing; there is no "meaning" or "proposition" that may be "made" true or false by the facts. Indeed, for this theory, there is, strictly speaking, "no such thing" as either truth or falsity. There are only symbols that are either useful or useless, either good instruments or bad, *and* facts. It is also indifferent, for this theory, whether so-called conscious processes are regarded as facts or not, and likewise whether there is, behind the qualities of the so-called physical world that can be measured, "anything deeper" or not. It is sufficient that, there are, on the one hand, facts or data, and, on the other hand, symbols, and, of course, thirdly—*and this must not be forgotten, although it usually is*—some *observer* of the facts, and some *user* of the symbols.

This is the theory, very briefly stated. Now, my criticism of it is, that it itself is by intent an account, formulated by word-symbols, of an objective "state of affairs" concerning symbols and facts, but that it explicitly omits from itself, as an account, the recognition of this very distinct and additional *third factor* [11] without which no account whatsoever can be communicated to another mind, and of which

[11] The three "factors" are, (1) symbols, (2) facts, (3) the proposition, the meaning; this third factor is that which is, on the one hand, symbolized, and, on the other hand, made true or false by the facts.

any account that is really communicated is an instance. This additional factor is the objective *propositional state of affairs* with which the account itself is really identical. But let this additional factor be recognized, and we no longer have the Nominalistic theory. Let it be omitted, and we have the Nominalistic account, but an account which is false, because it does not correspond to all the facts. Thus it appears that Nominalism, in denying the theory of meaning supported in this chapter, *i.e.*, in maintaining that there is "no such thing" as a proposition or meaning over and above and distinct from symbols and facts, and, possibly, also judgments, really presupposes that there *is* such an objective "state of affairs," denoted by its own symbols. Therefore the Nominalistic theory presupposes what it denies.

I conclude, then, that there are involved in any instance of genuine communication of one mind with another, even in any instance in which an opposed position is formulated, maintained, and communicated, a number of distinct factors, namely, (1), words or other symbols; (2), meanings or propositions "denoted" by words or symbols. There may also be, and in some cases there are, (3), facts which form the "locus of verification or of falsification" of the propositions. Indeed, perhaps there are in all cases such facts. Whether there are or not, we shall consider later. There may be also, (4), what is by many called a consciousness or an awareness of, (a), the words, (b), the meanings, and, (c), the facts, but, in the analysis I have made, I have thus far been indifferent to this possible fourth factor. Whether one accepts it or not depends, perhaps, upon one's general philosophy. Yet, if one does not accept this factor, something else takes its place, namely, "Disclosure." For, even the behaviorist, *e.g.*, presupposes that there is *disclosed* the objective "state of affairs," that there is no consciousness, no awareness, no mind. For the behaviorist, this "state of affairs" is, on his own terms, the stimulus for a response or reaction the result of which is the *disclosure* of this very "state of affairs"—to himself, at least, and, he hopes, to others.

Now the problem in which I have been especially interested in this chapter concerns primarily the second factor, the meaning or the proposition, and I have endeavored to show that this factor cannot be either physical or mental in character; that it is neither a word, nor a physiological reaction, nor an idea, nor a mental process, yet that it is a fact, a reality of some kind. It must be this in order that there may be "such a thing" as genuine communication between two or more minds, or, if there are no minds, then between the "end-terms" of "the communication relation," whatever the character of these end-terms may be.[12] *But it may be that mind is to be defined as just that which is identical with these "end-terms," i.e., that minds, whatever else they may be, are the "end-terms of the communication relation."* This means that, reduced to its lowest terms, mind is, in part, at least, that to which there is the disclosure of meanings or propositions.

The investigation of what is involved in the genuine

---

[12] Closely related to the position concerning *meaning* that is defended in this chapter, and yet not so explicit as my own account, is the view contained in the posthumous work of Professor G. H. Mead, *Mind, Self, and Society*, and expressed as follows: "Meaning is not psychical, . . . not an idea as traditionally conceived" (p. 76). And again, "Awareness or consciousness is not necessary to the presence of meaning in the process of social experience." "Meaning is thus to be conceived . . . objectively, as having its existence within this field itself"—the social field (p. 78). I am inclined to think that the position which I have developed is implicit in that of Professor Mead.

communication of one mind with another discloses, then, as was formerly suggested, important philosophical principles. These principles I would communicate:

(1) Reality is not limited to the two realms of what are usually called the physical realm and the mental, but there is another realm that is identical, at least in part, if not completely, with *meanings or propositions*.

(2) This realm includes also the *logical relations* of these propositions, and constitutes the realm of Possibility in the broad sense of this term. This realm is, accordingly, the field in which Reason, as opposed to Sensation and Emotion, operates, for if there is genuine Reasoning, then there are disclosed in this activity the logical relations of propositions.

(3) Whatever realm may be rationally investigated,— and no realm is exempt from such investigation, whether it be the realm of sense-data, of emotional experience, of reactions to stimuli, or of anything else, including the realm of meanings and of propositions themselves,—the investigation takes place by way of discovering *propositions* about the entities of these realms. There is then the possibility of communicating the results of the investigation to another mind.

It is, then, with the purpose of communicating with other minds in the sense in which this "process" has been defined in this chapter, that this and the other chapters of this book are written. But I may not succeed. It may be that, for one reason or another, exact or perfect communication is impossible, even the specific communication as to both *this* possibility itself and the reasons for it. All that I maintain is, that if and when there is an instance of perfect communication (perhaps the communication that there is no perfect communication), then this takes place upon the basis of the conditions that have been presented in this chapter,[13] and that make the propositions which constitute the *theory* of this chapter *true*, as opposed to other theories (Behaviorism, Mentalism, and Nominalism), as *false*.

[13] I may further comment that the theory of communication which I have presented in this chapter has, I think, a very definite bearing on the interpretation of the nature of literature, especially of poetry. Poetry, and, in particular, lyric poetry, is, in my opinion, not only the expression of what the poet thinks and feels, *i.e.*, of insights that are much finer and more delicate than are those of the average mortal, but it is also the poet's means of communicating, or of endeavoring to communicate, to other minds, those meanings that are thus present to him. According to the theory of this chapter, then, those meanings are not the poet's invention,— they are not the products of his imagination; rather, they are *objective realities* in the world, to observe or discover which only the poet is a sufficiently sensitive instrument.

II

PROPOSITIONS ABOUT PROPOSITIONS *

At the beginning of this chapter the conclusions of the preceding chapter are taken as a starting point. Nothing is exempt from rational investigation. Reasoning itself, then, and its method, of "using" propositions, may be investigated. Such an investigation will result, then, in discovering propositions about reasoning as well as about propositions and the logical relations between them. Both the propositions (the "investigating" as well as the "investigated") and the relations are realities. Realities they must be in order that there may be rational communication between minds, whatever minds may be. But propositions and the relations between them are neither physical nor mental realities. They are "no-where" in space, and "no-when" in time. They have no mass; they are not instances of energy; they have no chemical properties; they do not reproduce, grow, develop, and react as do organisms; they do not communicate, etc., etc. Even if one said, after investigation, as does, *e.g.*, the nominalist, "There are no propositions," one would be aware of, or would be discovering, at least one proposition.

When there is genuine communication there is a two-fold or n-fold awareness of, or at least, disclosure of, (1), a proposition, or of many propositions, and, if the com-

* This chapter, which is technical, may, perhaps, be omitted by the reader who finds it too difficult, without this seriously interfering with the understanding of the rest of the book.

munication is rational, (2), of the logical relations between the propositions.

With this our starting point, it is our plan in this chapter to present some of the results of recent investigations regarding the further nature of propositions and of their logical relations to one another. In making this presentation, we are convinced that we have been investigating not nothing, but something. Therefore, since this "something" is not what it usually called Nature, or Existence, to include under this term all physical realities, including organisms, and all conscious processes, it may be called the realm of Possibilities or of Subsistents.[1] We therewith return to the principle stated in Chapter I, that all existential entities are possibilities, although not all possibilities are realized in Nature, but that nevertheless all possibilities are themselves realities. We shall therefore investigate, in this chapter, these realities. It will be found that these realities are of different kinds, and that these kinds have definite relations to one another.

The subject-matter of this chapter will accordingly be, in some respects, an outline map of later chapters, a scheme of the whole. Much of its material is drawn from investigations and studies in the field of modern Symbolic Logic, yet it is not in any way my purpose to write either a chapter or a book on this subject. I am convinced that studies in Symbolic Logic have been productive of many important results, especially within the limited field denoted by this term, but I also find that these results have not been extensively "applied" to other fields, where their "application" is legitimate and throws light on important philo-

---

[1] *Cf.* Spaulding, E. G., *The New Rationalism*, 1918, pp. 294 ff., 305 ff., 377 ff., 444 ff., Chap. XLIV, *et passim.*

sophical problems. It is my purpose, then, in this and in later chapters, to make use of these results, and to develop their bearing on broader problems. Further, the study of the literature of the subject also shows that, contrary to the claims of the Symbolic logicians themselves that their method alone gives accuracy and precision, there are, nevertheless, in their writings, any number of instances of ambiguities and equivocations, of terms left undefined that should be defined, and of problems left unanswered that at least demand that an answer be attempted.

To answer some of these problems, to remove some of these ambiguities, to apply some of the results of Symbolic Logic to problems of broader interest and, possibly, of greater importance is, then, my purpose.

The remainder of this chapter will, then, be written in accordance with, and by the use of, some of the more elementary and fundamental technical symbols of modern logic; but these symbols will be employed only because they contribute to clarity of meaning. Perhaps the symbols with which we may most advantageously start are the $\phi(x)$'s, $\psi(x)$'s, $f(x)$'s (the parentheses are sometimes omitted when there is only one variable, x, *and they will subsequently be omitted in this book*) of Symbolic Logic. Each of these symbols is, or stands for, a *"form,"* a *"matrix"* in which ϕ, ψ, f each stand for *any property*, x for *any entity*. Φx, ψx, and *fx* are, then, each a symbol *for any entity with any property* (neither the entity nor the property being specified), or, perhaps better stated, for the "state of affairs" of some (*undetermined*) *entity x*, having, or possessing, some (*undetermined*) *property*, ϕ, or ψ, or f. Either ϕ or ψ or f could, then, stand for any one of such properties (so-called "abstractions") as *possibility, contingency, goodness, humanity, dimensionality, atomicity, spaciness, redness,* etc. But, also, ϕ, ψ, and f might each stand, not for *any* property whatsoever, but only for *some* (undetermined) properties (of a specific class) and not for others. However, if this were the case, we should then need a symbol for the *more generic* "state of affairs" of "*property (any)—possessed by—entity (any)."* It is, then, this *generic* "state of affairs" that is, according to the first usage symbolized either by ϕx or by ψx or by $f x$.

But there are not only the *forms or matrices,* ϕx, ψx, and $f x$. There are also $\phi(x,y)$, $\psi(x,y)$, $f(x,y)$, and $\phi(x,y,z)$, $\psi(x,y,z)$, to denote, or symbolize, in the first case, *any* situation or "state of affairs" consisting of two terms "connected" by a dyadic relation, and, in the second case, *any* situation consisting of three terms "connected" by a triadic relation, and there are, of course, "situations" in which there are four, five, or, to generalize, N terms. In the "actual" situations the terms and the relation are specific, so that $\phi(x,y)$, $\psi(x,y)$, $\phi(x,y,z)$, $\psi(x,y,z)$, etc., "stand for" *any* of these specific situations, dyadic or triadic respectively, but not for any particular one to the exclusion of others.

In the matrices, ϕx, ψx, $f x$, both ϕ, ψ, and f, and x, are variables. This means that ϕ or ψ or f (whichever is used), and also that x, may have "values." If, now, ϕ (or ψ or f) is "given," or has, a "value" (*e.g.* mortal[ity], red[ness], round[ness]), but x is not "given" one, a *propositional function* "results." Thus, *e.g.,* "x is mortal," "x is red," "x is round," are each a *propositional function. Any propositional function* may, now, according to *varying usage,* be symbolized by $\phi(\hat{x})$,[2] or by ϕx,[3] or by $\phi(x)$,[4] but, since there is occasion, for the sake of clarity, to distinguish, because they are distinct, between, (1), the "state of affairs" in which neither ϕ nor x is "specified," and, (2), that in which ϕ *is specified* but x is not, and, (3), that in which both x and ϕ are *specified*,[5] the symbol, ϕx, is sometimes used for the first situation, and $\phi \hat{x}$ for the second, *i.e.*, for *any* propositional function. In accordance with this usage, ϕx "expresses" *any* situation *of a something* that has a property, ϕ, while $\phi \hat{x}$ "expresses" *any* situation of *a (specific) property (the property)* that something has.[6] In accordance with this symbolism, then, propositional functions would be expressed by such symbols as "$\hat{x}$ is mortal," "$\hat{x}$ is red," etc., and not by "x is mortal, x is red."

However, for the sake of simplicity, I think this symbolism ($\hat{x}$) can be advantageously dropped.[7] The *matrix* or form can then be symbolized by (a), ϕx or ψx or fx, the *propositional function,—not any*, but in each case, a specific one,—by specifying ϕ or ψ or f, so that we have, *e.g.*, (b), "x is mortal," "x is square," etc., and then, (c), *the proposition* that results when x is also specified, by *stating the proposition itself*, (1)—*e.g.*, "a is mortal," "b is square," etc.[8] We may also [9] "obtain" propositions in *three* other ways. Thus, instead of "specifying," first ϕ, and then x, (1), we may, (2), specify ϕ, but *generalize, or "quantify,"*

---

[2] Stebbing, L. S., *Modern Introduction to Logic*, pp. 133–134; Eaton, R. M., *General Logic*, p. 411.

[3] Lewis and Langford, *Symbolic Logic*, p. 91 f.

[4] *Ibid.*, p. 272 f. Lewis, *ibid.*, pp. 90–262, drops the parentheses when there is only one variable, x; Langford, pp. 262 ff., keeps them.

[5] *Cf.* Lewis and Langford, *opus cit.*, pp. 272 f.

[6] See Stebbing, *opus cit.*, pp. 133–134, also Eaton, *opus cit.*, p. 411.

[7] It is by Lewis and Langford.

[8] *Cf.* Lewis and Langford, *opus cit.*, p. 272.

[9] See *Ibid.*

x (instead of assigning a value to it), so that we have "$(\exists x) . x$ is round," *i.e.*, *the general proposition*, "There are round things." Or, (3), we may assign to x, in the matrix $f(x)$, the value a, so that we have the function $f(a)$, and then *generalize f* by writing, say, $(\exists f) . f(a)$, "giving" the *proposition* "a has some property." Or, finally, (4), we may generalize both f and x by writing, say, $(x) : (\exists f) . f(x)$ "giving" the proposition "Everything has some property or other."

However, in this book, it is chiefly with *propositions* of the first *two types* illustrated respectively, by "a is mortal," and "There are round things," that we shall be concerned. For example, I shall wish to show that there are such objective "states of affairs" or *propositions* as (Type 2) "There are *contingent* entities," and "There are necessary entities," and also (Type 1) "Space-Time is four-dimensional," "Negation is necessary" (a necessity), and "Necessity is (itself) contingent."

In the matrix ϕx (or ψx or fx) all "abstract" terms such as humanity, mortality, atomicity, necessity, impossibility, negativity, divisibility, etc., may be values of ϕ. Any such specific value constitutes together with x, in each case, a *propositional function*. Each such value of ϕ, or of ψ, or of f, is *a property*, or, broadly speaking, *a quality* which something may or may not have, or which may or may not be *realized, satisfied, exemplified, instanced*, or not, but with the fact of this realization, exemplification, etc., I am not, at this point, concerned. There may be nothing that is, *e.g.*, necessary, or impossible, or negative, etc., but, whether there is or not, *the properties of necessity, impossibility, negativity, etc., as specific possibilities-of-realization, nevertheless are.* This is the important point for us at this juncture. Each of these properties is *a specific possibility-of-instances, first of possible instances, secondly, of actual instances,* but the property itself does not "generate," "determine," or *necessitate* the *actual* instances. These must "come from outside," "from a source," and "in a manner" that is independent of the property itself. If these *actual* instances are found, then there *is* a class, the *x*'s, all members of which possess the property; if the actual instances are not found, then there is no class (of actual entities), but only the property itself and the *possible* instances. These alone may be said to be "determined" by the property itself.[10]

There may be, then, and, indeed, it is found that there are, not only those properties, *e.g.*, necessity, which *are* realized by actual instances, but also those which are *not* realized, either because they merely *are not*, *e.g.*, "disembodied spiritness" (*cf.* psychical research), or because they *cannot* be. In these two last cases we have, on the one hand, an empty class, *i.e.*, a class with no members, or a property with no instances, and, in the second case, a null class.[11]

[10] I am quite aware that, in taking this position, I am "going" somewhat counter to orthodox views, but I am quite willing to do this. The distinction which I make between the *possible* instances and the *actual* is, perhaps, quite basic to my argument. Such a statement as "The modern view is that any possibility of instances generates a class" does not convince me. *Actual* instances are also *possible* instances, but, conversely, even if it be granted that, if, *e.g.*, there *is* the property, there *are* also the *possible* instances, from these the *actual* instances cannot be discovered. Thus, *e.g.*, granting the property of Necessity, or the property of Atomicity, one cannot, either from *necessities* as possible instances of the first property, or from atoms as possible instances of the second property, derive or discover what the *actual* necessities or atoms in either case are. It is for this reason that I "attach little importance" to the *possible* instances, whatever this attitude of mind may mean. If no actual instances are found, but if such instances are nevertheless possible, the class is empty; if they are impossible the class is *null*. All null classes are, then, one null class, by virtue of the fact that they have no members because their "defining" property is itself an instance of Impossibility.

[11] The *Class of Null Classes* is itself, however, not Null, for it has one member, namely, *the* null class.

If, now, as above stated, in the matrix ϕx, ϕ is "specified," we have a propositional function. "X is human," "x is necessary," "x is divisible" are each such a function.[12] Further, if for x, there is substituted a specific value or values, so that we have, in the examples chosen, "Socrates is human," "The law of contradiction is necessary," "The universe is divisible," then we have *propositions* that, in some sense, are either true or false.

Important for us is the fact that the proposition, "*There are propositional functions or properties of some kind,*" is itself presupposed by the attempt to deny it, *i.e.*, *the reality* of at least *some* entities that are propositional functions, or "*properties*"—of *something*—is presupposed by the assumption of the negative. Thus, *e.g.*, anyone who asserts that *all properties* (abstractions) *are* (1) *fictions*, or *non-realities*,[13] *presupposes*, respectively, the two functions or properties, *fictionality* and *non-reality*, as those properties of which all other so-called functions or properties, such as divisibility, negativity, atomicity, etc., are instances. But, since there are some,—in this case,—two such *realities*, —there may be others. Indeed it is the position taken in this book, that there are many such others (properties), and that most if, indeed, not all of them are to be accepted as *real*, perhaps, because, in some cases at least, *to deny their reality is to presuppose it*. Thus it will be found that there *are*, as especially important for our consideration, the functions or properties:—Ultimacy, Functionality, Possibility, Necessity, Contingency, Impossibility, Actu-

---

[12] As I have previously noted, some writers, *e.g.*, Stebbing and Eaton, use $\hat{x}$ instead of x for such propositional functions as those of this paragraph, but Lewis and Langford do not do this. Their symbolism is simpler; so I will use it. *Cf*. Stebbing, *opus cit.*, pp. 133–134.

[13] Which the Nominalist and Instrumentalist do.

ality, Logical Priority, Relatedness, Similarity, etc. It will be found not only that each of these is a *property* which something *might* have, but also that each is a property which something, as a matter of fact, *does* have, *i.e.*, we shall find that *there are x's*, entities, which are instances of each of these functions, or *that there are x's*, or entities, which are, respectively, ultimate, functional, possible, necessary, etc. Thus we shall be finding or discovering not only *actual classes* of entities with certain specific properties, but also *propositions* such as "Contingency is *a* possibility," "Possibility is a function or property." Thus, in the case of the examples just given (of properties), we find that each of the word-symbols used stands for *something other than itself*, *i.e.*, for an *objective function or property that is a member of that class all members of which are properties, and, therefore, all of which have in common the property of Propertiness or of Functionality.*

The propositions, "Contingency is *a* possibility," and "Possibility is *a* function," are each *a proposition* that is identical with a specific relation of *membership* in a class that is "determined" by a specific property in each case.[14] The generic relation of membership in a class is symbolized by ϵ. Thus, *e.g.*, if *a* is the class of functions "determined" by the specific property, or propositional function, Functionality, and *y* (Possibility) is found to possess this property, and so to be a member of this class, then there is the *specific proposition* of the *form y ϵ a*, and of the content, "Possibility is *a* Function or Property."

---

[14] This is in accordance with the position defended in Chapter I, that *a proposition is an objective situation or "state of affairs."* A specific "belonging to a class," or "having a specific property," *is* such a "state of affairs." The proposition just stated, "as to what a proposition is," *is itself just such a proposition.*

The foregoing examples illustrate one type of *proposition*, as distinct from propositional functions and matrices. Several other types are to be distinguished from this type, as follows:

General propositions: One type of these is symbolized by $(x) . \phi x;$ *i.e.*, this symbol stands for the *form* of all such general propositions, whether true or false, as are illustrated by the propositions, "Everything is physical," "Everything is mental," "Everything is contingent." In the case of these propositions, first, ϕ, *in the matrix*, ϕx, is "specified," so that there are the propositional functions, "x is physical," "x is mental," "x is contingent," and then, secondly, each of the properties is "assigned" to all x's,— to "everything." Obviously, as regards the first two propositions, both cannot be true; also, both might be false. This illustrates the fact that a proposition has, or is, among other things, *the (objective) specific possibility* of being "made" *true or false by something external to itself*, *i.e.*, by something which is the "locus" of its verification or its falsification.

General propositions are of the *form*, then, $(x) . \phi x$, which means that, for all x's, ϕx. This becomes *a general proposition* when, first, ϕ is "assigned" a value, and then, for this property, a definite range of values, *i.e.*, *all* x's, is also "assigned." [15]

Another type of general propositions is symbolized by $(\exists x) . \phi x$. This is the *form* for all such propositions as are illustrated by "Some 'things' are living," "Some things are contingent," or, "There are living beings, at least one," and, "There are contingent entities, at least one." If, for

[15] For a presentation of the different types of propositions, *cf.* Eaton, *opus cit.*, Part III, Chapter II.

ϕx, "x is living" or "x is contingent" is "substituted," then $(\exists x) \cdot \phi x$ becomes, in the case of the foregoing examples, $(\exists x) \cdot x$ *is living*, and $(\exists x) \cdot x$ *is contingent*. Other examples of propositions of this type that are important for our later considerations are: "There are necessities," "There are impossibilities," "There are functions," "There are values (ethical and aesthetic)—at least one, in each case." Any of these propositions may be true, any, false.

Another, and perhaps more "frequent" and important type of *general proposition* is of the *form, $\phi x \supset \psi x$*, in which the symbol $\supset$ stands for *material implication*, which may be defined as meaning that *it is not the case (or, not the fact,—whatever this may mean) that a "something," x, has one (specific) property and not another*. The expression, $\phi x \supset \psi x$, then, symbolizes the *form* of all "states of affairs," or propositions that are of the type, "If x has one property, ϕ, it has another property, ψ." This "situation" may, now, be "assigned" either for *all* x's, or only for *some*, at least for *one*, so that, in the first case we have the *form $(x) \cdot \phi x \supset \psi x$*, *i.e.*, for *all* x's, if x has the property ϕ, it also has the property ψ, and, in the second case, the form $(\exists x) \cdot \phi x \supset \psi x$, that, for *some* x's, at least for one, if x has the property ϕ, it has the property ψ. As illustrating propositions of the first kind, we have, (1), "If anything is physical, it is temporal;" (2), "If anything is actual, it is possible;" (3), "If anything is implied by its own negative (or its own denial), it is necessary;" (4), "If anything is such that its alternative is neither necessary nor impossible, it is contingent." [16] Or these propositions may, perhaps, be stated in the form, to select some of them, (1) "Existence implies temporality,"

---

[16] These are the *extensional* forms.

(2), "Actuality implies possibility." [17] Propositions of the second kind, of the *form* $(\exists x) . \phi x \supset \psi x$, are illustrated by: (1) "For some instances, some x's,—at least one,—if anything is divine, it is good;" (2), "For some x's,—one at least— if anything is such that its negative is impossible, it is necessary," or, *perhaps* better stated, (1) "There are some things which are good if they are divine," and, (2), "There are some things which are necessary if their negative is impossible."

There are also *general propositions* of the *forms*, (1), $(x) . \phi x \vee \psi x$ and (2) $(\exists x) . \phi x \vee \psi x$, in which the symbol $\vee$ stands for the relation "either-or," and also, (3) of the *form* $(x) . \phi x . \psi x$ in which the second dot stands for the relation (?) *and*. As examples of propositions of the first two *forms* we have the propositions: (1), "For *all* x's, either x is physical or x is mental, *i.e.*, everything is either physical or mental," (—a false proposition, for the writer); (2), "For some x's, x is either possible or impossible"; of the third form, "There are some things (at least one) that are both actual *and* possible;" also, "Some things are both possible *and* necessary."

The next type of proposition to consider is of the *forms*, $(x) . \phi x \equiv \psi x$, and $(\exists x) . \phi x \equiv \psi x$, in which the symbol $\equiv$ stands for *equivalent to*. $(x) . \phi x \equiv \psi x$ symbolizes the "situation" that, for *all* values of x, ϕx is equivalent to ψx; $(\exists x) . \phi x \equiv \psi x$, the equivalence of ϕx and ψx, for *some* values of x. As illustrating propositions of the first type we have: (1) "In all cases, being implied by the negative (denial) is equivalent to being necessary;" also, "In all cases, having an alternative which is necessary is equivalent to being impossible."

[17] The intensional form. Whether or not the intensional forms are (always) the equivalent of the extensional, is a matter of doubt. The extensional form may be true, the intensional false, and conversely.

In the paragraphs immediately preceding, it has been found that, if, in the matrix, ϕx, ϕ is specified, or given a "value," such as, *e.g.*, humanity, necessity, divisibility, there result the propositional functions, "x is human," "x is necessary," "x is divisible," and, in turn, that these propositional functions may become further specified so as to give propositions of the forms $(x) \cdot \phi x$, $(\exists x) \cdot \phi x$, $(x) \cdot \phi x \supset \psi x$, $(\exists x) \cdot \phi x \supset \psi x$, etc. The propositions which result from the "substitution" of values for ϕ and for x in these functions may be true, or they may be false. Whether they are the one or the other depends, however, on "factors" external to (the propositions) themselves, but, whether true or false, they *are propositions, meanings, realities*.

There is the important question, then, that concerns these "factors" which are external to, and that make, the propositions true or false, *i.e.*, the "factors" by virtue of which the proposition is, or is not, realized or validated. These factors are those entities to which the proposition "applies," or, the class or classes to which it applies. Thus, *e.g.*, in the general propositions of the form, $(x) \cdot \phi x \supset \psi x$, and the contents, (1), "If anything is living, it is reproductive," and, (2), "If anything is expedient, it is good," there is the question as to the actuality of the x's that are respectively *living* and *reproductive*, *expedient*, and *good*, *i.e.*, there is the question as to the actual occurrence of the entities of which "livingness" and "reproductivity," "expediency" and "goodness," respectively, are properties. These entities constitute in each case the *real or actual class* that, as real or actual, conforms to the possible class that is "determined" by the propositional function or property, *i.e.*, the class of entities that are the possible instances of the specific property that is substituted for ϕ in the matrix ϕx.

Every specific property that can be substituted for ϕ in the matrix ϕx, or for ψ in the matrix ψx, etc., to give a propositional function (*e.g.*, "*x* is living," "*x* is necessary," "*x* is divine," "*x* is perfect") "determines" in each case such a class of at least *possible* entities, all of which, conversely, "have" that property. But the "occurrence" of *actual* entities which conform to the possible entities of a class as "determined" by a property, is *not* "determined" by that property. It may, indeed, be "determined" by nothing. In other words, either there is, or there is not, such an occurrence, as "a matter of brute fact."

Properties, then, may be of three kinds. There are, first those properties, *e.g.*, *atomicity*, "for which" there are entities *both actual and possible*. Secondly, there are properties for which there are *no actual entities, but only possible ones*, *e.g.*, the properties, Perfect Goodness, Perfect Justice, Moral Obligation, Divinity, Natural Right, the properties of a Perpetuum Mobile, etc.[18] These properties "determine" classes which I call *empty*. Then, thirdly, there are properties which are such not only that they do not, but also that they cannot, have instances. Such properties are illustrated, perhaps, by *round-squareness*, *dead-livingness*, *contingent necessity*, etc. Thus, *e.g.*, if "round-squareness" is *an impossibility*, then, on the one hand, it itself is *an instance of this property*, but, on the other hand, it is an instance which is of such a character (impossibility) not only that it *is not*, but also that it *cannot be*, exemplified,— *i.e.*, there are no possible instances of it. There are, then, *some properties* (if, by courtesy, they may be called this), some pseudo-properties, that, as themselves *instances* of Impossibility, *cannot be possibilities-of-instances*, of classes.

[18] I am not at all sure of this list.

With this exception, then, there is the proposition that, on the one hand, if there is a specific property as a value of ϕ in ϕx, *e.g.*, "living," then there is the propositional function (in this case) "x is living," and this function "determines" the class of living things, as *possible* entities, and, on the other hand, that this "set" of possible entities satisfies or realizes the function, "x is living." The relation is, therefore, reciprocal: if there is the function that "determines" the class, then there is the *possible* class that satisfies the function, and conversely. However, these possible entities need not be *actual*.[19] There *can* be no entities that satisfy a property (pseudo-) which is self-contradictory, but there are *possible* entities for any self-consistent property such as *immortality, perfect goodness, social progressiveness*, even though these entities are not found empirically to be realized. Such entities are possibilities, if not actualities.

We thus reach an important "principle" as regards classes, and discover an important distinction between three kinds of classes, as follows:—If propositional functions "determine" classes, then there are (1) those functions that "determine" classes not only of possible but also of actual entities, *e.g.*, (using the *property*) *Atomicity and Atoms;* (2), those functions that "determine" classes of possible entities which are not also actual in the sense that they have not as yet been found empirically, in the broad sense of this term, *e.g.*, "disembodied spiritness" (as per psychical research); (3), those functions that "determine" classes, not of possible entities, but of impossible ones, *i.e.*, entities that not only are not found, but cannot be, *e.g.*, round-squares. That there must be null classes of this last type

[19] Just what I mean by *actual*, by *fact*, etc., I shall discuss in Chapter V.

would seem to be "implied" by those propositions which are themselves values of the propositional function, "x is impossible," or "x is absurd." If there are the properties, *Impossibility* and *Absurdity*, then there are at least *possible* the subordinate properties or entities that are *impossible* or *absurd* and that, as such, cannot themselves have instances.

We may conclude, then, that the factors which are external to a proposition and upon which its truth or falsity depend are *independent* of the proposition itself. They are not "generated" by it, but must be found quite independently. But, also, the proposition is itself independent of these factors, not as regards its being true or false, but as regards *its status as a proposition*. Whether true or false, *it is a proposition*. Its only norm is *self-consistency*. If it is self-consistent it is *valid*, but not, therewith, either true or false. Yet, as self-consistent, it may also be either false or true. If it is not self-consistent, but self-contradictory, then, it is false, not only because nothing *can* confirm it, but also in the sense of being *invalid*. Indeed, one may then doubt whether it is a proposition at all.[20]

[20] This matter of the *self-consistency* of a proposition, and, therefore, of its validity, *apart from its truth and falsity*, (which are dependent upon factors external to the proposition itself) presents a difficult problem, which will be discussed in further detail later. In general, there are two positions with reference to the problem that is involved. One position is, that the proposition is self-consistent (therefore valid) or, perhaps better stated, that a system of propositions can be (and is) internally consistent (and therefore valid) quite independently of any application, any "concrete representation," any external factor. Lewis, in *Mind and the World Order*, pp. 237 f. *et passim*, Langford in Lewis and Langford, *opus cit.*, p. 347, Eaton, *General Logic*, pp. 46–47, and Sheffer as quoted by Lewis (*Mind and the World Order*, footnote to p. 245) support this first view. On the other hand, there is the position, taken by many mathematicians, that the consistency can be "*established*" only by an "appeal" to an external factor, to a "concrete representation." This is, of course, *an appeal to truth*, and means, I take it, that there is no consistency, and so no validity, apart from truth, indeed, that it is not only difficult but impossible to ascertain

One discovers, by such considerations, that the reciprocal relation of a propositional function and a class "determined" by it, enables one "to pass" from "the connotative form" of a proposition to "the class or denotative form," and conversely. Thus, from the proposition, "Humanity implies wickedness," one may, perhaps, pass to the proposition, "All men are wicked," (whether there actually are men, or not), the latter being an example of the traditional class-form of a universal affirmative proposition, and then one may go back again to the connotative form. The first proposition, as is well known, is "in intension," the second, the class-form, "in extension." [21]

Whether the two "forms" are identical or not is closely

whether a proposition is self-consistent *or* self-contradictory, and likewise with a system of propositions, by mere inspection of the proposition or propositions themselves.

With this second position, however, I do not agree, and for the following reasons: A proposition has a "content," or, it is a *meaning*. This is what distinguishes it from a matrix, such as ϕx, or a propositional function such as "*x* is human." The latter is *partly meaning*, partly (in a sense) not. In contrast, a proposition or a set of propositions is a *full meaning*, and it is by virtue of this full meaning, consisting of many constituent meanings, that there is discoverable either consistency (absence of contradiction) *or* contradiction, and, in the former case, *validity*, as distinct from truth (or falsity). Whether, however, in this position of maintaining that *propositions as propositions, meanings as meanings*, are such as to reveal their consistency or inconsistency, there is a concealed reference to an external factor, and therefore to a "concrete representation" and so to an external test, is an open question. There may be this reference, and there may not, but I am inclined to maintain that there is not, at least in all cases. Accordingly I would maintain that one can deal with *meanings*, ascertain their consistency, and so their *validity*, and yet never raise the question of their *truth or falsity*. The actual development of logical systems in Mathematics, Geometry, and perhaps other sciences, is, I consider, a confirmation of this interpretation. *Cf.*, as in essential agreement with this, Dr. P. Henle's article, *A Definition of Abstract Systems*, Mind, XLIV, N.S. No. 172, pp. 341–346.

[21] See footnote 17. This matter of the intensional and the extensional form of propositions, and of the relation of these two forms to one another, I purposely refrain from discussing in detail, since such a discussion is not demanded by the main thesis of this book. *Vide* Lewis and Langford, *Symbolic Logic*, pp. 60 ff., 271–274, 277 ff., 322; Eaton, *General Logic*, pp. 265–272, 411 ff., 419.

related to the question as to whether a class is "really" *many*, because of its *members*, either possible or actual, or both, or *one*, because of the *property* which "determines" it, or *both one and many*. But how can a class be both *one and many* (not-one), or *many and not-many* (one)? However, this question will not be further discussed, at least at this point. Rather, we shall revert to the problem that is suggested by the fact that there are at least two kinds of classes, namely, (1), the class of those classes of individuals that are *actualities*, and, (2), the class of those classes of individuals that are not actualities, but only *possibilities*. Examples of the last would seem to be: angels, perpetual motion machines, perfectly functioning democracies. Further, as previously suggested, there may be also the class of those entities or properties, all of which have the common property of Impossibility.

This problem leads us to the consideration of a subject-matter which is of extreme importance both theoretically and "practically" (*i.e.*, in the application of the principles involved), namely, the subject-matter which has received considerable discussion, since the publication of the First Edition of *Principia Mathematica* under the caption of *The Theory of Types*. It is not my purpose to go into great detail concerning, but only to state the essentials of, this theory. The theory has been given much "abstract" or theoretical discussion, but has not been "applied" to the extent that its importance deserves. The theory is important because the recognition of various instances of it reveals the character of any number of different situations in different fields.

To return to our examples: If there are, at least, the *two* classes, (1), the class of *actual* entities, and, (2), the class of merely *possible* entities, then we have, (3), the *two properties, φ, bare possibility*, and *ψ, actuality*, of which, (4), *merely possible entities and actual entities* are respectively the members, and then, (5), *the property, F,* of the next, the 2nd order, of which φ and ψ are themselves *instances*, forming a class. F_1, in turn, may itself be an instance of a property of the next preceding order, F_2, and so on, with the result that there would (seem to) be an infinite series of properties (and so of propositional functions, of classes, and of propositions) of different and of successive orders. If this is the case, we should have the matrix $F_{N+1} \cdots \{ F_1 [\phi (fx)] \}$.

Now the fundamental principle of the Theory of Types, stated very simply, is, that, if φx represents a function φ of the argument *x*, then the "things" for which *x* might stand, *i.e.*, the "values" of *x*, cannot include φx (nor anything "represented" by an expression in which φ occurs). In other words, no propositional function (as well as no function of the same type as a given function) can be a possible value of its own argument.[22] Thus, the principle means, to take two examples, namely, the two propositional functions, (1), "*x* is heavy," and, (2), "*x* is necessary," both of the form, φx, and with φ specified in each case, in, (1), as *heaviness*, in, (2), as *necessity*, that, in (1) heaviness not only is not, but cannot be, heavy, and in (2) necessity is not necessary. In other words, if any propositional function, of the form, φx, "determines," when φ is specified, a class of possible entities, and also if "for" this class of entities *actual* ones are found, then that specific property, φ (in the above examples, *heaviness* and *necessity*), is not an instance, either possible or actual, of itself.

[22] *Cf.* Eaton, *opus cit.*, pp. 455–456.

Not to go into any great detail concerning the matter, it may be said that the Theory of Types was developed by Messrs. Whitehead and Russell in *Principia Mathematica*, in both the first and second editions,[23] and by Mr. Russell in his *Introduction to Mathematical Philosophy*, in order to avoid certain difficulties or contradictions in certain specific situations. The Theory is given an excellent discussion by Langford in Chapter XIII, *Symbolic Logic*, Lewis and Langford.

The situations just referred to are called "illegitimate totalities" and "vicious circles." Such "totalities" or "circles" (to be avoided) are, seemingly, got into, if one "starts" with such propositions as, *e.g.*, "All rules have exceptions," (Lewis and Langford, *opus cit.*, p. 441) and "All generalizations are false" (Eaton, *opus cit.*, p. 457). Thus, to consider the second example, and to quote: "This" ('All generalizations are false') "being itself a generalization" it would seem that "if the *all* is inclusive, this very statement must be false. Since it is then false that all generalizations are false, *some* [24] are true; and the original generalization may be among the true ones. Thus, if the original generalization is true and includes itself, it may be false. This *contradiction* is reached by *disregarding the principle that a function cannot be a value of its own argument.*"

In further comment on this it may be asked, however, What about the "statement," "All generalizations are *true*"? Cannot (or does not) this "apply" to itself without contradiction? And the answer is, "Yes, it does." Then why not avoid the difficulty which the Theory of Types aims to

---

[23] A. N. Whitehead and B. A. W. Russell, Vol. I, 1st Ed., 1910; 2nd Ed., 1925, Ch. II, pp. 37 ff. and pp. 161 ff. The theory is Mr. Russell's. See American Journal of Mathematics, XXX (1928), pp. 222–262.

[24] The italics are mine in each case.

avoid, merely by excluding the possibility of ϕx being a value of x in $\sim \phi x$ (false)? "Why *extend* the Theory of Types so as *not* to permit ϕx or any expression containing ϕ, or any function of the same type as ϕ, to be a value of ϕ?" "The reason is that we are considering the *possible* values of the arguments of propositional functions, *the range of values* which these arguments *could* assume, *whether truly or falsely*, rather than any specific value that the argument does assume. If ϕ can be *significantly* asserted of x, giving ϕx, then $\sim \phi$ can be *significantly* asserted of x. If, *e.g.*, it can be significantly asserted of *any generalization* that it is true, the negative of this can also be *significantly* asserted of any generalization, namely, that *any generalization* is not true. Thus *a contradiction is always possible* by taking a function as a value of its own argument, though in some specific cases it may not arise." [25]

This means that the "range of meaning" of a propositional function, *i.e.*, the range of entities to which a specific property applies (or which have a specific property) is limited. It is limited, (1), in that the property itself is excluded from this range, and, (2), in that all entities that are *not significant* are also excluded.

---

[25] Eaton, *opus cit.*, p. 460. The italics are mine in some cases.

The matter can be stated very simply in symbolic form. The question is, If the rule is $(x) . \phi x \supset \psi x$ (all generalizations are false), then, can this generalization itself be a value of x without contradiction? If the rule itself is a value of x, then we have $(\phi x \supset \psi x)$ is ϕ (a generalization), so that, as a generalization, it is false. But if it is false, then some generalizations (at least one) are not false, $(\exists x) . \phi x . \sim \psi x$, which contradicts the "original" rule.

On the other hand, if we "start" with "the rule," All generalizations are true, $(x) . \phi x \supset \psi x$, $(\phi x = x$ is a generalization, $\psi x = x$ is true), and ask the same question, Can this rule itself be a value of x without contradiction? and "try it out," we then have $(\phi x \supset \psi x)$ is a ϕ (a generalization), so that, since $\phi x \supset \psi x$, *it is true*. This does not, then, as in the first case, contradict the original rule, so *that all rules, including this rule itself, can be true*.

This may be illustrated and the meaning of the term "significant" be clarified by an example. From the range of individual lines, the reds to the violets, *in the solar spectrum*, there is excluded, existentially, not only, (1), the property, spectral color, of which these lines are instances, but also, (2), all such actual or merely possible entities as individual sounds of specific pitch, etc., angels, perfectly functioning democracies, electrons, logical principles, etc. If, now, the red lines be selected for attention, these last entities (under 2) are *not-the-red-lines*, as, also, the *other lines*, the yellows, greens, and blues, are *not-the-red-lines*. Two kinds of entities are, then, not-the-red-lines. The one kind is *identical with, positively*, although it may be formally symbolized by *not-x* (not-red), *the other spectral lines*, yellow, green, blue (y, z, q), whereas the other kind, also symbolized by *not-x*, are not even spectral lines, but entities that lie *wholly outside of the range of values of the property*, *(solar) spectral color*. This second kind of entity is, now, not a "significant" opposite, whereas the first kind is "significant." The "significant" opposite, *not-x*, of an entity, x, is, then, one that is resolvable into one or more positive entities (y, z, q) which, together with that entity (x) are the instances of a common property.[26]

The principle of the Theory of Types,[27] means, then, that a propositional function (or a property, *e.g.*, atomicity) which "determines" a class of entities that are ultimate individuals, (such as, perhaps, atoms) is itself, not one of these individuals, but of a "different type" from them, *e.g.*, atomicity is not an atom; but it also means that a

[26] This is my own "theory" of the "nature" of *significance*. I do not find that this term has received much discussion.

[27] I shall return to the discussion of the theory in the next chapter, and, to some extent, in other subsequent chapters.

propositional function or property that "determines" a class, the members of which are themselves propositional functions or properties, is not itself one of these functions or properties (we shall find, *e.g.*, that Necessity is not *a* necessity, Impossibility, *an* impossibility, Dimensionality, *a* dimension, etc.) *but is of the next "higher" type.*

The Theory of Types holds, it is clear, both for propositional functions and for classes. This it must do if, for every class, there is a specific propositional function or property, and, for every such function or property that is not self-contradictory, a class either of possible entities, or of actual. There is, then, a hierarchy both of functions or properties *and* of classes. There is a hierarchy both of properties or of functions *and* of classes, because a property or function may be "at once" both a property of which there are instances, possible or actual, (forming a class) *and* an instance, perhaps with other coördinate or "significant" instances, of a higher property, *and so on*—although it is a question how far back one can go. One may ask, "Can one find *a property of all properties*, a function of all functions, a class of all classes?" But, whether one can or not, there is a series of functions, to be symbolized by $F_2\{F_1[\phi(fx)]\}$, in which the x's, possible or actual, are the instances of f; fx and its coördinate functions, the instances of ϕ; and ϕ and its coördinates, instances of F_1, *and so on*. There is, then, both a hierarchy of properties and a hierarchy of classes. Thus, to illustrate, if, in the matrix $F[\phi(fx)]$ we "substitute," for f, temporality, for ϕ, serial order, for F, relatedness, and, for x, the *individual* development from fertilized ovum to maturity of organisms, we then have the propositions, of the "type" $(x) . fx$, and forming a hierarchy, "All individual development is temporal" (true), "All temporality is serial order" (true), and "All serial order is relatedness" (true).

The principle of the Theory of Types applies, then, to properties and functions, to classes, and to propositions. Whether it is universally true, *i.e.*, whether it itself, as *a theory that consists of a "set" of propositions*, is realized or validated in all cases, or only in some, *i.e.*, in those in which it is, as a matter of fact, found to hold, and not in others, is a question that is left for later chapters. However, the theory does seem to apply to certain situations some of which are of interest and importance for the considerations of the book. For example:

(1) Behaviorism can be logically defended, not by its own theory (its defense is not an instance of itself), but only *non-behavioristically*.[28]

(2) The drama can be *criticized* and evaluated only by canons or principles that are *not* those of dramatic construction itself.[29]

(3) The argument for Skepticism is *not* itself an instance of this Theory.

(4) The propositions which constitute Kant's *Critique of Pure Reason* are *not* themselves instances of those propositions which, within the limits of and according to the theory of this Critique, are alone "permissible," *i.e.*, the Critique itself is neither "phenomenal" nor "noumenal."

[28] *I.e.*, Behaviorism finds absolutely no place, in its scheme of stimuli and responses, for any such "theory" as *logic*, as this is *usually understood*. Yet the behaviorist in developing and in "arguing" his theory, does infer, does use logic.

[29] For example, in Aristotle's *Poetics* there are recognized, as the principles of the drama, *the three unities* of *place*, *time*, and *plot*, but the *Poetics* itself is not constructed on the basis of these unities.

(5) The Principle of Indeterminacy ("applying," *e.g.*, to the attempt to get "knowledge" of, or to measure, simultaneously, *both the position and the velocity of an electron*) does *not* apply to the knowledge of this Principle itself. Knowledge of the Principle is of a different type from (the attempted) knowledge of both the position and the velocity of an electron.

Each of these examples is of the same type as the "statement" previously discussed, "All generalizations are false," which forces us, in order to avoid the contradictions ("vicious circles," etc.) involved in "applying" this statement to itself, to the Theory of Types. That is, each of these examples is *an instance of taking certain properties which are necessary* (presupposed) *in order, respectively, to defend* Behaviorism,[30] *to criticize* the drama, and *to state* Skepticism, Kant's *Critique*, and Indeterminacy, *to be false*, and, therefore, if each of these *positive properties* is ϕ, of asserting that *each is nevertheless an instance of* $\sim \phi$. Thus, *e.g.*, if, in the case of the Skeptical position, in order to assert, "There is no truth," there is presupposed the *truth*, ϕ, *of this very proposition or "statement" itself, then this proposition cannot be a* value of the property, Falsity (not-truth), $\sim \phi$ and similarly with the other examples. In general, with properties of the "forms," ϕ and $\sim \phi$ ("significant opposites"), and propositions as values of the functions, "*x is ϕ*,"

---

[30] Any such thing as the *logical* defense of Behaviorism is denied or negated by Behaviorism, *i.e.*, Behaviorism is identical with the denial of a logical defense. On the one hand, this logical defense cannot be an instance of its negative, Behaviorism, and, on the other hand, Behaviorism cannot, by its *explicit* theory, be an instance of its negative, logical defense, since Behaviorism explicitly grants no such thing as logic. But both a logical defense and Behaviorism, as "*positive*" doctrines, *could each be an* instance of itself, *i.e.*, a specific logical defense could be an instance of logical defense "in general," and Behaviorism could be itself behavioristically interpreted.

and "*x is ~ φ*," "*x is ~ φ*" cannot itself be a value of *x* in "*x is φ*." On the other hand,—and this is, I think, very important,—in the case of propositions (positive) of the form, *φx* (*x is φ*), *φx can itself be a value of x, without contradiction.* Thus, *e.g.*, the proposition, "There is truth," [(∃*x*) . *φx*], can itself be "one of the things," *i.e.*, a proposition, that is true, *i.e.*, it can itself be *an x*.[31]

As further examples of this last situation we have the possibilities, (1), of examining, *by* propositions, *propositions*, including those that "constitute" the "examination" itself, and, (2), of studying, *by* logic, *logic—all logic*, including that by which we study. Only, in either case, we must issue with such "results" as to propositions and logic respectively, as will consistently permit us to obtain these results. This is the norm of *self-criticism*.

In the next and subsequent chapters "application" will be made of the principles which have been presented in this and preceding chapters.

[31] In brief, it cannot be true that there is no truth, since, if this were the case, then *this proposition itself would be false*, in which case there would be some truth, which *contradicts* the original proposition.

III

THE QUEST FOR THE ULTIMATE
UP THE HILL

The principle of the Theory of Types, just presented in the preceding chapter, readily (at least negatively) suggests a Quest, which may be called the Quest for the Ultimate. This quest, in one form or another is almost as old as philosophy itself. It is the search for ultimate principles, for categories, which, perhaps, are of the character not only that they *are* what they are, but also that they must be. Are there such principles?

The Theory of Types very naturally raises this problem, which will be investigated through the medium of a specific inquiry, thus not only to seek a solution to the more general problem, but also to illustrate the application and importance of the Theory.

The Theory of Types suggests this Quest in perhaps three forms, as indicated at the close of the last chapter. First, if there are classes of classes of classes,—and there are,—then, Is there a *Class of all classes* (including itself)? Secondly, if classes are "determined" by propositional functions, by properties,—and they are in the sense that a specific propositional function is the possibility-of-a-class (of possible members)—then, Is there an Ultimate Function or Property (or, are there Ultimate Properties) *of which* all other properties (as well, also, as this ultimate property itself) are instances, *i.e.*, members of the class of entities

47

that have this property? Thirdly, if there are propositions of various types—and there are, because there are propositional functions whose arguments are satisfied or realized, *i.e.*, have "values,"—then, Is there an Ultimate Proposition, or, Are there Ultimate Propositions (*about all propositions*)? [1]

The current theory as regards the answers to the problem or problems stated by these questions is designed to avoid the contradictions which an affirmative answer in each case is held to involve, or seems to involve. As regards these contradictions, it is not necessary to our purpose to trace the tortuous paths which lead to them. Suffice it to say that each of these "concepts" (if it is permissible to use this term for situations which seem to be impossibilities) is held to involve a contradiction for much the same reason. This "reason," in the case of classes, is admirably "formulated" by Langford [2] as follows: "Let us take the class of all classes K. Of each member of this class, we can ask whether it falls within its own membership; so that we can divide K into two mutually exclusive and jointly exhaustive sub-classes, C and $\sim C$, where the first comprises all self-membered classes and the second all classes that are not members of themselves, and where, of course, one class or the other might be null. It may then be asked whether $\sim C$ is or is not a self-membered class. If it is, then it must belong to C, which contains all self-membered classes, but if it belongs to C, it cannot belong to itself, and so cannot be a self-membered class; hence, it must belong to itself,

---

[1] For example, are the propositions, "A proposition is that which is true or false" and "A proposition is that which results from the substitution of values in a propositional function" (Lewis and Langford, *Symbolic Logic*, p. 90) either one or both about *all* propositions, including themselves?

[2] *Opus cit.*, p. 448.

and therefore must again belong to *C*." We are in a situation, then, "where," if it be assumed that ~ *C* belongs to *C*, this leads to the conclusion that it *does* not, but, rather that it belongs to ~ *C*, and then, in turn, that if it belongs to ~ *C*, it nevertheless does not, but, rather, belongs to *C*.

Langford's "solution" of the "paradox" of "the class of all classes" is, then, that it is not "significant to say of classes either that they are or are not members of themselves," which means that the "concepts 'being a class' and 'being a member of' cannot be synthesized into a genuine proposition." [3]

The two other "situations" as at least "entertainable" for examination, namely, the one, that of a Property of *all* properties, or a Function of *all* functions, and, the other, that of a Proposition "about" *all* propositions, present essentially the same paradox as does the "concept" (?) of "the Class of all classes" with, *perhaps*, essentially the same solution, namely: "Being *a property*," and "being *an instance* of that property," and "being a proposition," and "being *that* which this proposition is about" (namely, in the case under consideration, *other* propositions) cannot be "synthesized," in either case, into a genuine proposition. This means that a property, *f*, which is an instance of another property, ϕ, so that we have $\phi(f)$, does not, *as such an instance*, function *as a property*, although *in another relationship* it may so function, *i.e.*, it may itself have instances; and also, that propositions "about" which there is another proposition do not, in that situation, "function" as propositions.

But, whether this be the correct solution of these par-

---

[3] *Ibid.*, p. 448. The paradox is known as Russell's; Langford adopts Russell's solution.

adoxes or not, there are the problems presented, and the contradictions to be avoided, if possible,—if not by one method (or solution) then by another. One currently accepted "method," as was indicated in the preceding chapter, is to avoid the contradictions by *limiting the range* of classes, of properties, and of propositions. Indeed, the solution just given above is to this effect. The range is limited by introducing the term, "*other*," so that we have, (1), "a class of *other* classes than this class itself;" (2), "a propositional function, ϕx, for *other* entities than itself as *values;*" (3), "a proposition 'about,' and made *true* or *false* (we will have to define *true = realized*, and *false = not realized*), by *other* entities than itself, *i.e.*, by entities that are *external* in some sense to the proposition itself." [4]

But even this position does not avoid another problem. If the x's that are the values of x in any function ϕx are the instances or "individuals" [5] all of which possess the property, ϕ, and so members, possible or actual, or both, of the class that is "determined" by ϕ, then is it not possible that ϕ itself should be an instance or value of another property or function, ψ, of the next higher order, and so on, with the result that there is no "highest" or ultimate property or function, but an infinite regress of properties? In other words, or in symbols, so long as the principle of the Theory of

---

[4] *Cf.* Lewis and Langford, *opus cit.*, Chapter XIII: "The Logical Paradoxes": These "other entities" might in this case be the "other propositions" just referred to as, in relation to a proposition about them, *not* functioning as propositions.

[5] Just what an "individual" is, is open to discussion and criticism. (*Cf.* Lewis and Langford, *opus cit.*, pp. 465 f., and Eaton, *opus cit.*, pp. 455 f.) I shall throughout this book use the term "instance" or "value" in preference to "individual," and in accordance with the usage I shall consider what is called by some a "sub-function," or "sub-property," to be *an instance*. Which term is used is, I think, a matter of indifference so far as my main argument is concerned. Thus, *e.g.*, I shall consider *continuous order* (see Chapter VI) to be *an instance of order*.

Types is observed, so that we do not have $\phi[\phi(\phi x)]$, but $\phi[\psi(fx)]$, may we not have, or *is* there not, a hierarchy of properties *with no last property?* [6]

It may be that the "correct" answer to this question is, "Yes; there is this hierarchy; there is no ultimate property." But I am not certain of this, or at least I can envisage another possibility. That possibility rests on the "principle," which was discussed in the preceding chapter, that the Theory of Types is "advanced" to avoid the difficulty which is incurred when we consider the *possible* values of the arguments of a propositional function, the *negative* as well as the positive, $\sim\phi$ as well as ϕ, but that this difficulty is itself excluded if we exclude the possibility of ϕx being a value of x in $\sim\phi x$, and allow it to be a value of x in only ϕx. As an example of this, the *proposition*, "All generalizations are true," of the form $(x) . \phi x \supset \psi x$, ($\phi$ = is a generalization, ψ = is true) may *itself* be one of the generalizations, one of the x's, that is true, so that *it* may be said to "apply" to itself, with no contradiction, thus to be *one* of the entities by virtue of which it is true.[7] On the other hand, if we "take" the proposition, "All generalizations are false," of the form, $(x) . \phi x \supset \sim\psi x$, then this itself *cannot* be one of those "things," *i.e.*, be *an* x, that is false, *without contradiction.*

---

[6] Both Eaton, *opus cit.*, pp. 455–456, and Langford, *opus cit.*, Chapter XIII, *Logical Paradoxes*, accept such a hierarchy. These authors follow Russell.

[7] While *no contradiction* arises from taking $\phi x \supset \psi x$ as a value of x, the "vicious circle" situation still remains in the following form, and prevents one ever determining whether $(x) . \phi x \supset \psi x$ is true or not: For, suppose we know that all generalizations except $(x) . \phi x \supset \psi x$ are true. Then, in order to know whether $(x) . \phi x \supset \psi x$ as a generalization about generalizations is true, we must first know whether it is true as an *instance* of generalization (since the generalization is not true unless its instances are). But the instance is identical with the generalization; so we cannot know the *truth of the instance without knowing the truth of the generalization.* This in turn depends on the truth of the instance which depends on the truth of the generalization, etc. This "situation" was pointed out by Dr. Henle.

Although this may take us into much debatable ground, I shall, nevertheless, from now on maintain, and indeed later develop the point of view, that certain *properties* may be instances of themselves, with no contradiction. Accordingly, I take the position at this point, as regards the problem under discussion, that, although there may be no *one* ultimate property, nevertheless there may be a finite group of (= *many, and not one*) *ultimate* properties which *are* such because, although no one is an instance of itself, each is, nevertheless, an instance of all the others. Thus the principle of the Theory of Types is preserved. But there is the alternative to this, namely, that of "giving up" the Theory of Types at this point, thus to be able to grant that *each of such a finite set of properties is not only an instance of all the others, but, also, of itself.*

In brief, and to summarize: There is either an infinite series (regress) of properties or there is not. If there is, then, *ipso facto*, there is no ultimate property. If there is not, then either there is *one* ultimate property or there are many ultimate properties. But there can be *one ultimate property* provided only it is at once *both property and instance*, since, *if it is not an instance of itself, it must be an instance of a higher property*, and so on, in an infinite regress. There might, then, (conceivably, *i.e.*, hypothetically) be, (1), only one ultimate property,—on these conditions. But there might also be, (2), many ultimate properties—a finite number—on essentially the same condition, yet with the two "variations," (a), of each one of these properties being an instance of the others, but not of itself, and, (b), of each being not only an instance of the others but also of itself. It is this last possibility that will be found, later in this chapter, to be the one that is realized.

Let us now apply these principles to a special problem,—to one, indeed, which is not only of interest and importance for itself, but which, as examined in this way, may settle the issue just stated. This problem concerns the scientifically familiar process of Evolution, of theories as to the precise nature of the process, of what it involves, etc., etc. It is by starting with Evolution that we enter on our quest either for the Ultimate or for the Non-Ultimate, whichever may turn out to be the case. We shall carry out our quest by "putting to use" the principles we have thus far been discussing. Agreement with all the details of our quest will not be expected, but, that there must be agreement with the main features, I shall endeavor to show.

I shall begin with the *individuals*, the particular plants and animals that are now living and that have lived in the past, and assume for these, as they are grouped into distinct species, one current and well-known theory of evolution, namely, that theory which is called *Emergent Evolution*. According to this theory, the evolutionary process is, (1), a temporal one; (2), it is irreversible; (3), it is causal—within itself, needing no outside causal agent; (4), it is divergent, *i.e.*, more and more distinct species of plants and animals have appeared, "as time has gone on," so that there has been an ever-increasing variety and complexity both of form and of function; (5), here and there, in the process, novelties (*something qualitatively new*) have appeared, such as, (a), with the origin of life, living beings, organisms, out of the non-living, and later, (b), conscious processes out of the non-conscious, and, (c), strictly rational or logical thinking out of the non-rational; the physical basis remains, but is superposed by vital phenomena; these two remain, to be capped by the conscious, and, in turn, by the social, the rational, and the moral.[8]

I am not saying that this theory is true. It may be, and it may not be. I am merely "entertaining" it as *one* theory of evolution, one possible account of the process that includes living beings both past and present, and the first living beings, in order to ask what it, as distinct from other theories of organic (and social) evolution, involves.

I find that, in accordance with the "principles" previously considered, there are present as "constituents" of this theory, a number of *functions or properties*, some of which, if, indeed, not all of which, are independent of one another. The species of (individual) plants and animals, their organs and functions, their "connections of heredity," and adaptations to environment, etc., *all together form or are the existential process of Organic Evolution* (I am "taking" the theory to be true). I find, now, that this process, either as a whole, or in respect to certain parts, or both, is an instance of, or the realization of, the following functions or properties:—(1), Temporality, (2), Irreversibility, (3), Internal Causality, (4), Increasing Divergency, (5), Increasing Complexity, (6), Creativity, or, better, Emergence(y), (7), Physicalness (if I may use this term), (8), Vitalness (an apology due here, too), (9), Spaciness, and, perhaps, (10), Consciousness, and, (11), Rationality. Just what the relations are between these properties, and whether or not other properties should be added to the list, need not, for the purpose at hand, be considered. The question to be asked is, rather, Are these properties or functions, one, some, or all of them, *functions* that "determine" classes

[8] *Cf*. Conger, G. P., *New Views of Evolution*, 1929, *passim*.

which have one or more actual members, but that are themselves, in turn, members of a class or classes that are "determined" by functions still "further back"? My answer is,
They *are* such functions.

Thus, *e.g.*, I find that the functions or properties, Temporality, Spaciness, Causality, Increasing Divergency and
Complexity, and Creativity (I use the term to mean *Emergence*) are each an instance of *some sub-function* of the still
more general function, (Simple) Serial Order. Thus the
functions just enumerated as examples play a two-fold rôle.
On the one hand, according to the Theory of Types, they
themselves are at a level that is different from the level of
the instance or the instances (the species and the individuals
of the species constituting the evolutionary series) that
"satisfy" them, so that, if these instances are said to be
existents, and thus to constitute *nature*, at least in part, the
functions themselves must be said *not to exist*, but, nevertheless, *to be real*. On the other hand, the functions themselves
are each a "value," an instance, of some higher function,
namely, of a function which is itself, in turn, an instance,
at least indirectly, of a still more general function, namely,
(Simple) Serial Order.

It is my purpose, at this point, to go into only as much
detail concerning Serial Order as is necessary to the carrying out of my program.

Let us return to the functions just previously enumerated, and consider each briefly:

(1) Temporality: This is the function or property,
compound, yet single, of which empirical or actual time,
as this is usually "conceived," namely, as a continuous
series of instants, is the realization (= an instance).
In other words, empirical time is an instance of Tempo-

rality [9] (which subsists whether it is "instanced" or not) and Temporality is in turn an instance of a Continuous Series.

(2) Spaciness: [10] This is the compound, yet single, function or property of which empirical space as (seemingly) identical with a continuous series of points, lines, and planes (3-dimensional) is an instance, whether this space be Euclidean or non-Euclidean.

(3) Causality: This is the function, compound, yet also single, of which, with its sub-functions of continuous, discontinuous, and, possibly, "dense" causality (or causal series), *existential* processes or events in the realm of the physical, the biological, the psychological, and the social, are the instances. [11] Within the limits of the field of each one of these there would seem to be causality of the continuous or, at least, the "dense" type, but "the causal jump" from, *e.g.*, the physical to the biological, and from this to the psychological, would seem to be *discontinuous* or discrete.

The processes or occurrences that *are nature* differ, also, in other respects, whether they are continuous, discontinuous, or dense. Thus, some of these processes may have, (a), neither beginning nor end (Energy), or, (b), both a beginning and an end (the birth and death of an organism), or, (c), a beginning and no end (the case of immortality,

[9] The relation between time and Temporality may be more complex than I have indicated, but "the complications" are beside my main point.

[10] *Cf.* Whitehead, *Introduction to Mathematics*, p. 240. Whitehead says, "The '*Spaciness*' of Space and the '*Numerosity*' of Number are essentially different things. None of the applications of algebra to geometry . . . obliterate this vital distinction." Italics are mine.

[11] I have in mind, of course, not, *e.g.*, simultaneous events, but *causal series* as illustrated by a particular development of some fertilized egg, or a particular chemical reaction, or the whole evolutionary process.

if it is a fact), or, (d), no beginning, but an end (the "heat-death" of the universe, possibly).[12]

The special type of sub-function of Causality of which an emergent evolutionary process is an instance is one, (a), which "allows" cause and effect to be qualitatively discontinuous, (b), which is *not* an instance of necessity between cause and effect (so that some other effect than that one which is actually found is *not impossible*). It is also one, (c), which "allows," between "points of discontinuity," stretches of continuity (*e.g.*, the germ-plasm may be continuous, as *per* Weismann, from *its beginning to its end*), and, (d), which is not *ipso facto* identical with progress or betterment.

(4) Increasing Complexity: This is the function or property which is exemplified by the existential individual entities in a more inclusive evolutionary series,—atoms, molecules, colloidal solutions (protoplasm), cells, organisms (multicellular), behavior, psychological processes, social institutions. This series may have *a minimum* of complexity (*e.g.*, the "final" constituents of the atom, whatever these may be) or not, *a maximum* or not.[13]

(5) Number: This is the function or property (to be discussed in detail later) [14] with which, through *its* several sub-properties or sub-types of serial order, the several aspects of the evolutionary process as regards the *manifoldness* and the *order* of, *e.g.*, electrons, protons, atoms, molecules, cells, organs, etc., etc., are in *one-one correlation*. This means that the evolutionary series, in whole, or in

---

[12] *Cf. e.g.*, Jeans, J. H., *The Universe Around Us, passim.*

[13] That is, the series as a whole is characterized by more and more complexity as regards the "individuals" that "appear" in it. A human being is certainly more complex than an amoeba, an amoeba, than a molecule of water.

[14] Chapter V.

part, or both, instances, in one or more respects, one or more of the *several types of order of which different series of numbers are themselves instances*, so that, while there is a one-one correspondence between certain numerical series and certain aspects of the evolutionary series, the two are *not identical*. For example, there is, (a), the discontinuous or discrete series of whole numbers, 1, 2, 3, 4, 5, · · · $n + 1$, and, (b), the discontinuous series of individual organisms which bud-off, in the successive generations of a common stock, from the germ-plasm;[15] *both of these are instances of a more general discontinuous serial order*, but they are not identical with each other, although they are in one-one correlation.

(6) Irreversibility: This is the function or property (of a series) of which the evolutionary process both as a whole and as regards at least certain of its parts or "divisions," is an instance. The evolutionary process is irreversible in that, (a), both as a whole and in part, it is temporal; (b), in that it is a causal series characterized by, (c), increasing divergence, (d), by increasing complexity; (e), in that novelties appear in a certain order, namely, *following the inorganic, the organic*, then *the psychological*, then *the social*. These specific irreversibilities are not identical with that specific irreversibility with which the well-known Second (generalized) Law of Thermodynamics (The Principle of Entropy) is identical, and, according to which, all processes in nature tend toward a "heat-death," or a dead-level of energy-potentials, or a maximum of disorganization.[16]

[15] I have "in mind" Weismann's Theory of the Continuity of the Germ-Plasm.

[16] *Cf*. Jeans, *opus cit.;* also Eddington, A. S., *The Nature of the Physical World*, Chap. IV.

What we find, then, is that the Evolutionary process is an instance of certain properties,—Temporality, Causality, Increasing Divergency, Increasing Complexity—to select some of those that have been discussed—and that these in turn are instances of a more general property, Order or Irreversibility. Intermediate, however, between these properties and Irreversibility are the several *sub-functions* or properties, amounting to twelve, of this more general function. Thus, (1), Serial Order may be continuous, discrete (or discontinuous),[17] or compact (or dense); (2), it may also "at the same time" be characterized by, (a), no beginning, and no end (exemplified by the negative numbers, o, *and* the positive numbers all together, ... -4, -3, -2, -1, o, 1, 2, 3, 4, ... in order of magnitude); (b), a beginning, but no end; (c) no beginning, but an end; (d) two ends. The "product" of these two kinds of "variations" "gives" *twelve* different types.

Each of these twelve types is realized or instanced by specific numerical series, and anything which is, together with a specific "number-series," an instance of one of these types, is *in one-one-correlation with the members (numbers) of that "number-series," without being* identical with it. For example, if the evolutionary series is "marked" by *the specific discontinuous order, inorganic, organic, psychological, social*, then this series is in correlation with the discontinuous or discrete numerical series (with two ends), *1, 2, 3, 4*, and these two series are each an instance of the more general series which may be symbolized, $x < y < z < q$, in which $<$ stands for "precedes," and there is *no* member of the series *between x and y, y and z, and z and q.*

[17] I shall discuss *discreteness, compactness,* and *continuity* in some detail in a later chapter, and shall use discreteness and discontinuity as synonyms, although very technically this should not be done.

Temporality, Causality, Increasing Complexity, Increasing Divergence, Spaciness, Emergence, are each a "value" or an instance of, or a specific realization of, some one of these twelve *subordinate properties* (instances) of the more general property, Serial Order.

Not to give in detail at this point the *properties* which are identical with the specific sub-functions of Serial Order, since to do this is not requisite to our present purpose, the properties, however, which are identical with that property or function which *is Serial Order in general* will be presented.

These properties are, as stated in both words and symbols, the following: There is a specific relation, R, and there are the terms, x, y, z, etc., that are related:—

(1) X does not have the relation, R, to itself, but "always" to another term, *i.e.*, the relation is *aliorelative* or irreflexive. This is symbolized, using ~ for "not," by ~ (xRx) or by ~ (yRy).

(2) Either x has the relation to y, or y has it to x; *i.e.*, using ∨ for "either-or," $(xRy) ∨ (yRx)$. This means that the relation is *connected*.[18]

(3) If x has the relation to y, and y has it to z, then x has it (must have it) to z. In symbols, if $xRy . yRz$ then xRz. The relation is *transitive*.

This set of functions or properties forms *one* function or property, compound yet single, that of *Serial Order in general*. To this set of functions or properties there may be "*added*" those more specific functions or properties which define the specific sub-types or instances of Serial Order, and *each* of these different and more specific sets is

[18] *Cf.* Lewis and Langford, *opus cit.*, pp. 340–341. From these properties, (1) and (2), there "follows" the property of *assymmetry*, *i.e.*, if xRy, then not yRx.

in turn *one* compound yet single function or property. Each of these sets may in turn have instances.

The specific functions which we have been considering as constituent properties of the function, Evolution, are each such an instance. Thus, Temporality is an instance of that specific type of Serial Order which is, (1), *continuous*, and, (2), in which there is *neither a first nor a last member* of the series, and, (3), in which there is "substituted" for x, y, and z, etc., instants. With this "substitution" made, a proposition or a set of *propositions* results by which Temporality is "defined." This set of propositions is true or false according as it is or is not realized by "what Time really is." But to ascertain whether or not such a set of propositions *is* true or not, and to derive the propositions by "substituting" values in the propositional functions specified above, are two quite different things. The one is a case for empirical evidence; the other is to "set up" a *possibility* as to the nature of Time.

What has just been said of Temporality also holds of Spatiality, Causality, and Emergence. Each of these properties is an instance of a specific type of Serial Order that is "derived" by "substituting" for x, y, and z, etc., specific "values," namely, instants, points, events, and existential qualities, respectively.

"Starting," then, in our example, with the *individual* parts, processes, etc., of various kinds, which are "*connected*" so as to form the *existential evolutionary process*, and "working backward," we have found that these individuals, parts, *etc.*, are, according to the specific Theory of Evolution we are considering (The Theory of Emergence), *instances* of such functions or properties as Temporality, Causality, etc. But each of these functions is, in turn, an instance of *a special type of Serial Order*, as identical with a set of special properties which together form a compound yet single function or property. But these specific functions, as identical with specific types of Serial Order, are themselves instances of that compound propositional function which is identical with the properties *of Serial Order as such*. There is, then, a hierarchy of classes and of the propositional functions or properties which "determine" these classes. In this hierarchy, the classes have members that are not merely possible, but actual. These members are, in one case, the *existent individuals, in nature*, which make certain propositions, derived from certain propositional functions, true or false, but, in other cases, the members of the classes are other *propositional functions or properties*, actual, and not merely possible. A propositional function or property plays, then, *a two-fold rôle*. On the one hand, it "determines," or is the possibility of, a class, either possible or actual, and is itself not a member of this class, but, on the other hand, it may also be, and, indeed, *is*, a member of a next higher class whose members are instances of a next higher property. In other words, *properties have properties, and these properties in turn have properties, and so on backward, either with no end, or until an ultimate property (or properties) is reached.*

In this situation there are, also, *propositions of various orders*. Thus, conforming to the matrix, $\phi x \supset \psi x$, there are, *e.g.*, the propositions, of the type, $(x) \cdot \phi x \supset \psi x$, (1), "For all x's, to evolve implies being temporal," or "Whatever evolves is temporal," and, (2), "For all x's, being related causally implies being serially ordered," or, "Whatever is causally related is serially ordered"—either continuously, or discontinuously, or compactly.

Thus there is a hierarchy, not only of properties or propositional functions, but also of classes and of propositions.

In our quest, then, we have "gone as far back" as Serial Order. Can we go beyond this property to a property or properties of which *this* in turn is an instance? That we may be able to do this would seem to be implied by the propositions, of the form, $(\exists x) . \phi x$, "There are classes of classes," "There are functions which are instances of higher functions" (conversely, "properties of properties"). What, then, "lies back of" Serial Order? What functions or properties, What classes?

As in other cases, so, also, now, it is not my purpose at this point to attempt a complete answer to this question, but only to blaze a trail, as it were, in order to ascertain how far back one may go.

The inspection of the functions that "determine" Serial Order in general discloses the fact that this Order is itself an instance of functions which are still more general. Perhaps the most important of these is the function or property of *being related*, or of *relatedness*, R. The complex x, y, and z as aliorelatively, connectedly and transitively related, to form serial order, is an instance of this more general function, but it is not the only instance. Indeed, there are many other instances. But the specific relatedness which is involved in Serial Order is one that involves at least *three* terms, so that it may be said that this order is also an instance of the more general function or property, *Plurality* or Manyness.[19] Also, as the postulates for Serial Order have been formulated, namely, $\sim (xRx)$ and "$xRy \lor yRx$," (as well as the theorem) "if xRy, then *not*

[19] Any relation, except, perhaps, that of Identity, involves a Plurality of Terms.

yRx", there are instanced or *realized* or, at least, "involved," in Serial Order, the more general functions of "*Either-or*," i.e., of *Disjunction* (or *Alternation*), and of *Negation*.[20] Finally, since at least some of the constituent functions of the compound function, Serial Order, are *independent* of the others, this function itself instances or at least involves [21] the more general property or function, *Independence*.[22]

Have these properties (Relatedness, Manyness, Disjunction, and Negation, and, possibly, also Independence) in turn a common property, so that, while distinct from one another, they form the class consisting of the instances of this property or function? I find that they have, and that this property is *Necessity*.

To "demonstrate" this, let us consider various definitions of this last function, or property, in order then to see whether or not, *by these definitions*, one or more of them, anything *is* (*actually*) *necessary*. If something is found, *quite empirically* (again, in the broad sense of the term), that *is* necessary, even though it be the only instance, then there *is Necessity*, although of course, this property itself would *be*, even though there were no actual instances of it.

There are the following definitions, as values of the propositional function, "*x is necessary*," giving propositions of the form, $(x) . \phi x \supset \psi x$.

(1) That is necessary *which not only could be and is, but*

---

[20] *Cf.* Stebbing, *opus cit.*, p. 186.
[21] The order is the whole. A "whole" may instance or involve a number of properties; for example, an organism is at once developmental, self-regulative, chemical, and physical.
[22] *Independence must be something*—a *fact* of some kind; but it is not a substance or a process. I can find only that it is a property, a quality, a function, which certain *relational situations* exemplify, and others do not.

also must be. The comment to be made on this definition is, (a), that if anything is necessary, it not only *is*, but also is *possible;* (b), that necessity is defined in terms of "*must*," so that the definition is circular.

(2) That is necessary *to which no alternative is conceivable.*[23] Comment: This definition is in terms of the psychological concept of "conceivability." To avoid this criticism, the definition might be amended to read "*logically conceivable.*" But, the question then arises: What is it *logically to conceive?* thus to "refer" the definition back to logic.[24] Further, the definition is in terms of "alternatives," so that we must ask, What is *an alternative?* and, also, Is there more than one kind of alternative? Also, are some alternatives "significant," others not? Some positive, others (one, at least) negative? Are alternatives of the same order, or of different orders?

(3) (a) That is necessary *which is implied by its own denial.*[25] Closely connected with this is the definition: (b), That is necessary which can be deduced from its own denial.[26] Comment: The second definition depends on the first, since deduction is possible, logically, only "where" there is implication. We need consider, then, only the *first* definition. This definition is in terms of "implied by" and "denial." "Denial" must be either, (1), *purely* and exclusively psychological, *or*, (2), it must be a judgment *and a meaning, a proposition,* so that it becomes *the negative, the contradictory.* Accordingly, (3a) is better stated in the form:—

[23] *Cf.* Lewis and Langford, *opus cit.*, pp. 24, 119.
[24] Logical conceivability is defined as the absence of (self-)contradiction, *ibid.*, p. 161.
[25] *Ibid.*, pp. 134, 244.
[26] *Ibid.*, p. 160.

(4) That is necessary *which is implied by its own negative or contradictory*. Comment: The question then is, What does "implied by" mean? To answer this briefly at this point, it may be said that there are to be distinguished, as is well known, two kinds of implication, namely, "material" and "strict."[27] The symbol for the former is ⊃, for the latter ⊰. Using, now, each of the symbols, p and q, for "proposition," ~ for *not* (im-, etc.,), and, ◊ for "possible" we then have the two following definitions of implication: (a) $p \supset q$ when (if) it is *not the case* that p is true and q is false, or, *since this leaves "true" and "false" undefined*, $p \supset q$ when (if) it is not the case that $(p \sim q)$; (b) $p \dashv q$, if (when) ~ ◊ $(p \sim q)$, which means, p implies q if it is *impossible* that p should *be* and q not *be*. This leaves "*be*" undefined, but this may be defined as equivalent to "(to be) real"—in some sense.

The original definition, "X is necessary, if x is implied by its (own) negative," thus becomes, if we *generalize* [28]

---

[27] For "Material Implication" *cf*. Lewis and Langford, *opus cit*., pp. 136 ff.; for "Strict Implication," *ibid*., p. 124. For a discussion of both "kinds" of implication, see Stebbing, *opus cit*., pp. 221 ff., and Eaton, *opus cit*., pp. 226–234. Lewis, *opus cit*., p. 134, formulates the "proposition," *that "if a proposition is implied by its own denial, it is necessary*," by "$\sim p \dashv p \cdot \dashv \cdot p$."

[28] I realize that objections may be made to this generalization, perhaps on the ground that it is *only propositions that imply or are implied*. Very well. Then I am willing to use some other term than "imply," such as *demands, necessitates, presupposes*, or "is impossible without." The term "imply" has no special sanctity, and even *it*, in the case of strict implication, is defined in terms of impossibility; $p \dashv q$ if it is *impossible* for p to be true, and q false.

What I am especially interested in, is categories, functions, *properties*, and I think that it is a perfectly legitimate question to ask, not only if there are some *propositions* that are *necessary*, but also if there are any *properties* that are of this character, and, if there are, then in what sense. Accordingly, if it is maintained that propositions alone *imply*, and properties as such are not propositions, then, of course, no property could, by definition, either imply or be implied by anything else, so as, possibly, to be necessary. Nevertheless, some one actual specific property, *e.g., Temporality*, might be impossible were there not some one other specific property,

and use x not only for *proposition,* but also for *property,*
(a) x is necessary, if ~ x ㅓ x, and this becomes, ~ x ㅓ x,
if ~ ◊ *(~ x . ~ x), i.e.,* the negative of x implies x, *if it is
impossible for ~ x to be and x not to be.*

(in this case) Serial Order, so that the latter would be *necessary* as *demanded,*
or *presupposed,* by the former, even if not "implied" by it, provided one
wishes, by definition, to limit the use of this last term to propositions.

Accordingly, since I am interested not only in propositions that may be
found to be necessary, but also in *properties* that may be of this character,
I shall frankly *generalize* and set up my own definition, so that I can say
that anything, x, whether proposition or property or something else, is
necessary if it is demanded by, or presupposed by, or even *implied* by, *its
own* negative, ~ x, or if its negative is impossible without it. This is all
the more legitimate especially since *necessity,* as between propositions, is
first defined in terms of implication (*p* is necessary if it is implied by ~ *p*),
and implication (strict) is in turn defined in terms of *impossibility* (~ ◊).
This last property and (or) its *constituent* properties (*negation* and *possibility*), if they are not mere words, must have *some status as properties and
not as propositions;* they must be either necessary or contingent (just matters
of fact) or, if these alternatives are not exhaustive, something else, but, in
any case, they are not impossible. What their character is, is to be found
by empirical investigation.

However, there may be, even with the generalized definition granted, a
further difficulty in the situation. For, whether "imply" or "demand" or
"presuppose" be used, it must be asked, *how,* on the one hand, can something, x, be demanded, presupposed, or implied by its negative, ~ x, unless
this negative in some respect(s) *is?* And yet, on the other hand, how can
~ x be in any respect whatsoever, if, as, *e.g., the negative of the necessary,*
it is, or should prove to be, *impossible?*

My answer to this inquiry is, that ~ x, as the negative of some specific
value of x, must first, in order that it may be, and before it can be, *found
to be an impossibility,* be at least *entertainable* as "an object of thought,"
so that *it is* in just this respect, if in no other. But also, if ~ x is found, on
examination, to be *an impossibility,* then *it is* in a second sense, namely,
that *it is an instance* of this (more general) property, Impossibility. One
cannot say of *an impossibility* (a specific one) that it absolutely *is not,* since
to say this is to presuppose that it *is* in the sense at least of being "entertainable" in thought or to thinking, and so is more than a mere word. And
further, and thirdly, since any specific impossibility as an *actual* instance
of Impossibility must be *possible* in order to be *actual,* any negative, ~ x,
of x, as a *specific impossibility, is* in this sense, too.

I shall, then, in what follows, not hesitate to seek for the necessary, or
for *necessities,* elsewhere than among propositions, and also, in this quest,
I shall *generalize* the definition with which I started, so that it becomes:
(1) That is necessary which is implied by (demanded by) its own negative,
or (and) (2) Anything, x, is necessary if the negative, ~ x, is impossible without
x.

Thus, *e.g.,* in the "case" about to be tried out, that of Relatedness, in
order to ascertain whether or not this, as *an x,* is demanded by its negative,

This may be "tried out" by an example: Is *Relatedness* a function or property that is necessary? In order to answer, let "Relatedness" be a value of x in the above, final, definition. Making this "substitution," we have: Relatedness is necessary (*i.e.*, *is a* necessity), *if it is impossible for non-relatedness to be, and relatedness not to be*. But this *is* impossible, since the complex, Relatedness *and* its negative, non-relatedness, is itself *an instance of Relatedness*. This complex, $x R non\text{-}x$, could not *be*, unless Relatedness also *were* a function or property.

In further comment on this it is to be said, (a), that there is here occasion for the introduction of a new term, accurately defined, namely, the term "presupposed by," or the "active form," "presupposes." A function or property may be said to be *presupposed, if its denial or its negative is an instance of the function itself*. Also, there is discovered by our analysis a "new" property or function, namely, *Impossibility*, because, *if there are impossible entities*, or situations, or "states of affairs," then there must be *Impossibility*, and there *are* at least two such situations as instances, the one, *the impossibility* of p and $\sim q$, when (if) $p \dashv q$, and the other, *the impossibility of "$\sim x$ being, and x not being*," "when" x is *necessary*, as illustrated by *Relatedness*. On this last ground such functions as *Negativity* and *Possibility* ("of the Second Order," as I shall call it) are

---

Unrelatedness, this last, even if it were subsequently found to be *an impossibility*, must first *be* in the sense (1), that it *is a* "*something*" that is "entertainable" in thought, (2), that, if found to be *an impossibility*, *it is, as an instance* of Impossibility, and, therefore, (3), that, as such an *actual* instance, it *is a possibility*. In one or in all of these respects there is *a something*, although it is *a negative*, $\sim x$, which may be found to *demand*, to *presuppose*, even to *imply* (in the generalized sense) its "opposite" or contradictory, x. If this were not the case, the demanding, or the presupposing, or the implying, would be, as it were, *in vacuo*, "springing" from nothing, although "going" to something.

also *necessary*, since, obviously, (whatever this may mean) *the negative of Negativity could not be unless there were Negativity.* In symbols, Negativity is necessary if $\sim$ Negativity implies Negativity,—which means that Negativity is *necessary* if it is impossible for $\sim$ Negativity to be and Negativity not to be (N for Negativity: $\sim N \dashv N \cdot \dashv N$). And likewise with Possibility. In symbols, if P stands for Possibility, Possibility is necessary if $\sim P \dashv P$, *i.e.*, if $\sim \diamond (\sim P)$ *and not P.* This checks. *Impossibility* could not *be* unless it were possible, which means that Possibility is "necessary to" Impossibility. Disjunction or Alternation, and Plurality also, conform to this test. Thus there *could not be* Non-Plurality as the negative "other" to Plurality, except there were Plurality: *this and its "negative opposite" are* a Plurality. Also Disjunction; Non-Disjunction as the alternative to Disjunction is impossible without (the property of) Disjunction. And now I add Identity: Non-Identity (whatever this is) as the negative to Identity would be impossible were not it (as well, perhaps, as Identify itself) *identical with itself.* It is *what it is, and not something else.*

(5) That is necessary *whose contradictory (denial, negative) is not self-consistent* (the symbol for consistency being $\circ$).[29] Comment: This definition leaves "self-consistent" undefined. Having defined it, we take *its* contradictory, the not-self-consistent, to use *this* in the definition. But we must first define *consistent* or *consistency.*

Consistency is absence of contradiction or of self-contradiction. Thus we may say: (1), The two propositions, p and q, are consistent, if p does not imply $\sim q$; (2), the proposition p is self-consistent, if it does not imply its own nega-

[29] Lewis and Langford, *opus cit.*, p. 160; for " consistency " *ibid.*, pp. 153 f.

tion; (3), *if it (p) does imply its own negation, then it is self-contradictory, and impossible;* therefore, (4), as *self-consistent, p is possible,* so that we have, (5), *whatever* is self-consistent is possible, and conversely. To be contrasted with (3) is the definition of *the necessary*, considered previously, namely, "That is necessary which *is implied by* its own negation."

Our original definition becomes, then, "That is necessary whose contradictory is not self-consistent, *i.e.*, is of such a nature that it implies its own negation, and is, for that reason, self-contradictory, and therefore impossible." This applies to the example previously used: Relatedness is necessary because its contradictory is impossible.

There emerges from this discussion a definition of Impossibility. This is the property or function, with possible instances (and some instances have already been found), of being self-contradictory. Impossibility and Necessity accordingly appear as, in a sense, opposites. If anything is necessary, its contradictory is impossible; if anything is impossible, its contradictory is necessary.

The results of this discussion may, perhaps, be advantageously summarized. In the course of it, various definitions of, or criteria of, *necessity*, have been examined; some of these have been found faulty, others to be at least definite and clear.[30] That definition which has this character to the

[30] There are other definitions which have not been considered for one reason or another. Among such definitions there are the following: (1), "That is necessary which cannot conceivably be false." (L. & L., 212); (2), "That is necessary which cannot possibly be false" (*p* is necessary if it is impossible that *q* be false). (L. & L., 160.) Two comments are to be made on these two definitions: first, "false" is not defined, and, secondly, "impossibility" in (2) is defined in terms of *inconceivability* in (1).

Then there are also the following, (3), "That is necessary which has no contradictory." (L. & L., 477–478), and (4), "That is necessary which has no *significant* contradictory." (L. & L., 484.) Although these definitions should, doubtless, be taken in their context to be clearly understood,

highest degree is No. 4, amended so as to read, "*That is necessary which is implied or presupposed by its own negative.*" Also, it has been found what "a *logically inconceivable* alternative" is. It is an *alternative* which is a contradictory that is impossible because it is self-contradictory or not-consistent.

Starting, then, with Relatedness, Plurality, Disjunction, and Negation as functions or as properties that are instanced by or present in Serial Order, we have been led back to Necessity (and to Impossibility). These four functions are *necessities* because each is presupposed by its negative.[31] *Since they are necessities, there is the function or property, Necessity, of which they are instances.*

Can one go still further back? Is there an anterior function or property of which Necessity is itself an instance, a property "determining" a possible class of which Necessity is itself an actual member? This is our quest,—to "go back" as far as we can,—either to a stop, or to a "non-stop," and, which it will be, cannot at this point be foretold. In this respect our investigation is quite empirical.

Our analysis of the several criteria for Necessity has shown, however, that, coördinate with the function, Necessity, there is the function, Impossibility. *The necessary* is that which is implied by its own negative, the impossible; *the impossible* is that which implies its own negative, the necessary. These two functions must, now, themselves be members of a class that is "determined" by a function, Possibility, *of a still higher order than the function by the*

the comments may be made on them, in the form of questions: first, What is the difference between a contradictory and a *significant* contradictory, and, secondly, How can that which is *necessary* be (a) implied by its negative (denial, contradictory), or (b) deduced from its negative, or (c) *have a negative* which is impossible, *unless there is a negative?*

[31] See pp. 68–69, this chapter.

same name that is coördinate with Negativity, Relatedness, etc.
There must be this higher function. For, if there is the
property which some entities possess (namely, those that
are necessary) of "being implied by their own negative,"
and also, if there is the property, which other entities
have (those that are impossible), of "implying their own
negative," then, since these two properties of Necessity and
Impossibility *are*, they must each be possible,[32] and therefore *are instances of Possibility of a higher order*. As properties that *are*, *i.e.*, that are found empirically, they are, on
the one hand, not impossible, nor, on the other hand, necessary. This means, in accordance with the Theory of
Types, that, since Impossibility is not itself *an* impossibility,
and Necessity is not itself *a* necessity, then these two properties themselves, as *facts* (of some kind), *are possibilities*,
and therefore *instances of Possibility of the First Order*.

At this point an important question arises. We have gone
beyond Necessity and Impossibility to Possibility of a
higher order. Are there other instances, one or more, of
this higher function,—instances that are coördinate with
Necessity and Impossibility?

This question may be put in the form: Are there "somethings" (*x*'s) which, on the one hand, do not imply their
own negative (which impossible entities do), and, on the
other hand, are not implied by their own negative (as
necessary entities are)? I answer, "Yes." There are some
entities that *merely are*, without being either impossible or
necessary,—indeed,—much stronger than this,—with it
impossible for them to be either necessary or impossible.
Such entities are *contingencies*, and they all possess the
property of *Contingency*. This property is, then, coördinate

[32] Whatever is *actual* is *possible*.

with Necessity and Impossibility. It is the property, which some entities have, not only of not being, but also of *impossibly being, either necessary or impossible*.[33]

Thus there are three *kinds* of properties, as sub-functions or instances of the higher function, Possibility, that conform to what in simple language are called, (1), that which *must* be, (2), that which *cannot* be, and, (3), that which (merely) *is*.

It now remains to define this property, this function, Possibility of this higher order, thus to distinguish it from that Possibility, *of lower (second) order*, which is an instance or value of Necessity.

Possibility of this second order is *a necessity* because it is *implied by its own negative*, as are also Negativity, Relatedness, etc. In contrast, Possibility of this higher order is the property of (1), *not implying its own negative;* it is the not-impossible. Necessity, Contingency, and Impossibility each conform to this definition, and so are instances of this property. *Impossible* entities are such as *do* imply their own negative, but Impossibility (according to the Theory of Types) is itself not such an entity, nor is Necessity, nor Contingency.

Other definitions of Possibility of the higher order are:

(2) Possibility is Self-Consistency.[34] Comment: This reduces to (1) since the self-consistent is defined as "that which does not imply its own negation." [35]

(3) The possible is that which is logically conceivable, or capable of intellectual construction.[36] Comment: *This*

[33] Ultimately, *all fact* is of this character.
[34] Lewis and Langford, *opus cit.*, p. 123.
[35] *Ibid.*, p. 123. "◊ p is equivalent to 'It is false that p implies its own negation.'"
[36] *Ibid.*, pp. 119, 161; *cf.* Eaton, *opus cit.*, p. 48.

reduces to (2) *and then to* (1), for the reason that, only that which is self-consistent can be intellectually constructed and is logically conceivable.

(4) Possibility is the function for all complexes (sub-functions) that are open to realization.[37] Comment: "Realization" means having "instances," or "values," so that there is a class with actual members. "Open to realization," however, means "There *may* be such members," provided they are *logically conceivable* or can be *intellectually constructed*. This definition accordingly reduces first to (3), then to (2), and then to (1).

(5) Closely allied with (4) are the definitions:—That is possible, (a) which has "significance"[38] or "meaning," and, (b), "which conceivably might have an interpretation."[39] Comment: Having "significance," and "a conceivable interpretation" reduce to "open to realization," then to "logical conceivability" and "intellectual constructivity," and *so "go back" to* (1).

(6) Possibility is the property which an entity has by virtue of being *a coördinate alternative* to something else.[40] To be this, it must, however, "ultimately" have the property stated in (1) and the other properties that reduce to (1). To illustrate: There are *alternative* (various possible) Geometries, Theologies, Theories of Mechanics, Theories of the Nature of Life, Systems of Philosophy, etc.; etc. These examples could be extended almost indefinitely.

(7) The possible is "the non-existent."[41] Comment and Criticism: The non-existent, if it is "significant," "open

---

[37] *Ibid.*, pp. 480–483.   [38] *Ibid.*, pp. 474–475.   [39] *Ibid.*, pp. 67, 379 f.

[40] *Ibid.*, pp. 123, 153 f., Chap. VIII, especially pp. 257–261, Chaps. XI and XII, *passim; cf.* Eaton *opus cit.*, pp. 471–473.

[41] *Ibid.*, pp. 67, 182, footnote, 270, 318 ff., 471 ff.   Lewis says, "There is a definite intensional truth and falsity about non-existent but conceivable things, like unicorns." p. 67.

to realization," "logically conceivable," etc., is certainly possible, but existents are also possible; otherwise, no existents. This definition should, then, be inverted, so that we would have, "Both existents and non-existents are possible," so that we must go further back, to (1), in order to define the (purely) possible, *i.e.*, that which is possible *whether it is realized or not*.

I conclude that that definition which best stands criticism is: Possibility is the property, the function, ϕ, which anything, x, possesses, of "not implying its own negative (denial)," or, of being "self-consistent," *i.e.*, not self-contradictory, *i.e.*, *not impossible*.

Possibility of the higher order is, then, a property, a function of which a class of sub-properties or functions, namely, Necessity, Impossibility, and Contingency are instances, and these "instances" are, in turn, realized by certain sub-classes of properties or functions still "lower down," "going through," *e.g.*, Relatedness, Serial Order, the several sub-types of Serial Order, Temporality and Causality, until finally the ultimate particular individuals (the existential evolutionary process) of nature are "reached." But we now have the important question, Is this Possibility of the First Order itself an instance of a still higher property or function?

I find that it is, but in saying this I feel that I am on treacherous ground. Nevertheless I shall venture. Possibility of the First Order is *a property or function* of which there are the three instances, just discussed, Necessity, Contingency, and Impossibility. I ask, then, How could it (Possibility) be *a* property, *a* function, unless there were in the *structure* of things a *still higher* function, of which Possibility, as *a* Property, is (itself) an instance?

There might be other instances of this higher function; there might, indeed, be no instance of it at all, but this last is not the case, since Possibility is found empirically. *There might be no instances*, since a function or property, to be such, does not have to have instances—*actual* ones. If it does, then it is realized, satisfied, exemplified, and there is a class either of one member, or, perhaps, of more members, but, if no instance is found, the property is still *a specific possibility-of-instances, and so an element of "structure" in the universe.* Indeed, a function, a property (*i.e.*, any property, any function) may be defined as *a specific-possibility-of-instances*, and other, more specific properties may be found, quite empirically, to be the *actual* instances of this function, which, by the Theory of Types, unless we question this Theory, would not be an instance of itself. I find, then, that Possibility of the First Order, which is *a function or property*, must itself be an instance of the still higher property, *Functionality*, or *"Propertiness,"* or *"Possibility-of-Instances."*

This is, of course, very abstract, but it is intended to be this. We cannot, in our quest, be meeting with anything else than very abstract things; so it is well not to flinch, or to dodge, or to evade.

Can our quest, now, be carried any further back at the risk of being still more abstract? The risk should not be deterring; it were much better taken.

Possibility is *a* function, *a* property, and so is itself *an* instance of *Functionality*. There is, then, the function, Functionality. Is, now, this function ultimate? If it is, then it is *an* ultimate, so that it is an instance of *Ultimacy* which, accordingly, is "beyond." Then Functionality is not ultimate: but Ultimacy is itself *a* function or property, and so is itself *an* instance of Functionality, so that Functionality, and not Ultimacy, is "beyond."

Accordingly, we discover what may be called the Antinomy or Paradox or Dilemma of Functionality (or Propertiness) and Ultimacy. Each presupposes the other. Functionality, if, or as, *an* Ultimate, presupposes, or is an instance of, Ultimacy, and Ultimacy, as a function, presupposes, or is an instance of, Functionality.

But, not only is there, at this point, this paradox, but there is also a violation of the Theory of Types. There is no reason why this Theory should not be violated if it is found that the Structure of things violates it. The Theory, as a theory, is a set of propositions,[42] which, like other sets of propositions, are *true* in so far as they are (found to be) realized, or "confirmed" by fact, and *false* in so far as they are not thus confirmed. Accordingly, the facts concerning properties and instances may not confirm the universal proposition, that "*All* instances of '*properties and instances*' are such that *no* property can be an instance of itself." There may be exceptions. *There may be some properties that are instances of themselves.*[43]

Now it is with the discovery of Ultimacy and of Functionality that *two exceptions* to the Theory of Types are found. First, Functionality, Propertiness, *the* Possibility-of-Instances, is, itself, *a* property. It is quite arbitrary to call it anything else, for it is certainly not a process, nor a relation, nor a substance, nor a living organism, etc. By exclusion, it is *a* property. And, likewise, secondly, with

[42] That is, a set of propositions of which one may be aware, and by means of which one may, under certain conditions, communicate with another mind. These propositions are meanings, whether true or false by virtue of being realized or not.

[43] As previously found in this chapter, pp. 51–52.

Ultimacy. There is the paradox, then, that each of these functions is "beyond" the other, so that each is ultimate, and yet, that neither is, since each is an instance of the other. Ultimacy is, then, in one respect, although not in another, *an* Ultimate, and so, in violation of the Theory of Types, *an instance of itself*.

We have thus discovered an interesting state of affairs. Our quest, as we have made it, from the existential evolutionary series through properties which are themselves instances of other properties, to *Functionality and Ultimacy*, has led us to a Duality and not to a Oneness of Things. Must we stop here?

According to the general position which is being presented in this book, *Functionality and Ultimacy are not mere words, nor ideas, but realities. They are* and, *being*, they are instances of Reality.

Two questions then arise. First, one asks, "As *realities*, can they be impossible?" to which the answer is, "No." But, on the other hand, "Are they necessities?" Or, even more strongly, *"Is it impossible that they should be necessities?"* To which the answer is (for the second form of the question), "Yes." *As realities, then, that can be neither impossible nor necessary, they are, each of them, a contingency, and they therefore presuppose Contingency.*

To "Propertiness" and Ultimacy we must, then, seemingly, now add Reality and Contingency (of the First Order). What, now, is the "state of affairs" which these four present? I answer:

I.—*Reality* is not a word or an idea (mental), but, like Functionality, *an instance of itself; i.e., Reality is a reality.*

II.—*Contingency* is (likewise) real, and so, as neither impossible nor necessary, *is itself contingent.*

Thus, again, the Theory of Types is violated.[44]

We then have the interesting "state of affairs" that each of these four, *Reality*, *Contingency*, *Propertiness*, and *Ultimacy*, is an *instance of the other three as well as of itself. Thus:*

Reality is *a* reality, *a* contingency, *a* function, and *an* ultimate.

Contingency is *a* contingency, *a* reality, *a* function, and *an* ultimate.

"Propertiness" is *a* function or property, *a* reality, *a* contingency, and *an* ultimate.

Ultimacy is *a* property, *a* reality, *a* contingency, and *an* ultimate.

To this list we may now add Possibility of the First Order, with the outcome, (1), that Reality, Contingency, Propertiness, and Ultimacy are each *a* possibility. They must be this, if each is *a* reality, on the basis of the "principle" that *whatever is real is possible.* But, (2), Possibility is itself *a* Possibility, *a* Property, *an* Ultimate, *a* Reality, *a* Contingency.[45]

A "stopping place" has at least been reached in following a trail which started with the existential evolutionary series and which has led to properties or functions that are instances of higher functions, with these last, in turn, instances of still higher functions. The "point" that we have reached is a stopping place because the *hierarchical* form, in accordance with the Theory of Types, of "instances of properties which are not instances of themselves" *stops* when we find a certain finite number of properties or

---

[44] As usually formulated.
[45] One might, perhaps, add Identity to this list. Identity is, then, *a* Possibility, *a* Reality, *a* Property, *a* Contingency, *an* Ultimate, but also we may say, I (I),—Identity is an instance of Identity.

functions that are *both instances of themselves and of each of the others*. Possibility, Reality, Contingency, Functionality, and Ultimacy, in this respect, together form the stopping place.[46]

We are thus led, not to a Monistic, but to a Pluralistic Metaphysics; not to Mind, or Matter, or Self, or God, or Experience or an Unknowable, as, in each case, *the Ultimate One* of the Universe, but to a Pluralism of Five Functions or Properties.

Having made the ascent, we shall now, in the next chapter, make a descent. We have come up by one trail. May it not be possible to go down by another?

[46] In close agreement, I think, at least in many respects, with the critical position developed in this and the preceding chapter with reference to *The Theory of Types*, is the criticism made by Professor Paul Weiss in an article with that title published in Mind, N.S., Vol., 37, pp. 338–348. Professor Weiss states a number of "difficulties" that are involved in the statement of the Theory itself, and finds that we are led to the "acknowledgment of a theory of types of limited application." He finds that it must be admitted that there are certain entities, *e.g.*, certain general or "unrestricted" propositions which, as "formal principles" *are* capable of being taken as "arguments" to (instances of) themselves (pp. 345–346). This is, of course, the point which I have stressed. In conclusion, Professor Weiss says: "Not all the problems it (the Theory of Types) was designed to answer require it; another principle of greater logical import is desirable; while for the resolution of the problems in which it is itself involved, very drastic remedies are necessary."

IV

PROPERTIES AND INSTANCES
DOWN THE HILL

We shall consider in this chapter, as at least a beginning, some of the other trails that may be taken from the summit down, instead of merely returning over that trail by which the ascent was made. These other trails may be taken because they are real trails, not blazed in every case, perhaps, but nevertheless fixed by the terrain over which we are travelling.

In our quest for a function or property that is ultimate, we have reached Functionality, or "Propertiness," and Ultimacy themselves, and have found that each of these is not only an instance of the other, but also an instance of itself. It has also been found that these two properties are not mere words, or ideas, or fictions, but realities, so that each is an instance of Reality, which is also an instance of itself, since *it* is *real*. On the basis of the principle that whatever is real is possible, these three properties (Propertiness, Ultimacy, and Reality) are, also, each *a* possibility, so that there *is* Possibility. And further, on the basis of the principle that that which is, or can be, neither impossible nor necessary, is *contingent*, these four realities are contingent, as is also Contingency itself.

However, in what follows this complicated situation will not be repeatedly referred to. Rather, "Propertiness" and Ultimacy will be stressed, keeping "in mind" all the time that these are *realities* that are *contingent*.

The outcome of our quest might have been different. It might have resulted in finding that there is nothing Ultimate, but that each step in the series of properties necessitated another step, in an infinite regress.[1] This, however, has not been found to be the case, or the fact.

Accordingly, in this chapter we shall start with Functionality and Ultimacy, and "go down the hill," in some instances following a different trail from that which was taken in our journey upward. As we do this, it will be our effort to discover some of the more important details of structure that are present in the realm of properties that lie "outside" the realm of Nature, *i.e.*, the realm of *ultimate, particular individuals*, physical, living, conscious, and social. These individuals are indirectly, through the medium of "properties," finally instances of Possibility of the First Order, Functionality, Ultimacy, Reality, and Contingency.

The result is that *all* particular existent entities, whether inorganic, living, psychological, or social, all processes, such as Evolution, of which these entities are "parts," all the properties of which these entities and processes are themselves instances, indirectly and mediately "participate" in *the property, Contingency*. All of these entities, processes, and properties (of and with properties of different orders) *are; they are what they are*, but, beyond that, there is no reason. In fact no entity of any kind whatsoever *need be* at all. *Any entity that is might not have been.* All entities from the particular ones lowest down to the highest ones, such as Ultimacy and Functionality, then, simply *are*. However, *being*, and being *what* they are, they participate in the *structure that is*. What, then, is this

[1] An infinite regress is a *series* in which every "element" or member of the series is preceded by another "element" of the series; there is no beginning, no first "element"; there may be or may not be a last.

structure? What is the "scheme," the pattern, the arrangement, of the properties that compose it?

Possibility of the First Order is itself, as has been seen, *a* property or function, and, as such, an instance of Propertiness, of Functionality. In turn, Necessity, Contingency, and Impossibility, each being possible, are instances of Possibility of this order. These three constitute *the class* of actual, *i.e.*, of empirically found possibilities of the *First Order*.

There is no reason why Possibility of the First Order should have these three instances. It might have no instances at all, or three instances different from these three, or more than three instances. All that can be said is that, Possibility, being itself *a* function or *a* property, is, like other properties, *a possibility-of-instances*, or, that *instances of it are possible*. And then it is found that there *are*, as a fact, *three* instances, namely, Necessity, Contingency,[2] and Impossibility.

Each of these three properties or functions is, now, a property which other properties possess, a function of which other functions are instances. Each will be examined separately, first, Necessity, then, Impossibility, and, finally, Contingency.

NECESSITY

In endeavoring to find what entities, functions, or properties *are necessities*, *i.e.*, actual members of the class,— we shall define Necessity as the function or property of

---

[2] Contingency is defined as the property, which may or may not be "possessed" by anything, of *impossibly being either necessary* or impossible, *i.e.*, anything is contingent (= an instance of Contingency) if it neither implies, nor is implied by, its own negative. Contingency is, then, an alternative to Necessity and Impossibility, and each of them is an alternative to the other two.

"*being implied by its own negative.*" This was the definition which was found in the preceding chapter best to stand the test of criticism.[3] Anything which has this property is necessary.

What, now, are the functions or properties that have this property? In answer, I give the following list, which may be incomplete as well as open to criticism and correction:—

Possibility of the Second Order, Disjunction (either-or) Negativity, Plurality ("Manyness," Conjunctivity), Relatedness, Identity.

This is not a very long list. Noteworthy for their absence from it are certain functions (or "categories") which have been repeatedly and persistently, in the history of philosophy, regarded as necessary, notably Causation, Substance, and the "Law of Excluded Middle."

IMPOSSIBILITY

Impossibility is the function or property, as has previously been found, which "something" has, if this "something" *implies its own negative,*—this negative being, for this reason, necessary. That there is this entity, Impossibility, is presupposed in saying that *anything is impossible.*

What, now, are instances of this function? In answer a list is again given which is, doubtless, open to criticism and correction, and so to additions or deletions:—

The list: the Contingency of the Necessary; the Necessity of the Contingent and of the Impossible; the Impossibility of the Contingent, of the Necessary, and of the Possible; the Impossibility, if $p \dashv q$, of p being true, and q being false ("strict" implication).[4]

[3] Chapter III, pp. 68–70, especially footnote.
[4] One may well ask why, if Disjunction, Negativity, Plurality, Relatedness, and perhaps Identity are each *a necessity*, the *negative of each of these*

Perhaps the list might be, seemingly, expanded indefinitely, to include anything which is not consistent with itself, such as round-squares, variable cardinal numbers, living-dead men, etc., but at this point there are included in the list only those impossibilities that are essentially *coördinate with the necessities in the foregoing list.*

Another name for Impossibility is Self-Contradictoriness. The list given is made up of subordinate functions or properties each of which has *this* property. One could not "significantly" speak, *e.g.*, of an *impossible proposition*,[5] unless there were (a) *propositions*, as entities distinct from symbols, judgments, and facts external to the proposition, (b), the property, Impossibility, and (c), the *possible instances* of this property. The list I have given consists of instances that are more than possible; they are *actual* and *specific* instances, found quite empirically, and distinct both from the symbols (words) for them, and from the awareness of them. Obviously, if I think that, *e.g.*, a contingent necessity, or a necessary contingency, or, at lower levels, a triangular ellipse, or a living stone, is impossible, it is not my thinking that is of this character, *but that of which I think.* My thinking in this case is *an occurrence, a fact,* and so cannot be impossible.

But, even though Impossibility is a *property of properties,* a higher function of lower functions that are *actual,* and not merely possible, it does not follow that these "lower" properties or functions, in turn, have instances. Proper-

is not *an impossibility.* I would reply that this is exactly what is found to be the case. Each of these negatives *is* an impossibility by the criterion, that *the impossible is that which implies its own negative.* Thus Non-Disjunction as *an alternative* to Disjunction implies Disjunction; Non-Negativity as *the negative* of Negativity implies Negativity; Non-Relatedness, as "*the opposite*" of Relatedness, implies Relatedness (R = "negative opposition"), and Non-Plurality as "*the other*" to Plurality implies Plurality.

[5] Lewis and Langford, *Symbolic Logic,* p. 174.

tiness,—Functionality in general,—has been found to be *Possibility-of-Instances*, and *a property* to be *a specific possibility-of-instances*. This holds for most properties, namely, for those that are not self-contradictory or impossible. But some properties, such as round-squareness, contingent necessity, etc., are *specific impossibilities-of-instances*, and so are themselves instances of Impossibility. Such properties not only do not have, but cannot have, instances, either actual or possible; or, conversely, they are properties not only which nothing does have, but which nothing can have. They may be said thus to "determine," in each case, a *null class*.[6]

CONTINGENCY

Contingency is the property which something has, or the function of which something is an instance, if that "something" not only is not, but also *cannot* be, either necessary or impossible. For, if anything that is contingent could also be necessary, then it might be this, and if it were, then it would no longer be contingent. Likewise, if anything that is contingent could also be impossible, then it might be this, and, if it were, it would, again, no longer be contingent. The reason for accepting Contingency, then, as a property or function distinct from both Necessity and Impossibility, is that there are certain entities which *cannot be either necessary or impossible*. By exclusion, then, such entities must be contingent, and so *instances* of the property, Contingency.[7]

[6] Another type of class is found in the case of those properties which lack instances not because instances cannot be but because they merely are *not found*. Such a class I have called "empty."

[7] *Cf.* Stebbing's statement, *Introd. to Logic*, p. 201, "The system of the actual world *cannot* be logically necessary, and anything that is the case might have been other than it is."

What, now, are the properties or functions that, *at this point*, are to be accepted as the instances of Contingency? The list includes only three, and they are:—Necessity, Impossibility, and Contingency itself, *of the Second Order*, if one is to conform to the Theory of Types.

This means, stated simply and clearly, that (1) Necessity is on the one hand *a* possibility of the First Order, but that on the other hand it cannot itself be either necessary or impossible. By exclusion, then, it is contingent. (2) Impossibility, also, is not either necessary or impossible; by exclusion, then, it, too, is contingent. (3) Contingency, likewise, is not impossible, nor is it necessary; therefore it is *contingent*. One can thus admit, frankly, that the Theory of Types is violated, or one can save the Theory by taking the position that Contingency is of *two orders*, and that the First Order is not an instance of the Second.[8]

Let us now return to Necessity,—the function, the property,—and to the instances of this property which were enumerated in a preceding paragraph, namely, Possibility of the Second Order, Disjunction, Negation, Plurality, Relatedness, and Identity. Each of these is itself *a* function or property, identical with a specific possibility-of-instances. What, now, are the *actual* instances that are found for each of these properties?

To answer this question completely would demand the consideration of a very large number of details, the presentation of which would take us into diverse fields. Accordingly, our discussion will be limited to certain illustra-

[8] See the discussion of this in Chapter III.

tive details that are germane to the main purpose of this chapter, which is to trace "downward" certain lines of properties of properties of properties. Accordingly, no attempt will be made, either in this or in later chapters, to have this "tracing" complete, since it is not our intention or desire to present, *e.g.*, either a Symbolic Logic, or a System of Geometry, or a specific Mechanical Theory.

Possibility of the Second Order, Disjunction, Negation, Plurality, Relatedness, and Identity are, according to one of our main theses, properties or functions. These properties are symbolized respectively by $\Diamond$, $\vee$, $\sim$, $.$, R, and I. Now, according to our main thesis, each of these as a property or function is *a* specific possibility-of-instances, and as such is a reality, whether there are *actual* instances or not. But, in the case of these properties, as with, *e.g.*, the property, Impossibility, *actual instances* can be found, *and* in great number, so great, in fact, that these instances themselves prove to be of *different kinds*.

The first class of *instances* will have as its members the so-called "elementary functions of propositions." [9] Now to have "*functions of propositions*" there must be, it is evident, not only functions, but also *propositions*. Let us again ask, then, *What is a proposition?* In Chapter I a proposition has been identified with an *objective meaning* that is distinct from, (1), symbols, (2), the fact or facts to which the proposition refers, and, (3), the consciousness

---

[9] Lewis (Lewis and Langford, *opus cit.*, p. 123) calls these "functions" "ideas," but (p. 153), he uses the phrase "ideas *of* possibility and of impossibility," thus at least to suggest their *objective* character. To call them "ideas" is to introduce "mentalism" of one sort or another into "logic," and, accordingly, to raise many debatable questions. The second meaning conforms to the point of view of this book. If there are ideas *of* possibility and impossibility, then these properties are not identical with the *ideas* of them.

of (a) the symbols, (b), the meaning, and (c), the facts. And, in Chapter II, several kinds of propositions have been distinguished. Also, in Chapters II and III, and in this chapter, the "concept" of "propositional function," *i.e.*, of a property which something may have, has been fundamental to our discussion. At this point, then, a proposition may be defined as that "state of affairs" which is *identical with the fact of a specific property having a specific instance, or, instances*, or, with the fact of *a* variable (x) in a propositional function, x is ϕ (specified) having one or more "values." [10] Thus, with, *e.g.*, "x is mortal" a propositional function, "man is mortal," "Mussolini is mortal," and "time is mortal," are each a *proposition*. Each is capable of being *true* or *false* (the first two are true, the third, false) by reference to a "state of affairs" that is, in each case, external to the proposition itself. By themselves, with no "reference" to such a state of affairs, these propositions are neither *true* nor *false*, but since such a reference is always potential, a proposition is itself a specific *possibility of truth or falsity*, which is to "translate" "potentiality" into possibility.[11] In contrast with this "kind of truth," there is, secondly, another "kind" which has to do with the proposition as a *consistent meaning*, and thus as something that is quite independent of any external "state of affairs." According to this definition of truth, any self-consistent meaning is *ipso facto* true. Thirdly, there is the kind of truth, to be distinguished from the two preceding kinds, that is identical with facts, at least with facts of a specific character. Such truths may be

[10] *Cf.* Lewis and Langford, *opus cit.*, pp. 90–91.
[11] Eaton, *General Logic*, p. 26, defines *propositions* as "objects of our thought possessing the *capacity for truth and falsity*." The italics are mine.

illustrated by "logical truths," [12] or the "truths of logic." To this matter of "different kinds of truth" we shall shortly return (in Chapter V).

Propositions of different types "result," then, or, propositions *are*, when there are "values," both for x and for ϕ, in the forms or matrices, $(x) \cdot \phi x$, $(\exists x) \cdot \phi x$, $(x) \cdot \phi x \supset \psi x$, $(\exists x) \cdot \phi x \supset \psi x$, etc. Propositions, of different types, are *realities*. Examples of some of these different types have been given in Chapter II.

However, with the possible analysis ignored by which the type might be disclosed, "any proposition," of whatever type it may be, may be symbolized by p, even as *any* property may be symbolized by ϕ. If the analysis into contituents, *e.g.*, into subject and predicate, or into terms and relation, be made, the proposition is said to be "atomic," [13] even as when a molecule is analyzed into its constituent atoms. But also, just as molecules act as units in certain circumstances, so also, propositions are units in certain circumstances, and they are then called "molecular." Accordingly, the symbols p, q, r, will, in what follows, be used to symbolize molecular or unitary propositions.

There are *four* symbols here. Using the symbols ◊, ∨, ~, ., for (the functions) *possibility, disjunction, negation,* and *conjunction* respectively, it is found that, as *instances* of these functions or properties, there are subordinate "*functions of propositions*," p's, q's, r's, etc. These functions constitute the basis for what is sometimes called the Logic of Propositions, in contrast with the Logic of Classes, and the two are sometimes held to be *Logic per se*. But into this

[12] *Cf.* for "statements" in which "purely logical truths" are recognized, Lewis and Langford, *opus cit.*, pp. 24 and 355, and Eaton, *opus cit.*, p. 26.
[13] *Cf.* Eaton, *opus cit.*, pp. 49 ff.

matter of names I shall not enter. I am concerned with establishing the fact of *a series of instances of properties which are in turn instances of other properties*, back to the properties of Functionality, Ultimacy, etc., and in then retracing my steps by various routes. This is what I am doing in the present case. "Starting with" negation, possibility of the second order, disjunction, etc. (each *a* necessity), there are found as *instances* of these functions the following "functions of propositions":—

(1) *Strict Implication*,[14] symbolized by $p \dashv q$. Definition: $p \dashv q$ *if* $\sim \Diamond (p \sim q)$. "Translated," this means, "p implies q," (thus making it possible to deduce q from p,—the deduction being *psychological*) if it is impossible for p to be *true* and q *false*, or, better, for p *to be, and q not to be*, in some sense of *being*. Comment: "True" and "false" here are undefined. This is unsatisfactory. Obviously, for clarity's sake, these "terms" should be defined. *Three* definitions (of true or truth) are found in the literature, each of which may be stated *in the form of a propositional function*. These three definitions are:—

(1) Any proposition, p, has the *property*, ψ, of being *true*, if the proposition is *realized*, ϕ,[15] or, whatever proposition, p, is realized, is true. This is itself a proposition of the form $(x) . \phi x \supset \psi x$ (for *all propositions*, being realized implies being true).

(2) Any proposition, p, is true if it has the *property* of

---

[14] *Cf.* Lewis, *Survey of Symbolic Logic;* Lewis and Langford, *opus cit.;* Eaton, *opus cit.;* Stebbing, *Modern Introduction to Logic,*—each book in various places. The "expression" "strict implication" is due to Lewis. Stebbing, pp. 221 ff., calls "strict implication" "entailing," and Eaton calls it (pp. 226–230) "necessary implication."

[15] Instead of "realized" (see Lewis and Langford, *opus cit., e.g.,* pp. 318 and 472), we might say "exemplified," "agreed with," "validated," "represented." All of these terms are used. For the discussion of these symbols (if they are that) and of "the meaning of truth," see Chapter V.

being *self-consistent*.[16]   In the form, $(x) \cdot \phi x \supset \psi x$, this is: All self-consistent propositions are true propositions. This is itself a proposition.

(3) Any proposition, p, is true if it has the *property* of being a *fact*, at least *a fact of a certain kind*,[17] *i.e.*, in the form, $(x) \cdot \phi x \supset \psi x$, Whatever is a fact of a certain kind is true. This, again, is itself a proposition.

Obviously, these definitions of "truth" in terms of "realization," "consistency," and "fact of a certain kind" leave these terms in turn undefined.   Accordingly they should be defined, if possible. To this task we shall shortly come—in Chapter V.

The *Strict Implication* of q by p is, then, an instance (compound) of *negation, possibility*, and, perhaps, of "truth" and "falsity" in some sense of these last two terms, but it itself (Strict Implication) is a function or property of which, in turn, there may be, and, indeed, there are, many instances, namely, *all* those instances (thus forming a class) of one specific proposition implying another specific proposition in the sense defined.

Material Implication: symbolized by $p \supset q$. Definition; $p \supset q$ *if* $\sim (p \sim q)$; "translated" this means p implies q, if it is *not the case or the fact*, that p is true and q false. Comment: Not only are "true" and "false" undefined, but also "the case," "the fact." According to this definition, p *implies* q, if (1) p is true, and q is true; (2), if p is false and q is false; (3), if p is false and q is true. These are the well-known "paradoxes" of material implication.[18]

The material implication of q by p is, then, a complex

[16] *Vide* Lewis and Langford, *opus cit.*, p. 163.

[17] *Ibid.*, pp. 256, 355.

[18] Lewis and Langford, Lewis himself, Stebbing, and Eaton, *opera cit.*, each discuss "Material Implication" in various places.

instance of *negation,* "*fact*" *or* "*case*" (factuality), and "*truth*" *and* "*falsity*." Material Implication is also defined in terms of *negation* and *disjunction,* symbolized as $p \supset q$. $= . \sim p \vee q$, and translated, *p implies q if either p is false or q is true.*

Disjunction: symbolized by $. \sim p \vee q$. This is defined $p \vee q . = . \sim (\sim p . \sim q)$; "translated," this means that "either p is true or q is true" is the "defined equivalent" of "it is false that both p is false and q is false." Comment: "True" and "false" are undefined, and Disjunction is defined in terms of Conjunction and of "true" and "false."

Conjunction: symbolized by $p . q$. This is defined, $p . q . = . \sim (\sim p \vee \sim q)$. Translated, this means "p and q" is the defined equivalent of "It is false that either p is false or q is false." Comment: Conjunction is defined in terms of Disjunction and of "false."

Principle of Contradiction: symbolized by $. \sim (p . \sim p)$. Translated, this means that p (*i.e.,* any proposition) is not both true and false.

Excluded Middle: symbolized by $p \vee \sim p$; "translated": either p is true or p is false.

Syllogism: symbolized either by $p \supset q . q \supset r : \supset p \supset r$, for material implication, and by $p \dashv q . q \dashv r : \dashv p \dashv r$, for strict implication.

Strict and *Material Implication, Disjunction, Conjunction,* and the "principles" of *Contradiction, Excluded Middle* and the *Syllogism* are, then, *each* a (compound) function that, on the one hand, is an *instance* of the more general functions of possibility, negation, etc., but that, on the other hand, is also a function of which there are instances. *There are these instances if there are "values"* for p, q, and r, as related "implicatively," disjunctively, etc., *i.e.,* if specific propositions, capable of being true or false, are "substituted" for p, q, and r, as the case may be.

There are still other "principles" included in "the logic of propositions" that are at once both instances of the more general functions we are considering, and also, in turn, themselves functions or properties with instances *lower down*, but, for our purpose, it is not necessary to consider these other principles. The subordinate functions already presented, such as *implication,* suffice to show that there *are* instances of the "higher" properties or functions, Possibility of the Second Order, Negation, Disjunction, etc. These "higher" properties are each *a specific possibility-of-instances,* but *what* the instances "shall be" is not determined or implied by these properties. The actual instances—in this case, implication, disjunction, etc.,—are, on the one hand, *not necessitated* by the functions or properties, nor on the other hand, are they impossible. As neither necessitated nor impossible, these actual instances, are, then, *contingent.*

This outcome is, perhaps, a paradox, at least, from the traditional point of view as to the nature of logic. For, if logic is identified, at least in part, with the specific relations of propositions just considered, then the traditional view is, that *logic is not contingent, but necessary.* But, according to "the view" just presented, this logic is quite contingent. It is, on the one hand, an instance of certain *necessities,* such as negation and disjunction, which are themselves instances of necessity, though *not necessary instances.* And Necessity itself is also, as we have found, neither necessary, nor impossible, but contingent. So, *indirectly, logic, the logic of*

*propositions, which has been the stronghold of the abso-
lute and the necessary, turns out to be an instance of contingency, and, therefore, to be contingent.* Stated simply, this
means that *logic is*, but that there is *no necessity why it
should be.*

But, not only is this logic contingent as regards its more
remote "ancestry," but it is also of this character as regards its immediate parentage. For, given Negation,
Possibility of the Second Order, Disjunction, etc., logic, as
an *actual instance* (compound) or value of these functions,
is not necessitated. No actual instance ever is. So again, it
(logic) is contingent. It is contingent then, both in its
remoter "source" and also as regards its own distinguishing
characteristic functions, or properties, as *actual instances*
of functions or properties of the next higher order.

THE LOGIC OF RELATIONS

Having examined the logic of the unanalyzed propositions,
p, q, r, as one part of logic, "derivable" from more general
functions, it would, perhaps, seem "logical" next to consider the "logic of classes." Propositional functions, or
properties, are specific possibilities-of-instances, and, therefore, of-classes; if there are *actual* instances, then there *are*
actual classes. *Instances* of actual classes, and, therefore,
of the "logic of classes," have, however, already been met
with, *e.g.*, in the case of the classes that consist of, (1), those
entities that are *necessities*, (2), those entities that are
impossibilities, and, (3), those entities that are values of
Possibility of the *first order.*

However, classes involve relations of different kinds. The
specific relations present in a specific class are, therefore,
instances of the more general function or property, *relation.*

The actual members of a class are *similar* in the respect that they are all instances or values of the *same property or properties*, and *similarity is a relation*. At the same time, however, that the members of a class are similar, they may or may not be different from one another, but if they *are* different, then the relation of *different from* (or the fact of difference), if this may be called a relation, is present.[19] But the members of a class may be related in still other than these two ways, *e.g.*, they may be so related as to, (1), form a simply ordered series, as do, *e.g.*, instants of time, or, (2), as to "give" a whole of the type of a living organism whose parts mutually "influence" one another. In each of these cases, *"organizing" relations* of a definite type are present. Classes, then, by virtue of specific relations, are, some of them, organized, *i.e.*, they are more than a mere class, while others are not, or may have at least the minimum of organization. But in any case, classes involve relations, so that it would seem to be more "logical" first to consider the "logic of relations," and then to examine the "logic of classes."

Specific relations are found in great variety. "Similar to," "equal to," "next to," "greater than," "less than," "father of," "ancestor of," "cause of," "better than," etc., are each a specific relation. But these relations, while specific and different from one another in certain respects, may also be similar in that they themselves are instances of "higher properties." In other words, *specific relations are themselves related*, and as related in certain *specific* ways, namely, as *similar* to one another in one or more respects, they themselves form *classes*, or *types*. What, then, are some of the more important classes or types of relations? To answer this

[19] The members of the class are at least *distinct* from one another.

question, recourse is had to what has become the orthodox classification.[20]

(1) A relation (with the possible exception of *Identity*) relates terms,[21] at least two, but sometimes more than two. Accordingly relations are classified as *dyadic, triadic,* etc.

(2) A relation has *sense* or *direction*. Thus, if xRy, (*e.g.*, x is greater than y) the relation R is said to "go" from x to y. X is the *referent*, y the *relatum*.

(3) Every dyadic relation, R, has a converse, $\breve{R}$, *i.e.*, if xRy, then $y\breve{R}x$. This is a case of strict implication. It is also an instance of the property of "conversity."

(4) A relation may "go" from, (a), one term to *one* term, or, (b), from one term to *many* terms, or, (c), conversely, from many to *one*, or (d) from many to *many*. Accordingly relations are either *one-one, one-many, many-one,* or *many-many*. Instances: of (a), monogamic marriage,—one husband, one wife; of (b), the center of a circle, and the points on the circumference; of (c), the converse of this; of (d) parents (two) and offspring (two or more).

Specific relations of these three types are, therefore, instances of the *properties*, "*one-oneness*," *one-manyness, many-oneness,* and *many-manyness*.

(5) A term may have a relation, R, to itself. Example:

[20] This account of relations is presented, although it contains little, if anything, *new*, both because it is required in order to make my general plan complete, and because definite "use" will be made of it in later chapters.

The account which I give is orthodox. It may be compared with accounts in Lewis and Langford, Eaton, Stebbing, *opera cit.*, and also with accounts in Huntington, E. V., *The Continuum as a Type of Order*, and in Russell, *Scientific Method in Philosophy*.

[21] This is a relation's "function in life." A relation "simply" relates, and doesn't need anything else, *e.g.*, any other relation or any "higher" or any "deeper" entity, of any kind, to help it out. *Cf.* my discussion of Theories of Relations in *The New Rationalism*, Chaps. XXVI–XXVII.

a is identical with itself, *i.e.*, *a* is *a*. This relation is an instance of the property, *reflexiveness*.

(6) In contrast with (5), a relation has the property of being irreflexive or *aliorelative* if the relation is such that no term has the relation to itself. Examples: "greater than," "father of."

(7) A relation is *symmetrical* when the converse relation, $\breve{R}$, "equals," or is the same as, the "original" relation, *R*. This property is Symmetry. Examples: "equal to," "similar to," "cousin of."

(8) A relation has the property of *Asymmetry* when $\breve{R}$ is "incompatible" with *R*, *i.e.*, if *xRy*, *then not yRx*. Examples: "greater than," "father of," "better than," "before," "superior to."

(9) *Non-Symmetry*. A relation has this property when *R* is "sometimes" "the same as" $\breve{R}$, and sometimes not. Examples: "brother of," "sister of."

(10) *Transitiveness*. A relation *R* is transitive if it is such that, if *xRy*, and *yRz*, *then xRz*. This is an instance of strict implication. Examples: "ancestor of," "before" (in time), "inferior to."

(11) *Intransitivity*. A relation *R* has this property, if it is such that, if *xRy* and *yRz*, then "never" *xRz*. Examples: "mother of," "next to."

(12) *Non-Transitivity*. A relation has this property if "sometimes" it is transitive and sometimes not. Examples: "friend of," "similar to."

Relations have *domains*, *converse domains*, and *fields*. The domain of a relation is the class of terms that have the relation *R to* "*something;*" the converse domain is the class of terms to which "something" has *R*. The field is "the sum" of the domain and the converse domain. Example: If a "cut" (a point) "divide" a line into two groups of points, namely, those that "precede," and those that "follow," then in the case of the relation, "precede(s)," all the points that precede are the domain of this relation, all the points that follow are the converse domain, and the field is the "sum" of these two domains.

(13) *Connexity.* A relation has this property "when," given any two different terms of its field, viz., x and y, either xRy or yRx. Example: Given the field of the natural numbers, 1, 2, 3, 4, etc., of any two different numbers, x and y, either x precedes y, or y precedes x.

The *Independence* of the properties of relations: Many of the properties of relations are *independent* of one another. For example, a relation that is symmetrical can be either transitive or not; likewise with a relation that is asymmetrical. These four properties are, then, independent.[22] Yet these properties are themselves *related* to one another. They are, *e.g.*, *similar* in that each is an instance of the more general property, *relational property.* Accordingly there is here an instance of *the important principle that relatedness (by some specific relation) does not necessitate the dependence on one another of the terms of the relation, i.e., the terms of a relation may be related yet independent.* However, in some cases of relations, dependence sometimes is present and sometimes not, so that we have "*nondependence.*" This is illustrated by the oxidative processes of an organism; these are sometimes dependent on distinctly vital phenomena, and sometimes not. In other cases independence is always present, or dependence. Thus, (1), a relation as regards its "symmetry" is always independent of both transitivity and intransitivity; (2),

[22] *Cf.* the author's *The New Rationalism*, Chap. II.

every property is "always" independent of its actual instances, *i.e.*, no property need be realized (by actual instances); (3), the physical world, "taken" as a "single" term, is always independent of the specific instance of value, *goodness*.[23] On the other hand, at the social level, economic, social, and political life are always (causally) *dependent*.[24]

With at least some instances of terms, and some characteristics of relations (*e.g.*, symmetry and transitivity— which are, also, terms, as related) *both related and independent, combinations* of these characteristics or properties may "hold" of certain relations.   Thus, *e.g.*, a relation, *R*, may, "at one and the same time," be aliorelative, transitive, connected, and asymmetrical. A relation having these properties is a *Serial Relation*, and a Serial Relation "generates" a simply ordered class or series.

Such a series, which is a common property of many subordinate series, *e.g.*, the (series of) the points of a line, the colors of the spectrum, the individuals of the evolutionary series, etc., is an instance of *organization*.

Organization is a property or function of which there are a number of kinds. But first there is:—

(1) Negative Organization: This is total lack of organization, which, in turn, is total lack of relatedness, if there is any such thing. But there is not. "At a minimum," terms (if there *are* terms, and there is no necessity why there should be) must be either all similar, or partly similar and partly different, or *all different*,—in which last case it *might be claimed* that they would be similar in just this respect (of all being different).[25]   Total lack of (some) organization, *e.g.*, of that organization which is identical

---

[23] *Cf.* Chapter X.   [24] This may be questioned.
[25] I do not regard this claim as "justified."

with at least some similarity between terms, may, then, be *an impossibility.*

(2) The minimum of organization possible "occurs," then, "when" there is present a single specific relation of similarity between terms, *i.e.*, when terms are similar in that each possesses, or is an instance of, a single specific property. There is, then, (a) the *singleness* or identity of this property, and (b) the *manifold* of the terms,—two or more (excluding "the identity of a term with itself" from the discussion). When this "situation" occurs, there is, then, (1), the property, (2), the instances of the property, and therefore the class. Each instance is a member of the class, (ϵ), but each instance is in this relationship *quite independently of any one order of the instances,* as are also the instances similar to one another, as instances of *a* property, *quite independently of any one order.* Accordingly we can say, if R_s is a specific relation of similarity, "between" the terms x, y, z, and q, that $R_s(x,y,z,q)$ is equivalent to, or implies, $R_s(x,q,y,z)$ as well as any other order. In other words similarity is a *commutative relation,* and it "generates" an *unordered class.*

In this whole situation, however, there are, as distinct: (1) the specific property, (2), the instances of this and the relation of each of these instances to the property, (3), the converse relation of the property to the instances; and, (4), *the whole* that is constituted by these several relations and their terms. This whole is not the property, nor any one term, nor all the terms, nor any one of the relations. It is *something more* than each or any one of these "constituents." It thus "represents" a rather complicated *organization,* after all. As distinct from this minimum of organization there are:

(3) Terms that are organized by such relations as the so-called "reciprocal causal" relations between the parts, both structural and functional, of a living organism. This is *organic organization*.

(4) Terms are also organized by relations which are asymmetrical, transitive, connected, and also one-many (and the converse) as regards the number of terms involved. Such an organization is *hierarchical*. It is illustrated by the Roman Catholic Church, the "natural classification" of the species of all plants and animals, the "descent in time" (Evolution) of all such species, and by the series of properties with instances that are, in turn, properties of other properties, etc., which is the theme of this chapter.

There are many other types of organization,[26] but it is not necessary to consider them at this point. Most "things," indeed, perhaps all "things" *except absolutely simple entities with no parts*, such as, *e.g.*, electrons, h's (Planck's constant), points, instants, and some properties (Necessity, Possibility, Negation), are organized wholes, and many, if not all, such wholes have properties which their parts do not have. To this matter we shall return in a later chapter.[27]

Our results may be advantageously summarized: *Relation*, or Relatedness, (a relation is a possible relatedness) is a general property or function which is itself an instance, as we have found, of Necessity, but there are, in turn, specific relations that are instances ("sub-relations") or values of this more general function. For example, Symmetrical relations, Asymmetrical, Transitive relations,

[26] See the writer's *The New Rationalism*, pp. 193–200, for a more complete statement.

[27] Chapter VIII.

Intransitive, are instances [28] of *Relation*. But these "more specific relations" in turn have instances. For example, a *serial relation*, which is a compound of Asymmetry, Transitivity, Aliorelativeness, and Connexity (and yet single) is such an instance. And there are, in turn, various instances of a serial relation, giving continuous, discontinuous, and dense series, and series with no ends, with two ends, etc. And then come Temporality, Causality, Emergence, etc., and, *finally*, the *existential organic evolutionary series itself*, consisting of the individuals of the several species of plants and animals that have evolved in a certain order. So back to the individuals we return, with which individuals we started in Chapter III, although our descent has been made by a somewhat different path than was the ascent. The journey up was characterized by the repeated discovery of properties, of functions, that were, in turn, themselves instances of properties or functions still higher up, until the top was reached. There were, thus, classes of classes, and classes of those classes, until, toward the end, there were found *the three classes of the necessary, the impossible, and the contingent.* And then beyond these, there were found Possibility of the First Order, and finally Functionality, Ultimacy, and Reality. There a stop had to be made, then to about-face and make the descent.

However, both the trail up and the trail down have been found, not to be a gradual incline or decline, respec-

---

[28] Again, as concerns my main thesis—Contingency—it does not matter whether I call these "instances" or "sub-relations," as it does not matter, in other contexts, whether I speak of, in reference to a Property or Function, "sub-properties," or "sub-functions," or, in other contexts, of "sub-types," or of instances. The point is, that these "subs" are in each case, as regards that to which or of which they are "subs," *contingent*. They are not made more contingent by calling them instances, nor less so by calling them something else.

tively, but, rather, to go over sharply broken contours, in some cases rather steep and precipitous, thus to make the descent uncertain and hazardous. One who has scaled high peaks well knows that it is the descent that is the more difficult, and so with the descent we are making here. There are properties and functions "at the top," and also all the way down, but just where they are and just what they are is uncertain, so that we do not know just where to put our feet, just which projection will support us, until we "feel around" and try it out. Even then our footing may give way, and we may fall.

CONTINGENCY—CHANCE

Contingency has been defined as the property "of impossibly being either necessary or impossible." *Anything is contingent*, if it has this property. All "things" having this property are, then, members of the class that is "determined" by this function. Accordingly, if there is nothing that does not have this property, then there is nothing that is not contingent, and *Everything is Chance* (in the precise and definite sense of being contingent).

Is there anything, now, that is an "exception to this rule"? Let us attempt an answer. There has been discovered *a series of properties or functions*, each property, *with the exception of those properties that are instances of Impossibility*, being a specific possibility-of-instances. But this possibility does not in any case determine or necessitate the further, specific character of the instances. For example, Necessity does not imply what its instances, *necessities*, shall be. For this reason these cannot be deduced. They must be found or discovered both as to their specific character and as to their number. They are thus contingent in three respects, namely (a), as regards the *specific differences between them and the more general property*, *e.g.*, the difference between negation (*as an instance*), and necessity (*as the property*), (b), as regards the *specific differences among themselves*, *e.g.*, the difference between negation and disjunction, and, (c), as regards their number.[29]

This situation may now be generalized. All *instances* of properties, including, *e.g.*, Possibility of the First Order, as an instance of Functionality and of Ultimacy, are contingent in *three* respects, namely, (a) as to their qualitative difference from the immediately preceding, more general property, of which they are instances, (b) as to their qualitative differences among themselves, and, (c), as to their number.

Accordingly, the following are the characteristics of the terrain down which we have been making our descent, and up which we may again go.

I.—From Ultimacy, Functionality, Contingency, Possibility, and Reality, "at the top," down to the *existent individuals* of the world of Nature, there is a *discontinuous series* of properties and their instances. This series is "generated" by relations that are aliorelative, asymmetrical, transitive, and connected.

II.—The series has both a first and a last, *i.e.*, it has two

---

[29] In the Introduction the seeming paradox was discussed, that instances of Necessity, as *having* this property, are *necessary*, and yet, as *instances* of this property, are *not necessary*. This paradox is solved by the "principle" that each of these instances (necessities) is necessary in one relation, but not in another, *i.e.*, that it is necessary *as implied by its own negative but contingent as not implied by the property or function, Necessity*.

Accordingly there is also the seeming paradox, that "something"—in this case any instance of Necessity—is both contingent and not contingent, and this paradox is "solved" by the same "principle."

At this point, however, I am stressing,—"selecting," perhaps, *contingency* —the contingency even of there "being any such thing" as a "something that is implied by its own negative," *i.e.*, of there being *a* necessity.

"ends," the one consisting of Propertiness, Ultimacy, Possibility, and Reality at the top, the other of Nature, at the bottom.

III.—"At the same time" that the series is serial, it is also both divergent and convergent, *i.e.*, as one comes down, it spreads out, and, conversely, as one goes up, it converges. In it there is present, then, a many-many relation, *i.e.*, a "few-more" relation, "starting" from the top, and, conversely a "many-fewer-still-fewer" relation, if one "starts" at the bottom and goes up. Accordingly, the organization is *both serial, hierarchical, and oligarchical*.

IV.—This hierarchical series is an instance of *emergence* "as one comes down." This property runs through the whole "state of affairs" from "top to bottom," *i.e.*, at each step down there is "something new" both qualitatively and numerically, until, it may be said, the world of Nature itself finally emerges. This characteristic of the whole, this emergence, is, of course, *non-temporal*. Indeed, one must say, Time itself is born of it, not it of Time. It is not a process, a happening, an event, yet it *is* emergence or creativity (identifying the two). As such, its one law is, that it conforms to no law. In other words, there is "no reason why,"—no necessity, as one comes down, step by step, from property to instance,—even from Functionality and Ultimacy themselves. These ultimate properties *are*, but even they themselves need not be, as, also, they are not impossible. So they, too, are quite as contingent as is anything else. Born of Chance, they but "start" the series which throughout inherits its remote birthright.

Such a scheme of things may well seem to be the apotheosis of non-rationality, and, indeed, the scheme has exactly this characteristic. For, according to it, rationality itself (both the "logic" and the psychological process) is but *a* contingency—a mere incident—in the much larger field of the non-rational.

Rationality may be, on the one hand, identified with *the logical* as objective, or, on the other hand, with "something" which may "use" *the logical*, or by which *the logical* may be apprehended. Let *this* "something" be called *reason*. Then, in either case, rationality is quite contingent.

The logical is *a set* of special properties which "traces its descent" back to Necessity, but this property is, as has been seen, itself *contingent*. *The logical* is, then, itself (indirectly) contingent. And likewise with reason or reasoning, defined as a specific process, occurring in some human beings, which, whatever else it may be, is identical with the apprehension of, and so with the disclosure of, the logical. This specific process is "a product of" *the existential evolutionary* process as itself one "aspect" of Nature. But, therewith, reason or reasoning, as thus defined, is quite contingent, quite a matter of Chance. Nature, the whole of Nature, is this; each "aspect" of Nature is this, and reason itself, as a specific product of one of these aspects, is also this.

That there should be, in a world that is shot through and through with contingencies, either logic itself, or any disclosure or apprehension of logic or of anything else, is, then, a matter of pure chance. These "things" *are*, else there could not be the *discovery*, by *logic*, of the "more ultimate" non-rationality of both the discovery *and* the logic, but they *need* not be, therefore, they *might not* be, but, since they *are*, their *being* is not impossible.

V

TRUTH, KNOWLEDGE, AND BELIEF

Is the "scheme of things," the pattern, the structure, just presented, especially in Chapters III and IV, *true?*

This is, obviously, an important question,—one that certainly demands an answer.

Few problems have been the subject of philosophical inquiry more than has the problem of truth, but, ironically, perhaps, few are still in such a nebulous condition. To show that this is the case the following definitions of truth may be considered:

I.—A proposition is true if it is "realized," [1] "exemplified," [2] "satisfied," [3] "fulfilled," [4] validated or made true,[5] or if it "agrees with," "corresponds to," or is "represented by," [6] something external to itself.

This complex definition is, evidently, itself *a complex proposition*, of the form, $(x) . \phi x \supset \psi x$, and of the content, "Any proposition (x) that is 'realized,' etc., (ϕ) is a proposition (x) that is true (ψ). So the question arises, Is this proposition itself true by its own definition? Or, is it itself exempt, according to the principle of the Theory of Types, from this test? Personally, as I have indicated in Chapters II and III, I think it is quite arbitrary to exempt it, but, leaving this question undecided, it is evident that this

---

[1] Lewis and Langford, *Symbolic Logic*, pp. 317–318, 472–475, 482–483.
[2] *Ibid.*, p. 318.   [3] *Ibid.*, pp. 356, 365; Stebbing, *opus cit.*, p. 150.
[4] Russell, B., *Analysis of Matter*, p. 4.
[5] Lewis and Langford, *opus cit.*, p. 348.   [6] *Ibid.*, p. 473.

definition opens up the further questions, What are "realization," "exemplification," "satisfaction," "fulfillment," "validation," "agreeing with," and "being represented by"? The definition must be supplemented by answers to these questions in each case.

In sharp contrast with the definition just given, according to which the truth and falsity of a proposition depend on "something" *external to the proposition itself*, there is the definition which is involved in the following statements or propositions: (a) "The *truths* about the relations of propositions are . . . *logical facts.*" [7]   (b) "There are, clearly, purely *logical truths* . . ."; "*a proposition will be a logical truth* if it is constituted *wholly in logical terms* and certifiable *wholly on logical grounds, a priori.*" [8] "Logical principles are themselves true, and they state the conditions under which *propositions—objects* of our thought possessing the capacity for truth and falsity— . . . determine one another's truth and falsity." [9]

The definition which is involved in these statements or propositions is, that Truth is identical with *a certain kind of fact*, namely, with "logical fact." Truth in this sense is, then, *not dependent on anything external.* At least certain kinds of facts are, *ipso facto, true.*

(3) Distinct, in turn, from the two definitions thus far given, is a third definition, which identifies truth with *meaning.* Thus, to quote:—

(1) "To be a logical fact . . . does not mean to be a part of logic." "Logic . . . is the order of our *chosen* ways of ordering in general." [10]   "The only truth which

---

[7] *Ibid.*, p. 256; the italics are mine.
[8] *Ibid.*, p. 271, italics mine; *cf.* pp. 24, 118, 211–212.
[9] Eaton, R. M., *General Logic*, p. 26.
[10] Lewis and Langford, *opus cit.*, pp. 256–257.

logic requires . . . is that which is contained in *our own conceptual meanings*, . . . what our language or symbolism represents." [11] "What is true is logically possible or conceivable." [12] This means, of course, that a proposition is true if it is self-consistent, *i.e.*, not self-contradictory.

As quite distinct from these three definitions of truth, none of which has to do with the truth of *ideas*, or of *knowledge*, but with the truth of *propositions*, is the *pragmatic* definition of truth, which I take from James' *Meaning of Truth* as typical. The following are some of James' statements as to the nature of truth: "Truth is a property of ideas." [13] "It means their *agreement* with reality." [14] "Agreement" means sometimes "*copying*," sometimes not; *if not*, it means "making a difference in life." [15] "Truth happens to an idea." An idea "is made true by events." "*Its verity is in fact an event*, a process." This process is "verification," "validation." [16]

According to this pragmatic view, quite clearly, it is *ideas* that are true or false, and not propositions. Accordingly, I deliberately omit the further discussion of this view, since its whole point of departure is radically different from that of this book. Only in comment may it be said, to recur to the discussion of Chapter I, that the pragmatist himself presents his theory *by means of propositions*, of which he is aware, and of which he would have other minds aware in his desire to communicate, and that "really" what he himself is concerned with is, *not the truth of his own ideas, but the truth of the propositions (about ideas) that constitute the pragmatic position.*

There is also the (Modern) Idealistic definition of truth,

[11] *Ibid.*, p. 211.
[12] *Ibid.*, p. 163.
[13] James, *The Meaning of Truth*, p. v.
[14] *Ibid.*, p. v.
[15] *Ibid.*, p. v.
[16] *Ibid.*, p. vi.

or I should say *definitions*, because there are *many*, but these, also, I omit from consideration because of what I find in every case to be their obscurity and incoherency, notwithstanding the fact that some of them are called "coherent" theories. I select what I regard as a fairly typical example: "Truth in its essential nature is that systematic coherence which is the character of a significant whole. A 'significant whole' is 'an organized individual expression, self-fulfilling and self-fulfilled.'" "Its organization *is* the process of its self-fulfillment, and the concrete manifestation of its individuality." "A significant whole . . . can in the end be most adequately described only in terms of . . . self-conscious thought." [17] But there is no use in quoting further to elucidate these quotations, since one thing at least becomes quite evident from them, and that is, that truth is defined by the Idealist in terms of experience, of consciousness, even of self-consciousness, and not as a (possible) characteristic of propositions. Since the idealistic definition is, then, so remote from the whole view-point of this book, I deliberately ignore it from this point on.

The critical examination of these various definitions of truth,—*to omit the Pragmatic and the Idealistic*—results, I think, in the disclosure that the definitions reduce to three, or that there are, or may be, *three* kinds of truth, as follows: (1) *The truth* (of a proposition) *that depends on something external to that which is true.* (2) *The truth* (*of something*) *that is not dependent on anything external.* Fact (of *certain kinds*, at least) and truth are "one and the same"; they are identical, at least in certain cases. (3) *The truth of meanings:* any *meaning* that is self-consistent, *i.e.*, not self-contradic-

---

[17] Joachim, *The Nature of Truth*, pp. 76–82, *passim.*

tory, is, *of itself*, true. This is like (2) if *meanings are facts,—and they are*,[18]—but it is different from (2) if *some meanings* are not *the kind of fact* that is identified with truth in (2), and to accept such facts (logical facts = truths) is the "intent" of (2).

Truth defined as identical either with certain kinds of facts (2), or with self-consistent meanings (3), may also be called *validity*.[19] If it is, then we have a clear distinction between *validity and truth* (1). However, this is a matter of terms.

Each of the kinds of "truth" that have been distinguished may be discussed briefly:—

First, let us examine Definition (1). The essential feature of this definition is, that truth is "made" dependent *in some way* on a "factor" *external* to that which *is true*, namely, *the proposition*. But this dependence is stated in different terms. The expressions "realized," "exemplified," "satisfied," "fulfilled," "made true," and "validated by" are not as definite in what they suggest as are the two terms "represented by" and "agreeing with." These last two suggest a *correspondence*, a similarity of pattern or structure, a "copying relation" between that which is true and the external factor. The external factor is *fact* of some kind, but this by itself is neither true nor false. Also the "factor" (the proposition) that *is* true or false by virtue of "corresponding to" (etc.,) this external factor, is, *by itself*, neither true nor false. The truth, in any instance, is identical with the specific dyadic relation, symbolized by "correspondence between," "agreeing with," etc.

[18] Lewis and Langford, *opus cit.*, p. 472.
[19] *E.g.*, Lewis and Langford, *opus cit.*, say, p. 259, "We are familiar with the fact that there is a variety of abstract geometries . . . no more than one of which is *true* of space, but all of which are *valid*." Italics mine.

In contrast, the other terms, such as "realization," do not necessarily suggest this "correspondence." "Realized," "exemplified," "validated by," etc., might be "evaluated" in terms of "correspondence," but, again, they need not be. "Validated by" and "made true" (the Latin and the English) are rather question-begging or "circular,"— indeed very much so. These terms throw absolutely no light on *what truth is*. All that they really say is, that a proposition *is true if it is true*. Accordingly they may be dismissed from further consideration.

There remain the two terms "realized by" (and its synonyms), and "agrees with" (and its synonyms). If one of these "reduces" to the other, then both terms are not needed except to secure "variety of expression." But it is doubtful if these two terms do have the same meaning. "Agrees with," "corrresponds to," etc., suggest "similarity of pattern or of structure" between the external factor and that which is "made true" by this factor, whereas "realized by," etc., do not, of necessity, mean this.

That meaning of "realized by," "satisfied by," "ful-filled by," which seems to be least open to criticism is "exemplified or instanced by," so that one can say that a proposition is true if it is "exemplified" [20] by something, or, conversely, if it "applies" [21] to something in this sense. This definition of truth results in considerable, if not per-fect, clarity, especially if "to be exemplified" means to be *"instanced."* Thus, to illustrate, the proposition, "All living beings are reproductive" would be true if this proposition, which is to the effect that the property, *living*, implies the

---

[20] *Ibid.*, p. 318. The N.E.D. justifies my use of "exemplified," "instanced" and "realized" as synonyms, so I shall use them as such, although some logicians may criticize.

[21] *Ibid.*, p. 317; *cf.* Stebbing, *opus cit.*, pp. 208–209.

property, *reproducing, is exemplified or instanced by all living beings, i.e., by all existent living beings actually being reproductive.* Whether or not this *is* the case—the actual "state of affairs—is a different problem from the problem of what truth is. *It* is the problem of evidence, of establishment, etc., but with this we are not at present concerned. Our present interest is directed only to the definition of truth, to the problem of *truth's nature,* or of what truth is. Truth might accordingly turn out to be of such a character that it would be difficult, perhaps impossible, ever to show that in any particular situation it had been attained. However, to show *that there is truth,* and to show *what* (proposition, theory, law, etc.) *is true,* are two quite distinct matters.

To the consideration of this problem at some length we shall recur, but at this point it may be said that the question, *What proposition* (or propositions), *what* theory, *what* law, *what* account, is true, concerns knowing and judgment. Knowing and judgments may be said, broadly speaking, to be, as they occur in human beings, conscious events or processes. Their immediate content or object (that *of which* there is a consciousness) is a proposition, or propositions related in specific ways, in some cases by the relation of implication. Propositions as thus merely "entertained" or "apprehended" are neither true nor false according to the definition of truth (and falsity) we are considering. The bare consciousness of them makes them neither. They are true or false according as the proposition is, or is not, realized, exemplified, instanced, by something external to itself. If a proposition is true on this ground, and one believes or judges it to be true, then one's belief or judgment is *correct.* If the proposition is true, and one believes or "holds" it to be false, one's "belief" is incorrect. If the proposition is false, and one judges it to be false, again one's judgment is *correct*, but one's judgment is incorrect if one holds the proposition to be true when it is false.[22]

Beliefs, judgments, are, then, either *correct or incorrect.* Propositions are *either true or false.* Knowledge is the "holding" of propositions to be true "when" they *are* true, and false, when they *are* false. And propositions are true or false, respectively, according as the property or properties which form their constituent parts according to the form of the proposition *are* or *are not* instanced. Thus the propositions, "Everything is necessary," and "All planets are inhabited," are false, but the propositions, "Some 'things' are necessary," and "All atoms are complex," are true.

It is evident, as the outcome of this discussion, that, according to this first definition of truth, a proposition (or a theory or law) is not true by itself. Rather, it is "made true," (and one could also now say "validated," *in this sense*) by *something external* that *instances* or *exemplifies* the proposition, and in this sense *realizes* it. This is a clear and precise definition of "realizing." This "something external" is a *fact* or *facts*, of some kind, which, as such, are neither true nor false, but just *are,—quite indifferent*, as it were, to whether they make propositions true or false, or whether, through the medium of propositions, they are known or not. But the facts which thus make propositions true or false are not limited to *existential* facts,—to *nature.* There are any number of different kinds of fact that do not belong to this realm. Thus I should say that, *e.g.*, Ultimacy,

----

[22] *Cf.* Lewis and Langford, *opus cit.*, p. 473. I here accept, essentially, the position of these authors on this point, and have followed rather closely their statement of it.

Possibility of two or more orders, Impossibility, "Serial Order," Implication, Contingency, Relatedness (of various kinds), etc., etc., *are all facts* in the universe quite as much as is any particular event, organism, or quality that is a specific part of what is called *Nature*.

With this the case (the fact), *truth*, by the definition we are considering, is not limited to those propositions that are "instanced" in, or by, the particular entities that *are nature*, but is, as it were, coextensive with *the entire realm of fact of any kind whatsoever, in so far as and in that any special or delimited part of this realm instances the properties which are the constituent parts of the propositions "about" this realm*. Truth is thus flung far and wide. We enter the "potentiality" of its realm the minute we enter the realm of propositions, as the *media* of our judgments, *about anything whatsoever*, for those propositions are themselves the specific possibilities of truth or of falsity. Thus there are *the facts* that "make" *true or false propositions*, (1) *about truth and falsity themselves*, (2) about the nature of beliefs and judgments, (3) about "fact" itself, (4) about "nothing" and about "something," (5) about propositions and propositional functions, (6) about Impossibility and Impossibilities, (7) about Contingency and Contingencies, (8) about God, and men, and angels, and about stars and machines and atoms, etc., etc. There are no limits to the list. There is nothing that is exempt from rational examination and criticism, and, since the method of this procedure is the use (awareness) of propositions, there is nothing in it (the procedure) that is exempt from (the possibility of) being "made true" or "made false" by facts (of some kind) that are external to the propositions themselves.

The propositions, identical with meanings, are symbolized; they are "understood," or not, by other minds than that of the investigator; and they are made true or false by facts. But the facts themselves care not whether or not there is truth or falsity, understanding, symbolization, rational examination, science, or philosophy; only, if there *are* these, then the realm of fact is by so much the richer.

This account of truth, which *as an account* is itself identical with a set of connected *propositions*, and which, by its own norm, is true or false according as these propositions are realized by fact or not, is not the only account of truth that can be given, as we have seen at the beginning of this chapter. There are at least two other accounts, one being an elaboration and defense of the definition which identifies truth with a certain kind of fact, *e.g.*, with *logical fact*, the other, an elaboration of the definition which identifies truth with the *self-consistency*, or logical conceivability, of *meanings*. According to this second view (the third of our original list), *whatever one means when one thinks is of itself true provided one's meanings stand the tests of self-consistency and logical conceivability or possibility*.

Now, with the first of these two views I have not much of a quarrel. If there *are* truth and falsity, then truth and falsity are facts, and *some facts* are identical with truth and falsity. It may be that for this reason *logical facts* are *ipso facto* true. But, *if* it is *only* logical facts that are thus true, and there are other than logical facts, then these other, non-logical, facts are, as facts, *either false, or neither true nor false*. It seems rather arbitrary, then, to identify truth with a certain kind of fact, namely, logical. Much less arbitrary is the view which (a) distinguishes fact and truth, as has been done in the preceding discussion of

Definition (1), and (b) maintains that fact itself is never truth, and "finds" this (truth) in *a specific dyadic relation* between fact and proposition, namely, in the relation of the proposition being "realized" or "instanced" by the fact or facts. But here, again, truth emerges as itself identical with *a certain kind of fact*, namely, with (1), *the fact of a proposition being realized by*, (2), *a fact or by facts other than itself.* There are, then, in this situation, *two orders* of fact, the one, *as fact*, neither true nor false, but merely the complex "*state of affairs*"—*proposition-realized-by-fact*, the other, *within* this complex, the fact or facts which realize the proposition or propositions whereby *there is truth.*

If now, I "make" certain propositions concerning truth, namely, that "a proposition is true if it is realized by fact," and these propositions (which I make about truth) are *themselves realized in this way*, then it is the propositions of my account that are true, and not the facts which in either or both cases "do 'the realizing.'"

I conclude that *in general* facts as facts are neither true nor false, *i.e.*, are not identical with truth or with falsity, but that this "privilege" (of being true or false) is reserved for that very special kind of fact (or situation) which *is a proposition-in-relation-to-other-facts (external to itself)-which-are-its-realization.* Truth is a property of this relational situation, and is itself a *fact* when there *is* this situation. Paradoxically, however, the *fact* of truth is not itself true; like other facts, it makes certain propositions true. Accordingly I give up that (possible) definition (2) in which truth is identified with fact, albeit, perhaps, with fact of a certain kind, namely, logical fact, and keep to definition (1). According to this definition there are *propositions about logical facts*, which propositions are true if the facts "instance" or "exemplify" or "validate" or "realize" them, and are false if this is not the case.

There remains only one other definition of truth to be discussed, namely, that one which identifies truth with self-consistent, logically possible, or logically conceivable, meanings.[23]

The critical inspection of this definition shows that logical conceivability depends on logical possibility or self-consistency, which is, in turn, the absence of "self-contradictoriness." According to this definition, then, any proposition is true if it is not self-contradictory. This last (negative) property is itself defined as follows: A proposition, p, is self-contradictory, and so impossible, if it implies its contradictory, symbolized by $p \dashv \sim p$. Accordingly a proposition is possible,—self-consistent,—conceivable, if $p \dashv \sim p$ is false, i.e., if $\sim (p \dashv \sim p)$.

This definition of truth opens up the floodgates. By it truth is wholly an *internal* matter of self-consistent meaning. It is dependent on nothing external. It is identical with fact, to be sure, but the fact, alone, of self-consistent meanings, as themselves facts consistently related *as another fact*. Almost any proposition or set of propositions can be true, then. Only one condition is to be observed.[24]

Now I grant that this definition of truth itself has the virtue of consistency as applied to itself, namely, *if "consistent meaning" is what I mean by "truth,"* then, this latter meaning is, seemingly, itself quite self-consistent,[25] and so,

[23] See previous reference to Definition (3): *cf.* Lewis and Langford, *opus cit.*, p. 211, *et passim.*

[24] Lewis, *Mind and the World Order*, pp. 237 and 245.

[25] Lewis and Langford, *opus cit.*, p. 497, say "For every proposition p, the statement 'p is self-consistent' is a self-consistent statement." I suppose they mean "a self-consistent proposition." If they do not, I would ask, then, *What is "a statement"?*

by definition, true, and so on, in an infinite regress. I can mean what I wish, and have this meaning *mean* what I wish, and, in turn, have this meaning again mean what I wish, and so on indefinitely, just *so long* as I conform to the norm of consistency. *But*, the minute that this definition is interpreted to *mean*, (1) that it itself is a proposition (and it *is*) which is exemplified by "an objective state of affairs" external to itself, namely, *by the objective fact, that self-consistent meanings are true*, and, (2) that it is, *for this reason*, a *true* definition (of truth), the jig is up, and we are back, to definition (1). And, what is more, I do not see how this second interpretation is to be avoided. For, certainly, the definition has to do not merely with itself as "a self-consistent meaning," but with *other propositions* as self-consistent meanings, so that the locus of its realization and validation *is external* to the definition itself. The definition *is* a proposition about other propositions,—about the "conditions" or "character" of their truth or falsity. Whether one wishes to "bring in" the Theory of Types or not, the definition is itself self-consistent, and therefore, according to itself, true. But, as *exemplified, realized*, or *instanced* by other propositions to which it "applies," it is *more than* merely self-consistent. Accordingly, I conclude that, although one may mean what one wishes and says, and so on, in an infinite regress, one *need not* get "thus carried away." *Rather, one can avoid this regress by the definition, which must finally be accepted anyway, that the truth of a proposition, even of a proposition which is itself a definition of truth, is a matter of being "exemplified" or "realized" by something external to the proposition itself.*

The self-consistency of a proposition or "meaning" is,

then, not enough to make a proposition true.[26] It is one condition, but not a sufficient one. To be true the proposition must also be exemplified. No self-contradictory proposition is true, for no self-contradictory proposition is or can be exemplified, but there are any number of propositions which are not self-contradictory, and so are consistent, but which are *not true*, just because they are not exemplified. To be true, a proposition, or a system of propositions, must be, respectively, not only self-consistent, or internally consistent, but also exemplified. If one's attention,—and attention is selective and can ignore,—is directed *away from* the locus of possible exemplification and toward and to the proposition itself, or the system of propositions by themselves, then the question of truth or falsity in the sense of exemplification is not raised, but "the demand for consistency" still remains. Accordingly, we have the definition:

A proposition, or a set of propositions, that is, respectively, self-consistent, or internally consistent, is valid.

Validity is, then, distinct from truth. Each is a function or property, but neither *is* the other. Truth is impossible unless there is validity, but, if there is validity, truth need not also be "present." For it to subsist, there must also be realization, or exemplification. If this is absent, there may or may not be validity; but this property is present if there is self- or internal consistency.

Accordingly one can say, to repeat, that I can mean what I wish and say, etc., etc., at least in an indefinitely long series, if not in an infinite one, and have a *perfectly valid set or system of meanings*, just so long as the heinous sin of introducing a self-contradictory meaning, or a contradiction

[26] The foregoing discussion is, I consider, quite consistent with one of the main theses of Chapter I, namely, the thesis, that *a proposition, a meaning*, is not mental, but a specific objective reality.

among meanings, is not committed, but that *that way no truth lies*. Indeed, the history of rational thought is replete with such *systems of meanings* in the diverse fields of Science, Politics, Theology, and Philosophy,—systems which have been mistakenly judged to be true because they were (and still are) internally consistent, but which really were and are only valid.

That system which is valid because it is internally consistent, and, as such, possible logically, and conceivable psychologically, is not, for these reasons, *true*. For this, something else,—exemplification, realization by actual or real instances,—is required. But these instances are not necessitated by their possibility. The actual or real is always possible, but the possible is far from being always actual.

We now return to the question asked at the beginning of this chapter: Is the "scheme of things" presented in Chapters III and IV (and in the other chapters of this book), and constituting the "meanings" of those chapters, true?

In Chapters III and IV it was found that there is a hierarchy of properties and functions "leading back," on the one hand to Functionality, Ultimacy, etc., and, on the other hand, "down" to the existential world (Nature) of particular physical, living, psychological, and social entities as all involved in an evolutionary process. In order to present this scheme of things, word-symbols were used, and sentences constructed. According to Chapter I these symbols should be symbols of *meanings*, of *propositions*, and it is of these last that I would have the reader aware or conscious. I would thus endeavor to communicate with his mind.

Now, at this point, I am not primarily interested in the symbols, nor in the consciousness either of them or of the meanings (or propositions), but in the *propositions* themselves, and especially in the question as to whether or not these propositions are true by that definition of the term which has issued from the discussion just preceding.

The problem then is:—Are the propositions, especially those of Chapters III and IV, true in the sense of "being realized" (with this term defined as meaning "being instanced," or "exemplified," or "satisfied") by something *external* to themselves? Now it is obvious that, if the propositions *are* realized (true), then they can well serve as the media for "getting at" the reality which realizes them, so that, if one holds (believes) that these propositions are true, then one's belief is correct, and there is *Knowledge*— not merely of propositions, but of the facts which make the propositions true. But the important and crucial question then is, *Are the propositions realized?* How can it be shown that they are? Obviously, merely to *assume*, in order to answer this, that the propositions *are true and therefore realized*, and then to infer that, because they are realized, they are true, is to proceed in a very vicious circle. I am not sure that this circle ultimately can be avoided, but I am sure that, if it can be, it should be. In other words, I am confident that one should, if one can, indeed, that one must, get at the "instances" which exemplify a proposition *by some other method than by means of the proposition itself.* To do this *may* be quite possible in the case of some kinds of knowledge or beliefs, and yet impossible in the case of other kinds. To do this might seem to be possible, *e.g.*, in the case of those sciences which use methods of observation by means of measurement and of experimentation, and yet I am not sure that the difficulty is escaped even here, for even these sciences,—*e.g.*, Physics, Biology, Chemistry, Astronomy, in part,—not only present their *results*, but also carry on their investigation by means of, and in the form of, propositions that are symbolized by words, ideograms, etc., so that the sciences may be in the same difficulty as are Logic and Philosophy. This difficulty may be called (*awkwardly*) "the proposition-predicament." [27] This is the predicament of being able, on the one hand, to get at facts by means of propositions provided only that the propositions are true, and, on the other hand, of being unable to show that the propositions are true in the sense of being realized, except by means of propositions.

It may well be that the only escape from this predicament is by way of getting data such as are obtained in some of the sciences by means of experimentation and measurement, but, if this *is* the case, one might as well recognize it, and proceed accordingly. However, *that this situation is or is not the fact, can itself be established*, if it can be established at all, not by physical experiment and measurement, *but only by the propositional method of investigation*.

As concerns, however, both the method and the results of the investigations of which this book is the presentation, we are unquestionably committed to the use of propositions as the only method of rational inquiry (in the field under investigation). Physical experimentation, and measurement, and sensuous observation are, for our purpose, quite useless. It is for us, then, a very important question whether or not there is an escape from the circle of "getting at facts

[27] There is, as is well known, quite a list of "predicaments," but I do not intend to discuss them. The list includes the egocentric, the logocentric, the biocentric, in physics, perhaps, the geocentric, and the "value-centric" or the axiological. If all values are human values, then perhaps there is an anthropocentric predicament. A predicament is, in general, an "uncomfortable situation," from some standpoint, to be in, and, so, a situation to get out of, if possible. The problem is, Is it possible to get off all centers, so that one is completely *excentric*, or is one in the predicament of always being on some one center if not on another?

by means of propositions that are assumed to be true, and of then 'regarding' these propositions as true because they are realized by facts."

Now it is obvious that at least those propositions which state the results of our investigations purport to be true, and so to describe "an objective state of affairs" other than themselves, so that it may be said that, if there really is this "state of affairs," then it realizes the propositions and so makes them true. But the question then is, How can we show that the propositions really do describe this objective "state of affairs," *i.e.*, that they *are* true, so that, through them, we are getting at the facts, *if* the only way, seemingly, of getting at the facts is through the propositions? Are we not, apparently, kept absolutely within our circle of propositions? Can we possibly get out of it by some such methods as, *e.g.*, those that the physicist adopts when he shows by independent, non-propositional methods of investigation, that the propositions constituting a certain theory are realized, and therefore true?

Now, in order to attempt to answer this question, it may first be pointed out that in this book we are, at least thus far, for the most part, investigating not physical, or biological, or psychological phenomena, but properties or functions, classes, propositions, the relations between and among these, etc., etc. Accordingly, it may be said that, *if* there *are* these entities, *i.e.*, if they are in some sense *real*, and if they are of the *kinds*, and have the *relations*, that have thus far been presented, then they do realize, instance, or exemplify our propositions, thus to make them true. But here again is the same problem: How can we show that there *are* properties, classes, propositions, and that these *are* of different kinds and *related* in different ways, etc., *except by propositions?* Both the method of investigation and the statement of results are propositional.

However, I think that there is a way out of the difficulty. It is a way, furthermore, which is, I think, both explicitly adopted and tacitly presupposed in any investigation of the field of logic, which is, in the broad sense of this term, the field we are examining. It is a way that is identical, in the first place, with the use of propositions in a dual rôle, namely, as (1), providing a means of investigation, and, (2), as offering the only means of stating results (for propositions are "content-full") and of communicating with other minds.

The position has already been taken that there is nothing that is exempt from rational examination and inquiry, and that therefore properties (such as *Necessity*), propositions, classes, relations, logical "principles" (*e.g.*, implication, the law of contradiction), can be investigated. But the method of such investigation is by means of propositions, for we are dealing with content, and not with mere "form." There is the principle, then, that, when propositions are investigated by propositions, the propositions investigated are not functioning (as propositions) together with, "at the same time with," either the propositions that constitute the means of investigation or those that are found as a result of this investigation. It is only on this basis that a logician can, *e.g.*, discover and then assert not only the *fact of propositions*, and of their relation to propositional functions, to classes, etc., but also such *facts about* propositions as (1) "All propositions whatever can be derived from logical matrices, such as $f(x) \cdot p \vee q$, and $f(x) \vee \sim f(x)$"; [28] (2), "Every proposition is a possibility

[28] Lewis and Langford, *opus cit.*, p. 272.

(conceptual) that is open to realization." [29]   Nor, also, except on this basis, could a logician write of "logical facts," and say *of* these facts, as *facts about them*, that, (1) "the multiplicity and variety of such facts is beyond all imagining," and (2) "to be a logical fact does not mean to be a part of logic," [30] and (3), "logical facts are not created" by logic (the science) nor are they "dependent on the process of inference; they either are related in certain ways or they are not." [31]

If there is not this propositional method of investigation and of *discovering facts* which may also be found to realize and thus make true *other propositions* ("stating" the results) not involved in the investigation, then such words as *Implication, Negation, Possibility, Necessity, Disjunction, Proposition, Propositional Function*, stand either for nothing, or for *mere* meanings, since the methods of observation, experiment, and measurement of *objects in Nature* disclose no content, no reality, for these terms. But, if the propositional method of investigation is admitted to disclose facts (*and to conclude that it does not, is but to assert as another fact something discovered by the propositional method*), then the "proposition circle" is escaped, and it is possible, within the limits of intellectual error, by *means* of propositions (analogous to the physical experimental method) to *discover such facts* as *Implication* and *Negation*, and also *such facts* about propositions, properties, classes, etc., *as exemplify and realize* certain other propositions, and therefore make them true.

If the propositional method of investigation, as the method of rational inquiry, is not one that thus leads to the disclosure of *facts* external to specific meanings (al-

[29] *Ibid.*, p. 483.   [30] *Ibid.*, p. 256.   [31] *Ibid.*, p. 257.

though these facts are neither physical nor mental), but is one that is limited entirely to *meanings*, then I cannot see that it results in anything more than *a merry-go-round of meanings* with the only norm that of consistency and the only outcome that of *validity*, but never that of truth. For the truth of a proposition is "dependent" on a state of affairs "external" to the proposition itself, and meanings as meanings do not "generate" such "states of affairs."

It is for these reasons, then, that I take the position, at this point, that the propositions which constitute the account which I have given of such *properties* as Necessity, Contingency, and Impossibility, of the *instances* of these, such as *negation* and *relatedness* (= *necessities*), and of still more abstract properties, such as Possibility of the First Order, *are true propositions*. These propositions constitute a true account, because these properties, their relations to one another, etc., are found to be *facts by means of the propositions that constitute the method of investigation*. This propositional method of investigation may now be used in order to discover further features or aspects (facts) of the *objective "state of affairs"* which our account thus far has portrayed.

It has been found that there is a hierarchy of properties or of functions. There are properties that are actual instances of properties higher up, with these properties in turn actual instances of still higher properties until certain ultimates are reached, and, at the bottom, there are instances that have "no further instances." This is Nature, consisting of concrete particular "things."

But if there are properties with actual instances, then these instances form a class; but these instances are in turn properties with actual instances, so that there are actual classes of actual classes of actual classes. Thus there is a hierarchy not only of properties, but also of classes.

What I next propose to do is, then, to show that there is not only a hierarchy of properties and of classes, but also of *propositions*, of *facts*, of *realizations*, and, therefore, of *truths*. In order to do this I shall return to earlier chapters, especially to Chapters III and IV. These chapters are in part identical with the propositional method of investigation. By using this method, certain facts have been discovered. These facts make certain propositions true in that they (the facts) are an *objective "state of affairs,"* external to the propositions themselves, that instance or realize the propositions. In this way we shall show that *the proposition* that "there is a hierarchy of properties, of facts, of classes, of realizations, and of truths" *is true*. The problem may best be worked out by returning to the subject-matter, especially of Chapters III and IV.

In these chapters it was found, *e.g.*, that, (1), "there is Possibility of the First Order," that, (2), "Necessity 'materially' (= as a matter of fact) implies Possibility of the First Order," and that, (3), " Negation is a Necessity." *These are each a proposition*, of the *forms*, respectively, (1), $(\exists x) . \phi x$ (a ϕ, not specified, is a property of something, x); (2), $(x) . \phi x \supset \psi x$ (all x's that are ϕ are also ψ); (3), ϕx (*something* specific, is ϕ). It is, however, with propositions of the first and second forms that I am especially concerned, for what I maintain is, not only that there is a hierarchy of propositions of *these two types*, but also that these propositions are *exemplified*, "instanced," or realized, so that they are *true*, and that accordingly there is *a hierarchy of truths*.

To show this, let us take the proposition, "There is

Possibility" (of the First Order), *i.e.*, "Possibility *is*." Is this realized? The answer is "Yes, by the facts (instances), Necessity, Contingency, and Impossibility." These instances are not themselves, as has been seen, necessitated by the property, Possibility, but are *contingent*, so that, if the proposition, "There is Possibility" is "made true" by them, *its truth is quite contingent*. This is a thesis which I desire to emphasize, namely, that *although truth is, in the sense of realization, it is not necessitated in any case, so that it is quite contingent, wherever it is found*.

To continue:—Possibility (of the First Order) is itself, like every other property or function, a specific possibility-of-instances, but these instances "have to be found" as "matter of fact," and cannot be deduced. The instances here are, Necessity, Contingency, and Impossibility. These instances make the (self-consistent and, therefore, valid) proposition, "There is Possibility of the First Order" *true*. But, in turn, there are the three propositions, "There is Necessity," "There is Contingency," "There is Impossibility," and the question again arises, Are these true? with the same answer: "Yes, if they are realized." *But they are*. Necessity *is* exemplified or instanced, as we have seen, by such facts or *necessities* as Negation, Disjunction, Relatedness, and Possibility of the Second Order; Contingency, by, *e.g.*, the fact of Necessity; and Impossibility, by a considerable number of instances. In turn, to select one instance of Necessity, namely, Relatedness, and the proposition, "There is Relatedness," this is true because it is instanced by the more specific types of Relations discussed in Chapter IV, such as Symmetrical Relatedness, Asymmetrical, Transitive, Intransitive, etc.

The situation need not be traced downward in detail further, for the principle involved becomes clear. The specific properties of each "level" are instanced by certain specific properties of the next lower level until, finally, we come to *Nature*, to the realm of existents. These "instance" or realize certain sets of propositions that immediately precede, thus to make them true, and at the same time *fail* to instance other propositions just preceding, thus to make these propositions false, although they may form internally consistent systems and thus be valid. For example, if Nature "instances" those propositions which as a set or system are identical with the Theory of Emergent (Discontinuous) Evolution, then this theory is *true*, and any theory of Evolution that is one of *continuity* is false, though it be internally consistent, and thus valid.

However, it does not follow, because a theory of continuous or non-emergent Evolution, or any other theory as a set or propositions, is false, that the propositions of the preceding level and levels are false. For the propositions that are not instanced and that are, therefore, false, must themselves, in their constituent parts, be instances of certain properties of a preceding level, so that the propositions of this level are true. For example, assuming that a Theory of Continuous Evolution is false, such a theory itself nevertheless instances the propositions that constitute *a still more general theory of continuity* which *applies* not only to Evolution, but, perhaps, to many other things.

But in the hierarchy of properties and of classes, there are propositions not only of the type just considered, but also of the type, $(x) . \phi x \supset \psi x$ (if anything has the property, ϕ, it has the property ψ). Thus, as propositions of this type, there are, (1), "If anything is necessary, it is possible;" (2), "If anything is self-contradictory, it is impossible;" (3), "If anything is serially ordered, it is related." These propositions may also be stated: (1), Necessity implies Possibility (of the First Order); (2), Self-contradictoriness implies Impossibility; (3), Simple Serial Order implies Relatedness.

These are the propositions. Are they true? That is, are they "instanced," exemplified, realized, by facts? The answer is, I think, quite evident. For (1) we have *the instances* of Necessity, namely, Disjunction, Negation, etc., as given in Chapter IV; *these are necessities; therefore, they are also possibilities.* For (2) we have such instances of self-contradiction as *a contingent necessity, a necessary contingency*, and *an impossible contingency*, etc., again, as given in Chapter IV. Each of these is *a* self-contradictory entity, therefore *an* impossibility. And for (3) we have *asymmetrical* and *transitive* relatedness, but this *is relatedness*. *These propositions*, then, are, by the definition of truth that we have accepted, *true*.

We have, then, very evidently reached an answer to the original inquiry of this chapter: "Is the 'scheme of things,' the pattern, the structure just presented (Chapters III and IV) true? " That answer is, "Yes." Yet in finally making this answer, certain comments are pertinent, by way both of summary and of further development of our main thesis.

In a preceding discussion the property of Contingency was discovered. This is the property which anything may have not only of *not* being, but also of *impossibly* being, either necessary or impossible. Broadly speaking, whatever has this property is "a matter of Chance," by which I mean neither Probability nor Freedom. Indeed, I would equate Chance with Contingency.

Now "the picture" which I have sketched is one of a fourfold hierarchy of properties, of instances of properties, of propositions, of the realizations of these propositions, and of truths (and falsities), from Functionality, Ultimacy, etc., "at the top" to Nature "at the bottom." But the "field" of the hierarchy spreads out enormously just this side of Nature, for the realm of the logically possible is "infinitely greater" than is that "one deal of the cards" which *is* "the *existent* world, past, present, and future." But I have *sketched* this hierarchical "picture" of properties, and then of instances, of propositions that are realized, etc., (which I have *discovered by* the propositional method) *by means of other propositions*, namely, those that, broadly speaking, *constitute my conclusion.*

I hold, now, that these last propositions are true in the sense of being realized by the "objective state" of affairs that is "pictured." I do not "derive" this realization from the *assumed* truth of my propositions, but, rather, on the basis of *the cogency of my propositional method as a means of discovering facts.*

Contingency, then, "appears," as it were, in two dimensions, namely, as it concerns (1), the truth of, *i.e.*, the realization of, my own propositions, and (2), as it is found "all the way through" the hierarchy, from Functionality and Ultimacy at the top, to Nature at the bottom. With Contingency defined as the property of impossibly being either necessary or impossible, I find, (1), that *all actual instances* of (higher) properties are contingent; therefore, (2), that the *reality of classes* is contingent; (3), that *all propositions* (which "arise" when the variables of a specific function, ϕx, have values) are contingent; (4), that, accordingly, *realization* is contingent, and, therefore, (5), that *truth itself is an instance of this property.* But I also find, as concerns my own propositions, which at least possess, I would claim, the virtue of being a *consistent* set, that their realization or truth is also contingent. In other words, if these propositions are true, they have *this* property, not because they must have it, but merely because they do have it, as a matter of fact. But, of course, that they *are* (actually) true, *are* (actually) realized by a "state of affairs" that is external to and independent of themselves, is what I would claim upon the basis of the defense of the propositional method of discovery as presented in this chapter.

If, now, the propositions of my own account are true, then, by means of them, through them, something other than themselves is *known*. Then there is *Knowledge*.

Nothing, however, in the objective scheme or structure of things as it has thus far been presented has the semblance of "Knowledge" or of knowing, of awareness, of consciousness. In that scheme, Necessity and necessities have appeared, as have also, *e.g.*, the properties of *Order*, of "Emergence," etc., etc., but not *knowledge* or *knowing*. Truth also has appeared, but not Goodness and Beauty. What, now, of these? Is there no place for them?

Only a brief answer to this inquiry will be given at this point, a detailed answer being reserved for later chapters. This brief answer is, that *knowing is a contingent event in an evolutionary process (the whole of Nature) which is itself contingent.* In other words, there is no necessity (and, of course, no impossibility), according to the "scheme of things" thus far presented, why there should be any "existent world," any Nature, at all, or why, with an evolutionary process a fact, there should appear in this process living beings, or conscious beings, or such a "thing" as *Knowing*, *or Knowledge.* These *are*, but they need not be. Because they *are*, both the realm of Nature and the realm of that hierarchy of properties of which Nature is one instance become known as regards their structure, at least in part. But one of the *facts* which thus becomes known, is the very fact of the pure contingency of this Knowledge itself.

VI

DIMENSIONALITY, SPACE–TIME, SPACE AND TIME, MATTER

There has been presented in a preceding chapter (IV) a summary of the various types and characteristics of relations, and in Chapter III the specific constituent properties of the single property, Serial Order. This property subsists as the *specific possibility-of-being-instanced by terms-related-in a specific manner*, namely, by a relation that has the properties of *aliorelativeness*,[1] *connexity*, *transitivity*, and *asymmetry*.

These properties are defined as follows: (1) A relation, R, is *aliorelative* or irreflexive, if a term, x, does not have the relation to itself, *i.e.*, if ~ (xRx). (2) A relation is *connected* if, for every x and y which are distinct and belong to the field of the relation, either xRy, or yRx. (3) A relation is transitive, "when," if xRy, and yRz, xRz. (4) A Theorem derivable from (1) and (2)—A relation is asymmetrical if "not both xRy and yRx."

This property as thus defined (the logical sum of four properties) is the generic property, ϕ, of which anything as a set of "values" of x, y, z, etc., as serially ordered, *e.g.*, the (ordered series of the) points of a line, the (ordered series of the) instants of time, the order of the chemical elements in the Periodic Table according to their "atomic number," is *an instance*.

[1] *Cf.* Whitehead and Russell, *Principles of Mathematics*, Volume II, p. 513, and Russell, B., *Introduction to Mathematical Philosophy*, Chapter IV. Also Stebbing, *opus cit.*, pp. 112–113; Eaton, *opus cit.*, pp. 469–477.

It is now proposed to present in detail some of the sub-types which are instances of this general property of Serial Order, and then in turn to present sub-types or instances of these sub-types, and so on down, until we reach the physical or material world. In this journey downward we shall go through several levels such as Dimensionality, Space-Time as used in Relativity, Space and Time, coming at last to Matter and Mass and perhaps to Electricity and Magnetism. In giving an account of at least some of the more important properties recognition of which is made in both the Restricted and the General Theories of Relativity, it is, however, my purpose not to attempt in any sense a complete presentation of this Theory, but only to consider such outstanding aspects of the Theory as are demanded by the main thesis of this book. To this task we now turn.

Our presentation will gain clarity if use is made of the "concept," the function, or the property of *number*, or *more specifically*, at first, at least, of *natural number, positive integer, or finite cardinal* [2]—for I shall use these terms synonymously, since I find them, as a matter of fact, thus to be used in the literature.[3] In adopting this program, I shall not consider many, perhaps most, of the very refined details concerning *number in general*, but will select only those details which are relevant to my main purpose.

To this end, we may, perhaps, advantageously begin with the question, What *is* an integer (a *positive* integer), a "natural" number, or a finite cardinal number? I reply,

[2] I use the "expression" *finite cardinal*, because there are, also, *infinite cardinals*. *Finite* may be defined as *not infinite*. *Cf*. Young, *Fundamental Concepts of Algebra and Geometry*, p. 63.

[3] *Cf*., *e.g.*, Young, *opus cit*., Lectures VI–XI. By some writers it would be said, however, that the positive integers are 1, 2, 3, 4 ..., the "natural numbers," 0, 1, 2, 3, 4, ... According to Whitehead and Russell, the terms "natural number" and "finite cardinal" are synonyms.

"Integer" (positive), "natural number," "finite cardinal" are each, really, (as these *words* are read) *a symbol for a specific property*, namely, "Integerness," etc., which is instanced by more specific "somethings" that are symbolized by 1, 2, 3, 4, *or* by I, II, III, IV, etc. That is, "integer," "natural number," "cardinal number" is *a property of which there are instances*, namely, "oneness," "twoness," "threeness," "fourness," etc., symbolized by 1, 2, 3, 4, etc.—to use the Arabic symbols, these subordinate properties being, in turn, specific-possibilities-of-instances.

My first thesis is, then, that the specific positive integer, natural number, or finite cardinal that is symbolized by each of these symbols is *not the symbol itself*. Symbol and symbolized are distinct. Accordingly there may be, as, indeed, there are, different symbols for *the same symbolized entity*, *e.g.*, I or α, instead of 1; II or β instead of 2; III or γ instead of 3, etc. If this were not the case, then, instead of, *e.g.*,—it is difficult to express—a *single* "two" or "twoness," we should have three "twos" (or perhaps more), namely, 2, II, and β. The "real" natural numbers, are, then, not the symbols, but that which is symbolized.

Just what, then, is that which is symbolized, i.e., just what *is* each specific "natural number," positive integer, or finite cardinal, such as "twoness," "threeness," "fourness," etc.? To this inquiry I shall give both a simple (relatively) and a more technical answer.

First, the simple answer—by means of an example: Let us make the assumption, which corresponds to certain orthodox views, that in "every human being," at least after birth, there is a soul—"a simple, indivisible, spiritual entity"—that is distinct from the body. Then there is "*instanced*" *the relation of* "*one-one reciprocal correspond-ence*" between bodies and souls, *i.e.*, for each body, one and only one soul, for each soul, one and only one body. There is, then, the "situation," or objective "state of affairs": Bodies are many; they form a group or manifold. Souls are also many, "forming" a manifold. Body and soul, as such, and so, bodies and souls, are *qualitatively different*, at least in many if not in most respects. *Yet the two manifolds, one of bodies, the other of souls, are similar, but only in a specific respect. They are similar as regards their manifoldness by virtue of the relation of one-one correspondence between the (two) groups.* There are *as many* souls as bodies, *as many* bodies as souls. But this "as many" is *specific*. It becomes a "how many." For the "manyness" or "manifoldness," in regard to which the groups are similar, is *specific*. It is, now, *this specific similarity*, in the case chosen, *that is a (specific) natural number, or integer, or finite cardinal.* This number might be 500,373,891 or 1,500,000,009, or any other positive integral number. In any case, there are *as many* bodies as there are souls, and conversely, and, in addition, there is *a definite number* of each. Each group "shares" this number, or has, or is, an instance of this property.

A specific natural number, or positive integer, or finite cardinal, may, then, be defined as that property which is the specific relation of similarity as regards manifoldness between distinct classes or groups (of distinct entities) that are in one-one correspondence, and that are also so related that one class is not a proper part of another, as, *e.g.*, a segment of a line *is* a "proper part" of that line. In this latter case, since there are *as many* points in the segment as there are in the whole, "because" of the one-one correspondence between whole and part as regards points, the line is *an infinite whole or an infinite class*. When this "situation" "holds," there is an "infinite cardinal" as *the number* of points of the line.[4]

A finite cardinal,[5] or positive integer, or natural number—a specific one—is, then, a specific relation of similarity (as regards manifoldness, "uniquely determined") and so *a property* that may be *instanced* by various manifolds, namely, by those that are in one-one correspondence with one another, *under the condition that one manifold is not a proper part of the other*. "Twoness," "threeness," "fourness," "fiveness," etc., are each such a property, a ϕ, for which 2, 3, 4, 5, or II, III, IV, V, are respectively more "compact" or economical symbols.

This is a *connotative*, an *intensional* definition. It "says" nothing about the instances of "twoness" or of "threeness" or of "fourness," etc. There might be such instances, and there might not, but, if there are, then the instances of "twoness" form a class of dyads, of "threeness," a class of triads, of "fourness," a class of quadrads, etc. *Denotatively* defined, then, a specific finite cardinal number, *e.g.*, 3, or 4, or 5, is in each case the *set* or *class* of all classes or groups that are in a specific one-one correspondence with one another, and so are similar in respect to their manifoldness.

But what about, not specific cardinals (finite), but *finite cardinal number in general*, or, even, more generally, about *cardinal number, whether finite or infinite?*

In answer: Each specific finite cardinal is a specific sim-

---

[4] The positive integers themselves, as is, perhaps, well known, "have" this same property of infinity, since the whole series (natural order), 1, 2, 3, 4, 5, 6, 7, 8, 9, 10, etc., is in one-one correspondence with a part of itself, the even numbers, 2, 4, 6, 8, 10, 12, 14, 16, 18, 20, etc., also, of course, with the odd numbers.

[5] I omit the consideration of *infinite cardinals* as not germane to my main thesis.

ilarity as regards manifoldness under specific conditions.[6] This is what 2, 3, 4, 5, etc., are. *But these specific similarities are in turn similar.* They are similar in that they are all instances of the still *more general property of similarity-(not specific)-as-regards-manifoldness*, as "conditioned" by one-one correspondence of classes with one another.

This more general property is symbolized by N. Abstractly defined, then, *finite cardinal in general*, N, is a property, ψ, (of similarity as regards manifoldness as conditioned by one-one correspondence between classes, with specific limitations) that is *instanced* by the specific finite cardinals, 1, 2, 3, 4, 5, etc., each of which is in turn a ϕ that is instanced by the members of the class or "set" that it "determines." As determined by this more general property, symbolized by N, these *instances* of $\psi = N$, form, then, *the class of all finite cardinals*, each finite cardinal, *e.g.*, 2, 3, 4, 5, in turn being a property that is instanced by, respectively, "actual" dyads, actual triads, etc., which dyads, triads, etc., each form a class or a set all members of which have a common property.[7]

It is possible at this point to go "even higher" by removing the restriction necessary for "finite cardinals," namely, that classes have the same *finite* cardinal number if they are in one-one correspondence, and one class is *not* a proper part of the other. *Remove this restriction*, and one can then define cardinal number, whether (*i.e.*, independently of its being) finite or infinite, as follows: The cardinal number of the class C—or the number of elements in C—is a property possessed by all classes that are, or that can be "put," into one-one correspondence with C. This definition does not

---

[6] Specified in the third paragraph preceding.
[7] *Cf.* Young, J. W., *opus cit.*, Chapter IV, *passim.*

"say" whether any one of these classes is a proper part of another, or not. If this is not the case, the cardinal number is finite; if it is the case, the cardinal number is infinite. But, common to both finite cardinality and to infinite, is *cardinality*. This is a "higher" property, of course, than its instances, which are in turn properties.[8] However, into further details concerning this matter we will not enter, although still "other kinds" of number will shortly be considered. Rather, we shall proceed so as to advance more directly toward our goal.

The human race, especially, perhaps, in its Western Civilization, has discovered a great many finite cardinal numbers, or integers, or natural numbers. It has also discovered an infinite cardinal, or, infinite cardinals.[9] But we shall be chiefly concerned with finite cardinals.

Each finite cardinal number, positive integer, or natural number is, now, a specific property or function of which there may be many instances, or only one, or none, but with this we are not, at least at present, concerned. Suffice it to say that each finite cardinal, *e.g.*, 2, 5, 3, 13, etc., is an instance of the more general property, *finite cardinality*, and that the finite cardinals constitute the class that is "determined" by this function. They constitute or are members of this class quite irrespective of any *order* (serial).

But the cardinal numbers have *a natural order* which is an instance of a Simply Ordered Series. The order is, of course, the familiar one, $1, 2, 3, 4, 5, 6, n - 1, n, n + 1$. In this, 1, $2, 3, 4$, or $5, 6, 7$, etc., are "values of the x, y, z's of a preced-

---

[8] *Cf.* Young, *opus cit.*, p. 65.
[9] Whitehead and Russell, *Principles of Mathematics*, Volume III, Part V, Section E, Theorem 265, 32; also Russell, *Principles of Mathematics*, Chapters XIII and XXXVII.

ing page (1). This natural order is *an ordinal series*.[10] Analysis of this class, which we will call C, or < C, shows that it exemplifies certain specific properties:—

(1) *Betweenness: e.g.,* 4 is between 3 and 5.

(2) *Nextness: e.g.,* 3 and 4 are next to each other since there is no integer "in between." Nextness is of two kinds: (a) Immediately succeeding(ness): *e.g.,* 5 on 4, 4 on 3. (b) Immediately preceding(ness): *e.g.,* 4 precedes 5, 3 precedes 4.

(3) *Firstness:* The property of having no immediate predecessor and also of preceding all other members of the class; *e.g.,* 1 is the first positive cardinal.

(4) *Lastness:* The property of having no successor, and also of being preceded by all others; *e.g.,* there is no last cardinal except as arbitrarily selected, *e.g.,* 100, or, as instanced empirically and physically, by, *e.g.,* the principle that the speed of no material body can *exceed* that of light, 186,243 miles per second. Even here it is the speed of light that has "nothing beyond," and not the number, strictly speaking.

(5) *Direction:* In addition to the *sense of a relation,* which is a characteristic of any relation whatsoever in that it "goes" from the *"referent"* to the *"relatum,"* *e.g.,* from x to y in xRy, there is *direction in the series we are considering;* this direction is from less to greater, or, the converse direction, from greater to less. This direction is neither spatial nor temporal, neither physical nor mental.

(6) *Magnitude:* This may be defined as the *stretch or "distance"* from one specific cardinal to another specific cardinal, *i.e.,* it is a property of a pair of cardinals.

---

[10] There are, of course, various types of order. The *natural order* of the positive integers is one of these types.

(7) *Discontinuity or Discreteness:* [11] This is the property, of which the series is an instance, by virtue of the
fact that between *any* two members of the series there is
not another member, i.e., some numbers are immediately
next to others, *e.g.,* 2 and 4 are *next* to 3 *with no integer
between either 2 and 3 or 4 and 3.*

NEGATIVE NUMBERS AND ZERO

Just as the positive or "natural" numbers are distinct
from the symbols for them, so also are there negative integral numbers, and zero, that are distinct from the symbols
for them. Thus, *e.g.,* 0, -2, -5, -3 are *symbols* that
stand for *realities*. This is implied by the fact, (a), that, if
there is *direction, e.g.,* from 3 to 4 to 5, etc., and also *the
converse direction* from 5 to 4 to 3, and, (b), if there are the
stretches or distances, *e.g.,* from 3 to 5, $(+2)$, and, in the
converse direction, from 5 to 3, (-2), then there are still
other stretches or distances in this converse direction. The
specific distance from less to greater is *the reality* "behind"
the "operation" of addition; that from greater to less,
the reality "behind" *subtraction*. These "operations" are
acts of attention given to an objective "state of affairs."
Accordingly there are many stretches or distances from
greater to less, with the result that, *e.g.,* the specific "dis-

[11] The more frequently used term is, I think, "discrete," but I shall, in
what follows, not distinguish between this term and "discontinuous."
Logically, "discrete" means *not continuous* and also *not compact* (terms to
be defined shortly), while *discontinuous* means *not-continuous*, which allows
of *compactness*, so that *a compact series* could be discontinuous but not discrete. However, for my purposes, I shall distinguish merely *three* types of
order at this point, namely, discreteness or discontinuity, compactness or
denseness, and continuity. I shall wish to play up the first as *the opposite*
of the last, and, for this purpose, *discontinuity* is more expressive than
discrete.
Cf. Young, *opus cit.,* pp. 62 to 86, *passim;* Lewis and Langford, *opus cit.,*
pp. 364 ff.; Russell, *Principles of Mathematics,* p. 271.

tance," −3, from 3, "reaches" 0, while from 2, it "reaches" −1, and from 1, −2. Accordingly there is discovered the *series of negative integral numbers and 0.* This series has a last member, −1, or 0, but no first, and shares with the series of positive numbers the properties of discontinuity, direction, converse direction, and, between specific members, distance.

From the foregoing discussion it is readily discovered that there are *four types of discontinuous simply ordered series whose members are integers,* with 0 "as good" an integer as any other. These four types are as follows:

(1) The series of positive integers; in this there is a first but no last. This series, or any series that is in one-one correspondence with it, is called a *progression, ω.*

(2) The series of negative integers; this series has a last but no first; any series that is in one-one correspondence with it, is called a *regression, * ω.*

(3) The series of negative *and* positive integers *and* zero; this series has no first and no last; it is "unlimited" in two directions (* ω + ω).

(4) A finite series; this has both a first and a last, with it, perhaps, an arbitrary or conventional matter as to what shall be selected as first and as last respectively, *e.g.,* whether 1, 2, 3, 4, 5, or −2, −1, 0, 1, or 2.

Each of these types is a specific set of properties forming *one compound property,* of which there may be instances or not. On the other hand, each of these numerical types is *an instance* of a more general type which, *as more general,* is quite independent of being exemplified by integral numbers, positive and negative, with 0 "in between," or by anything else. The exemplification is quite contingent.

As defining a property of this more general type, whatever, if there are instances, the instances of it may be, whether the integral numbers or "something else," we have the well-known "postulate" of Dedekind: "*If* C_1 *and* C_2 *are any two non-empty sub-classes of an ordered class* C, *such that every element of* C *belongs either to* C_1 *or* C_2, *and such that every element of* C_1 *precedes every element of* C_2, *then there exists an element* X *in* C, *such that every "element" of* C_1 *which precedes* X *belongs to* C_1, *and every element which follows* X *belongs to* C_2." [12] In other words, there is an element X in C which divides C into two non-empty classes.[13] X may be either the last element in C_1 or the first element in C_2. If it is the last in C_1, then all the elements of C_1, including X, precede all the elements in C_2; if it is the first in C_2, then it and all the other elements in C_2 "follow" C_1. In either case, the class C_1, of elements that precede, has a last; the class C_2, of elements that follow, has a first.[14]

If the class C is instanced by the series of integral numbers, positive and negative, and zero, ... −3, −2, −1, 0, 1, 2, 3, ..., then any number, negative, positive, or zero, "makes" a division.

DENSITY OR COMPACTNESS

Distinct from the property, Discontinuity or Discreteness, of an ordered series, C, and from Continuity, is the *property of Density* (or Denseness) or *Compactness*. This is the property (of the series) that is identical with the possibility of there being between *any* two elements of C another element of C.

This property is realized by the class of *all rational num-*

[12] Quoted from Young, *opus cit.*, p. 75.
[13] A non-empty class is a class with actual members.
[14] *Cf.* Young, *opus cit.*, pp. 72–76.

bers in their natural order from less to greater ($<$). All rational numbers include all integers and all rational fractions. A rational fraction, $\frac{m}{n}$, as distinct from an irrational, *e.g.*, $\sqrt{2}$, may be regarded as the pair of integers, (m, n). One rational fraction, $\frac{m}{n}$, then precedes (or is less than) another rational fraction, $\frac{m'}{n'}$, if $mn' < nm'$.[15] Thus $\frac{1}{5}$ $< \frac{1}{4}$. This property may also be realized by the points of a line, by the instants of time, and by the varying intensities in a field of force.

Any series that is dense is an instance of the following general properties:

(1) Since between any two elements of the series there is another element, there is an infinite number of elements between any two.

(2) No element is immediately next to any other, *i.e.*, no element has either an immediate predecessor or an immediate successor.

(3) Accordingly, if the series be "divided" or "cut" by an element, X, and if X is the first of those elements that follow, forming the sub-class, C_2, then the sub-class, C_1, that precedes, has no last; similarly if X be the last of C_1, then C_2 has no first.

Four *sub-types* of dense series are, however, possible, even as is the case with discontinuous series: the series as a whole, C, may have, (a) a first and no last, *e.g.*, the rational numbers "beginning" with o; (b) a last and no first, *e.g.*, the rational numbers "ending" with o; (c) neither a first nor a last, *e.g.*, all the rational numbers, negative, o, and

[15] *Ibid.*, pp. 101–102.

positive; (d) both a first and a last, *e.g.*, the stretches from o to 1, inclusive, and from −3 to 3, inclusive.

CONTINUOUS CLASSES

Continuity by the strictest definition yet obtained is that specific and distinct property which a class of elements possesses provided the class is dense and also satisfies Dedekind's Postulate.[16]

Although this property may be defined in these general terms, its further "constituents" have been discovered by the analysis of an instance of it, namely, that instance which is identical with the so-called "arithmetical," or "linear," continuum.

This continuum subsists by virtue not only of the rational numbers in their "natural" order, $(<)$, but also of irrational numbers or fractions, such as $\sqrt{2}$, in their order. Such a number is "demanded," *e.g.*, in order to correlate the length of the hypotenuse and the length of the legs of a right-angled isosceles triangle, assuming each leg to be of unit length. In this case there must be some number x, such that $x = \sqrt{2}$. If each leg is the stretch, o to 1, then the hypotenuse is the stretch, o to $\sqrt{2}$. In this case, as with integers and rational fractions, *the symbol and the symbolized (the number) are to be distinguished.*

An irrational number may, then, be defined as a number which, if "evaluated" decimally, "leads" to a non-ending and non-repeating decimal that may approach the irrational as "closely" as one wishes, but that never "reaches" this irrational. The irrational is, then, *the limit* which such a decimal approaches.

There are many such irrationals, and they are both

[16] *Cf.* Young, *opus cit.*, p. 82.

positive and negative. There is, *e.g.*, $-\sqrt{2}$ as well as $\sqrt{2}$.

There is a class, then, which includes both rational *and* irrational numbers, both positive and negative. This "more inclusive" class is called the class of "real numbers." *All these numbers together have a natural order* ($<$). *This natural order is the "linear," or arithmetical, continuum. Anything else* which has the same type of order that this continuum has, or that is in one-one correspondence with it, is also linearly continuous. Space of one dimension, time, a field of force, the flow of energy, the evolutionary series, *might* each be an instance of this type of order, or not. Even if nothing in nature or elsewhere instances it, *it is, nevertheless, a property made up of constituent properties, a specific possibility-of-instances.* Such constituent properties are the following:—

(1) As stated above, this series is *dense* and satisfies *Dedekind's Postulate.*[17]

(2) *Absence of Nextness.* No number of the series is next to any other; between any two numbers there is an infinity of other numbers; no number has either an immediate predecessor or an immediate successor.

(3) The series itself is the series of real numbers. In it, therefore, there is the series of rational numbers. This last series is denumerable, *i.e.*, it "can be put" in one-one correspondence with the terms of a progression. The series is of the character that, *between any two real numbers, there is a rational number. This is the "postulate" or "principle" of linearity.*

The Continuum we have been defining thus far is the *unlimited linear continuum;* it has neither a first nor a last

17 See p. 146, this chapter.

member. But the property of Continuity permits also of, (a), a first and a last element in the series; (b) a first, but no last; (c) a last, but no first.

To illustrate: Time as "conceived of" by Classical Mechanics (Newton) is an instance of an unlimited linear continuum of instants. A finite line may be defined as a linear continuum of points, with a first and a last point. The radius of intensity of a field of force is a continuum of potentials with a first (the center of the "sphere of force") but no last potential. In the inverse direction this radius has a last (the center) but no first.

SUMMARY

Simple Serial Order is a property, a function, ϕ, compounded of constituent properties, of which there are twelve sub-types or instances, namely, discontinuous, dense, and continuous order, with each of these varying as to the presence or the absence of a first term or of a last term, or of both. Each of these *twelve types* is in turn *a more specific property or function* that is instanced *in the realm of number*, so that we have the arithmetical continuum, the arithmetical "discontinuum," and the dense series, each open or closed in one or in both directions. Each of these arithmetical series is in turn a property which may be instanced or which may "apply" in one or more ways.

But between the arithmetical continuum, on the one hand, and the "discontinuum" and dense series, on the other hand, there seems to be, perhaps, an important difference. Each of the two latter series can be stated in general terms, *i.e.*, by "x's," "y's," *and* "z's" (as related in specific ways) that are not mathematical, but it is difficult, if, indeed, not impossible, to express an important constituent of the arithmetical continuum, namely, the presence in it of irrationals, *in general terms, i.e., in terms that are not numerical. Yet, there must be such terms.* For, if "anything" is continuous in that it is in one-one correspondence with the arithmetical continuum, then it is not for this reason identical with this continuum, but shares with it *the more general property of continuity.* There is, then, *this more general property*, although it is difficult, perhaps impossible, to state it without the use of numerical terms.

Characteristic of *this series* of sub-types of sub-types, etc., of Serial Order, is the property, discussed in preceding chapters, of contingency "at every step." Each higher type is a specific possibility-of-being-instanced, but this does not, in any case, imply the instances. These must be found in each case empirically. In no case can they be deduced. Accordingly we must say that, while there are, as a matter of fact, a *generic "discontinuum," continuum, and dense series*, each as an instance of the *still more generic serial order*, none of these is necessitated by this order. And likewise with each of the mathematical sub-types of each of these series, and, in turn, with any instance of any of these sub-types. *At each step, the instances are contingent; at each step there is the specific discontinuity of possibility and of actuality or realization.*

DIMENSIONALITY

The foregoing discussion prepares the way for the consideration of *dimensionality*, a property which, as regards certain of its specific instances at least, is one of great importance in certain aspects of contemporaneous science. Thus, *e.g.*, in both the Restricted and the General Theories of Relativity, we find the "concept" of Space-time, with this defined as "*a four-dimensional manifold.*" It is partly because of their bearing on the problem of the nature of this manifold that, in the preceding paragraphs, the various sub-types of Serial Order have been considered.

Just what, now, is a dimension? The answer is, of course, that *a dimension is anything that possesses the property of dimensionality*, though, of course, if there is the generic property of dimensionality, one could not *deduce* from this *anything* that would have this property. However, there *are* instances of this property, or of *its* sub-properties, 1-, 2-, 3-, ... *n*-dimensionality, each found empirically. Time is such an instance, *i.e.*, time is dimensional, so also is 1-, (2-, 3-, or *n*-dimensional) space, and there may be many other instances. The important question at this point is, however, *what is dimensionality generically*—the general property, the function, which is a specific possibility-of-instances?

The answer is, *Dimensionality is but another name for linear continuity;* anything which is *an instance* of generic linear continuity is *a dimension*.

But in this generic continuum, which is itself an instance of (generic) Serial Order, there are [18] both terms and relations. The relations are, as we have seen, aliorelative, connected, transitive, and asymmetrical. What are the terms?

There are various possibilities as to the nature of the terms, as we go "downward," but, before we do this, let us consider the generic possibilities at this level. Thus, (1), the terms or "elements" of a linear continuum may themselves, each of them, be *a linear continuum*, in which

[18] *Cf.* p. 136, this chapter.

case we have *a generic two-dimensional continuum;* or, (2), the terms may each be *two-dimensional*, in which case we have a *three-dimensional continuum*. It is obvious, then, that, by the principle involved, we may also have a *four-dimensional*, a *five-dimensional*, indeed an *n-dimensional continuum or manifold*, the principle being that *a linear continuum whose terms are each n — 1 dimensional is itself n-dimensional*.

The terms of each "constituent" continuum are in one-one correspondence with the terms of the arithmetical continuum, but are not identical with these terms, for correspondence or correlation does not imply identity. Accordingly, in an *n*-dimensional continuum, each term is in correlation with *n* numbers, each number being a "value" of, or in, one of the constituent dimensions or variables, so that each term is in correlation with a set of "simultaneous" numerical "values," rational or irrational, positive or negative. Such a set of "simultaneous values," if $n = 3$, is analogous to a point,[19] and is in correlation with a point in three-dimensional space, but if the set is one of four or more simultaneous values, then that which is *correlated* with it is not such a point (in three-dimensional space), although it may be called "a point" in four- or in *n*-dimensional space.

There are, then, one-, two-, three-, four-, *n*-dimensional manifolds or continua. "Points" in these can be specified by, or be in correlation with, sets of simultaneous "values" of the one, two, three, four, or *n* variables involved, with the set and that which is in correlation with it always distinct. The variables may be *qualitatively similar or different*, so that one and the same "point" may be a simultaneous

---

[19] And may be called "a mathematical point."

set of values of qualitatively similar *or* of qualitatively different variables or dimensions.

We shall now examine certain instances of this "abstract" or generic continuum (1- to *n*-dimensional), and then consider, in turn, certain instances of these instances.

I.—*N*-dimensional Space. Space of any number of dimensions may be analytically defined as above. Thus, "a 5-space" is the continuous manifold of "points" each of which is a specific set of "values" in five distinct dimensions,—one value for each dimension, and similarly for "a 4-space" and for a "3-space." But, of all these possible *spaces*, only one, the 3-dimensional, is *existent* or given to sense-perception. There is here assumed a qualitatively unique reality which may be called *Space, with the property of Spaciness*, and which is distinct from Time.[20]

II.—*N*-dimensional Time. If the elements which are in correlation with a simultaneous set of numerical values have, or "be regarded as having," the property, *Timeness*, as distinct from *Spaciness*, then there can be analytically defined "a 1-," or "a 2-," or "a 3-," or "a 4-," or "an *n*-dimensional time."[21] But, of all these possible times, only one, namely, 1-dimensional time, would seem to be *existent*, or to be the time of sense-perception, of our living, and, perhaps, of our consciousness.

III.—Color. Color is sensuously perceived. Psychologically considered, a specific patch of color is regarded as a

[20] Whitehead, *Introduction to Mathematics*, p. 240. "There is . . . a fundamental distinction between the properties of space and the properties of number. . . ." "The 'spaciness' of space and the 'numerosity' of number are essentially different things."

This book was written in 1911. I hold that the distinction which was recognized by Whitehead then has not been obliterated by *Time*.

[21] I have in mind a paper read a number of years ago by Professor C. J. Keyser of Columbia University at a meeting of the Am. Phil. Assoc., but I have not been able to find or to obtain the reference.

simultaneous set of "values" of four *non-spatial and non-temporal dimensions*, namely, *saturation, brightness, hue,* and *vividness,* and these four dimensions are qualitatively distinct.

IV.—Tones. A specific tone, psychologically analogous to color, is a simultaneous set of "values" of possibly six dimensions, namely, pitch, loudness, volume, density, timbre, and duration.[22]

V.—Space-Time. This is the interesting and novel 4-*dimensional* manifold to which the physicist is logically led in both the Special Theory and the General Theory of Relativity. The physicist is led to this manifold in his quest for *an invariant, an absolute,* "in the midst" of quantities that, as measured, are found, very definitely, to vary from one "observing" or recording instrument to another, and therefore to be relative to the frame of reference in which such an instrument is situated. Such quantities include most of those that were formerly considered (uncritically) in classical physics or mechanics to be *invariant,* namely, *length, area, volume, shape, time, mass, velocity,* etc. To get beyond these "relatives," the physicist finds himself *logically compelled to "go" into a four-dimensional manifold, space-time,* (1), whose dimensions are neither space nor time; (2), whose elements or terms, each a simultaneous set of values of four variables, are neither points nor instants, but "point-events;" (3), in which the "distance" between two point-events, each a simultaneous set of values of four variables, is neither a spatial nor a temporal quan-

[22] Steven, S. S., *The Attributes of Tones,* Proc. Nat. Acad. of Sciences, Volume 20, No. 7, pp. 457–459, July 1934, distinguishes *the first four.* I am not sure that he is right, but, whether he is or not, *a tone* is a "member" of a number of dimensions. This article was called to my attention by Professor S. H. Langfeld of the Department of Psychology of Princeton University.

tity, but an *interval;* and, (4), in which there is no motion from one point-event to another, in time, but *action.* These "concepts" are radically different from those of traditional mechanics, but they are *forced* upon the physicist by the "logic of the situation," and are not artificial or arbitrary.

Space-time is, then, not four-dimensional space, nor "four-time." It is found that it cannot be either of these if a quantity is to be discovered which is invariant when lengths and times are measured, *as they must be,* in and from frames of reference that are either in uniform rectilinear or in accelerated motion with reference to one another. When such measurements are made, the results as to space-and time-quantities do not agree. Thus, if two frames of reference, A and B, are in uniform rectilinear motion with reference to each other, then the lengths in the direction of the motion, and the times, "on B," as measured both "from A" and "on B," do not agree, and, conversely, for lengths and times "on A" as measured both "on A" and "from B." Measured lengths, areas, volumes "on B" as moving in reference to A as at rest are *shorter* as measured "from A" than they are as measured "on B" itself, and times are *slower or longer.*[23] The results are, however, reciprocal, and each set of values obtained by actual measurement can be transformed by certain equations into the other set. Thus, meter rod "on A" as measured both "on A" and "from B" will be, of course, one meter "on A," but only $\sqrt{1 - v^2/c^2}$ of a meter as measured "from B," v, in this equation, being the uniform velocity of A in reference to B, and, c the speed of light, 186,243 miles per second—*a constant.* And a

[23] The lengths and times "on A" as measured "on A" are called "proper lengths" and "proper times."

specific time period, say, one hour, as measured on A, will, as measured "from B," be longer on the ratio of

$$\frac{I}{\sqrt{I - v^2/c^2}}.[24]$$

With these differing lengths and times actually obtained by measurement and, therefore, relative, it is necessary, if one is to find a quantity that is *not relative, but absolute and invariant*, to "go beyond" these varying Spaces and Times, if this is possible. And this possibility is realized by means of the formula, $ds^2 = dx^2 + dy^2 + dz^2 - c^2dt^2$, in which x, y, and z are the three spatial coördinates, all capable of taking on any values whatsoever *as measured*, t is the time, also having different values *as measured*, and c is the speed of light (constant).[25]

This expression is of the same form as the expression for the well-known Pythagorean Theorem, that the sum of the squares of a right angled triangle is equal to the square of the hypotenuse, or, conversely, that $ds^2 = dx^2 + dy^2$, so that $ds = \sqrt{dx^2 + dy^2}$. This expression allows x and y each to vary, but the hypotenuse to remain invariant. For three dimensions, the expression is, as is also well-known, $ds^2 = dx^2 + dy^2 + dz^2$, so that $ds = \sqrt{dx^2 + dy^2 + dz^2}$.

The expression, $ds^2 = dx^2 + dy^2 + dz^2 - c^2dt^2$, from which $ds = \sqrt{dx^2 + dy^2 + dz^2 - c^2dt^2}$ is analogous to the expressions for two and for three spatial coördinates, with the difference that the fourth coördinate appears *with a minus sign*. It can be shown, however, that, only provided this minus sign is used, is the expression, $ds = \sqrt{dx^2 + dy^2 + dz^2 - c^2dt^2}$, *invariant*, while its constituents, the three dimensions of space, and the one of

[24] *Cf.* Einstein, *Relativity*, 1921, pp. 42–44.
[25] Here again, as elsewhere in this book, the position is taken that *the symbol and the symbolized are distinct*.

time, as measured, vary, or are relative. It is for this reason that the expression on the right hand of the equation does not stand for anything in 4-dimensional *space*, but for an *interval in a four-dimensional manifold that is neither space nor time, but space-time.*

The expression just used, $ds = \sqrt{dx^2 + dy^2 + dz^2 - c^2dt^2}$, is the symbol for an invariant quantity, *the interval, between two point-events* which are "determined" by two simultaneous sets of values, three of space, one of time, as obtained from measuring instruments in two frames of reference in uniform rectilinear motion with reference to one another. But this expression does not hold if two frames of reference, "from which" and "on which" distances and times are measured, are accelerated with reference to one another. In this case the expression is much more complicated, though of similar form. It is $ds^2 = g dx_1^2 + 2g_{12}dx_1dx_2 + 2g_{13}dx_1dx_3 \ldots$ or, more concisely, $ds^2 = \Sigma g_{ik}dx_1dx_k$, in which the *g*'s symbolize the *curvature* of the 4-dimensional continuum in which *ds* is invariant.[26] This more complex expression is that to which the physicist finds himself logically forced when there is not only uniform rectilinear motion "between" two coördinate systems, but accelerated motion. The "effect" of this accelerated motion is to "distort" the coördinate system, so that distances and times as measured are not only relative to the frame of reference "in" or "from which" they are measured, *but also* relative to the distortions of these frames as due to, or as identical with, accelerated motion between the two frames. The former, simpler expression is that which is used in the Special Theory, the second, more complex

[26] *Vide* d'Abro, *The Evolution of Scientific Thought from Newton to Einstein*, p. 99.

expression, that which is found in the General Theory. In each case, however,—it is to be emphasized—*the expression is but a set of symbols that stand for something symbolized. This "something" is an objective reality*, but it is *a reality* that is not identical with spaces,—lengths, areas, and volumes—and times *as measured*, or as we usually "conceive" them, and live by them. These it cannot be, for *they are relative, and it is invariant and absolute;* it (the reality) is to be found, then, only in *a different realm, that of space-time*, a realm that "contains," not points, instants, lines, and times, but point-events and intervals; and not mass, force, and energy, but, as we shall later see, curvature and action.

It is not my purpose, however, to give an account of Relativity. In preceding paragraphs we were considering the generic characteristics of an *n*-dimensional manifold, and we then passed to instances of such a manifold, such as *N*-spaces, *N*-times, and Space-Time. The discussion of Relativity has been in this connection. We may now, then, continue our discussion of *n-dimensional manifolds as such*, in order to examine two or three matters of importance.

First. An *n*-dimensional manifold as such—the generic form—has no "geometry," *i.e.*, even though it be "thought of" in analogy to space, especially "a 3-space" (which may have any one of a number of different geometries), still it is *amorphous*. It has no particular form, except that it is an *n*-dimensional continuum. But specific instances of this continuum may have a particular form, or some one of a number of possible forms or "geometries."

Secondly. An *n*-dimensional manifold may be "cut," the result being a manifold of $n-1$ dimensions. This may be *illustrated* in the case of a 1-, 2-, or 3-dimensional Euclidean space, *i.e.*, in the case of a straight line, a flat plane, and a 3-dimensional manifold. Thus, if a plane intersects a 3-dimensional spatial manifold, *e.g.*, a sphere, a plane results; if a flat plane, a straight line results; if a line, a point. In each case we have, owing to the "cutting," $n-1$ dimensions resulting from n-dimensions. Let us call this "cutting plane" a "*hyperplane*," and, still more generally, let us use the term "cutter." [27]

This second matter will now be considered in further detail, especially in connection with the previous discussion of space-time.

In the literature on both the Special Theory of Relativity and the General Theory we find it stated that the 4-dimensional manifold, space-time, is "split up," "carved up," "cut up," "sectioned," "separated" [28] into three dimensions of space and one of time, by the observing or recording instrument or by the observer. The values of these four dimensions will, however, as we have seen, differ quantitatively, *as measured* by the observing instrument, according to the frames of reference "in which" or "from which" the measurements are made and also according to the kind of motion of these frames, *i.e.*, whether it be uniform *or* accelerated. The results of the measurement would differ, also, according to the *geometrical form, or geometry, of space-time*, if it had a geometry, just as, by analogy, a different line results if a hyperplane "cuts" a curved surface, from what results if a flat surface is "cut."

However, what I particularly wish to emphasize at this point is, perhaps, the vagueness of the terms "split up," "carved up," "cut," etc., and the desirability of getting

[27] This statement is made as the basis for *an analogy*, to be developed in what immediately follows.

[28] d'Abro, *opus cit.*, *passim*, uses all of these terms as synonyms.

more precise terms for this "operation." As such terms, I take "cut" and "cutter," and define these generically as follows: A "cutter" is of such a character that it "divides" or "separates" an *n*-dimensional manifold into an *n − 1* continuum and a remaining, "single" dimension. Thus, *e.g.*, if a three-dimensional space is "cut," a two-dimensional surface results, leaving the third dimension as separate and distinct from this surface.

The foregoing is only an attempt, by the use of analogy, to make clear how space-time, as "cut" by an observer, or by a recording instrument in a particular frame of reference, results in three dimensions of *space*, or in a 3-dimensional space, and a distinct, single dimension of *time*, with the values and character of these varying with the "direction" of the "cut," *i.e.*, with the frame of reference in which the observing instrument is situated. This is somewhat analogous to the varying curves that result from the "cutting" of a cone at different angles. If the cone is "cut" at right angles to its perpendicular axis, a circle results, if not at right angles to this axis, an ellipse, etc. Still other curves result if the *surface* of the cone is curved in *two* dimensions, like the surface of a sphere, instead of being flat in one dimension.[29]

The result of the "cut" depends, then, not only on the "direction" (the frame of reference) but also on the *nature or structure of that which is "cut."* It is, then, to the question of the possible structures, the (possible) geometries, of space-time—of that which is "cut"—that we next turn.

Just as it is not my intention in the least even to attempt to give an account of the more important "points" in the

[29] One might derive the analogy from, *e.g.*, Dedekind's Theory of Number. Dedekind defines a "cut" as an "element" in a Number Series that "effects a *division*." *Vide* Young, *opus cit.*, pp. 103–106.

Theory of Relativity, but only to "draw" from this theory in so far as it is germane to my main thesis, so also it is not my aim to give a complete account of modern geometry, but only to use some of its accepted results. Use is to be made of these results because it is accepted doctrine in the Theory of Relativity, especially the General Theory, that *space-time is a 4-dimensional manifold that is curved.*[30] In fact it is "with remorseless logic" that the physicist is led to this curved manifold. But not only this. The "cutting" of this curved manifold results in both *a curved 3-dimensional space, and a curved time.*[31]

What, now, can such terms mean? "What in the world" can *a curved space-time, a curved space, and a curved time be?* It is in order to answer these questions with some degree of clarity that a brief excursion is made into the field of Modern Geometry,[32] especially into those aspects of it that have to do with *curved manifolds*.

I shall distinguish, at the start of my discussion (what I shall call) *Theoretical Geometry* from *Empirical* or *Physical Geometry*, and then I shall sub-divide the former into *Logical* and *Metrical*.

Now, it is quite possible, as is well known, owing to the researches of Bolyai, Lobatschewsky, Riemann, Gauss, and others, to develop "Plane Geometries" that differ radically from the Plane Geometry of Euclid. In one such geometry this development consists of a series of deductions that are made from the postulate (together with other postulates), that in a plane containing a line (*shortest, as measured, between two points*), and a point, there are, through this point, *two*, and perhaps, indeed, *an infinite*

[30] See Einstein, *Relativity*, pp. 108–110.
[31] See d'Abro, *opus cit.*, Chap. XXXI.
[32] I derive my account from a number of sources, not from any one source.

number of parallels.[33] There results, *e.g.*, the "theorem," that the sum of the angles of a triangle is less than two right angles. This geometry proves to be the geometry of a surface which a Euclidean geometrician would call *a surface of negative curvature*, illustrated by the surface of a saddle. It was first worked out by Bolyai (in 1832) and, also, independently, by Lobatschewsky (in 1835). In contrast with the two-dimensional space defined by this geometry, there is the two-dimensional space, first defined by Riemann (about 1850), which starts with the postulate (with other postulates), that through a point, in a *plane*, there are *no* parallels to a line in this plane. From this postulate *and* others there is deduced, *e.g.*, the theorem, that the sum of the angles of a triangle is "always" greater than two right angles. A Euclidean geometrician would call this surface one of *positive curvature*, and, if the surface were that of a perfect sphere, a surface of *uniform* or invariant, positive curvature.

The radius of curvature in either of these two geometries might be very large or very small (according to some selected unit of measurement), and if it were very large, the curved surface, in either case, might be indistinguishable, if one attempted to determine its character by measurement, from a flat or plane surface.

This latter surface can, however, also be *defined logically*. It is a surface in which there *is one, but only one*, parallel to a line, through a point. From this postulate, with other postulates, it follows (is implied), that the sum of the angles of a triangle is just exactly equal to two right angles. This surface is, of course, the kind that is defined by the orthodox geometry of Euclid (about 300 B.C.).

[33] These are two "limiting" or "principal" parallels.

There are other differences between these three geometries, *e.g.*, on a Euclidean surface there can be similar figures of various sizes, but not on a non-Euclidean. However, it is not necessary to my purpose that these further differences and details be discussed. Suffice it to say that each of these three geometries consists of a body of propositions (postulates, definitions, and theorems) that, (1), are all consistent with one another, but that, (2), only in some cases imply and are implied by other propositions, so that, (3), some propositions are, in this sense, *independent* of others. In these respects each geometry is a system, or set, of propositions, that is independent of the other two systems, and *contradictory propositions, e.g., the propositions that concern parallels, can co-subsist in different systems*. Each geometry is the *locus*, then, for the subsistence of some propositions which are the alternative to, or the formal contradictory of, certain propositions in another system. The "effect" of the contradiction is, then, to *exclude*, or to force, contradictory propositions into different *loci*.[34] Thus, *e.g.*, the specific proposition, *p*, concerning parallels in any one system, say, in the Euclidean system, has, as its formal contradictory, *non-p*, which can be "translated" into *positive* propositions, concerning parallels, in each of the other two systems.

The three systems under discussion have, however, at least one thing in common. The space, or two-dimensional manifold, which each defines, is *isotropic, i.e.*, it is of constant curvature, either finite, and therefore either positive (Riemann) or negative (Lobatschewsky), or zero (Euclid). In contrast with such a manifold, it is possible to conceive

---

[34] Exclusion into distinct and different *loci*, of some kind,—spatial, temporal, logical, subsistential,—is the "effect" of any specific contradiction. Given two *loci*, contradictories can always coexist or co-subsist.

of a manifold, here, two-dimensional, that is not isotropic, *i.e.*, that is *anisotropic*. While in some cases that are *anisotropic*, *e.g.*, the surface of an *ellipsoid*, it is logically possible to define the surface as a whole, in other cases it is not possible to do this; rather, only small areas of the surface can be defined, and this only approximately.

If the term *"logical"* is applied to geometries which are "constructed" as are the three kinds of plane geometry just discussed, then the term *"metrical"* may be used to characterize that method of "construction" which depends on the *possibility of measurement*. This *possibility* or property I shall call *Metricity*.

Metricity is *the possibility of measurement*, and measurement is in terms of some unit. The choice of the unit is, of course, quite arbitrary, as is evident.

Each of the three plane geometries just discussed can, now, be derived from certain assumptions concerning Metricity. Thus, *e.g.*, if there be assumed a specific unit of length, which might be instanced in the physical world by a metallic rod called *a meter* under certain specific conditions of temperature, pressure, etc., then, if it be assumed that this unit is used for measuring distances, there are three possibilities as to the "action" of this unit as an "instrument" of measurement:—In general, to be such an instrument, the "unit" must be movable, or, it must move. In moving, (1), it may remain *rigid*, *i.e.*, not change its length; (2), it may contract under certain specific conditions as a "result" of its motion; (3), it may expand. By *rigidity* is meant not changing size,—in this case, *length*,—as a result of changing position.

It is impossible, now, by actual measurements, in the physical world, of lengths or distances, either to prove or to disprove rigidity, for any such proof or disproof is circular. Thus, if we "check" the rigidity of a "meter-stick" by a "centimeter-stick," it is quite possible that each "stick" changes size as a result of motion, yet that the ratio established by measurement should remain constant. But this ratio would also remain constant if neither unit changed size. To infer from this ratio that the meter-stick has not changed is, therefore, to beg the question.

Accordingly, since both to establish rigidity by actual measurement and also to "disestablish" it, is impossible, we are left quite free explicitly to assume or postulate *rigidity* or its absence, and, in the latter case, either contraction or expansion as a "result" of motion.

Again, it is not my purpose to go into many details regarding this matter. Suffice it to say that, if a unit of length be assumed to remain rigid as it "glides" over a surface, then this surface is Euclidean, and the shortest distance *as measured* between two points, *defining shortest as that distance which contains the unit (of measure) the least number of times, will be what is usually called a straight line.* On the other hand, if it is postulated that the unit of measure decreases in size, *in inverse ratio to its distance from the center*, as it moves, *e.g.*, along the radii of a circle, away from the center, and toward, "a bounding circumference," then it can be shown to follow that all lines other than radii and diameters are, as shortest distances—with "shortest" defined as in the preceding sentence—, segments of curves or circumferences which "make" right angles (Euclidean?) with the circumference. To a hypothetical measurer on this surface, these segments would "appear" to be straight, if straight means shortest, as previously defined. Thus it can be seen that perhaps both terms, *straight and curved*, were better given up, and only the term, *shortest or least distance*, retained, with this defined as that distance which "contains" the unit of measurement the least number of times.

A surface with the properties just described is "Lobatschewskian." It is a surface which "a Euclidean" would call a surface of negative curvature, like the surface of a saddle or of a curved hour-glass, with a constant, but negative, radius of curvature.

But one may also assume that the unit of length expands in a certain way as it moves away from the center.[35] From this assumption, together with other propositions, it can be shown "to follow" that shortest lines, again as previously defined, are the segments of curves that do not "leave" the surface in which the triangle "exists," but that remain in the surface to "return" to themselves. In other words, all shortest lines are segments of great circles of a sphere of constant curvature. This surface is Riemannian. To a hypothetical measurer of this surface, limited to it, and knowing nothing of any other surface, it would appear, with certain limitations, to be, not spherical, but, rather, quite "flat." It is to be interpreted as *spherical* only in relation to a Euclidean, flat surface, by an interpreter who makes his standard Euclid. Conversely, however, if this Riemannian space were "made the standard," then, to a hypothetical observer of it, it would be flat, and Euclidean space curved.

However, if these terms of comparison be not used, and there is no necessity why they should be, it is nevertheless theoretically possible for a theoretical being theoretically inhabiting a 2-dimensional surface, and knowing nothing of

[35] *Cf.* F. Klein, *Vorlesungen über Nicht-Euclidische Geometrie*, 1928, pp. 296–298.

any other surface as a basis of comparison, to determine the character of that surface. This possibility was first found by Gauss a hundred years ago, and generalized by Riemann for *n* dimensions. The method of doing this depends on a generalization of the well-known theorem of Pythagoras, that the square of the hypotenuse of a right-angled triangle is equal to the sum of the squares of the two sides. This may be stated in the form, $ds^2 = dx^2 + dy^2$. The generalization is, $ds^2 = g_1 dx_1{}^2 + g_2 dx_2^2$. In this formula x_1^2 and x_2^2 stand for the coördinates (of any coördinate system whatsoever) and g_1 and g_2 are "multipliers" (variables) whose values are to be determined (theoretically) by measurement.[36] Theoretically, then, all that an inhabitant of a surface would have to do would be to measure up a number of triangles and, by comparing results, empirically determine the values of the *g*'s. If g_1 and g_2 were each found equal to 1, then the formula becomes $ds_2 = dx^2 + dy^2$, and the surface is Cartesian or flat, but if one *g* (or both) is not equal to 1, then the surface is curved. However, with it assumed that an inhabitant of a surface is confined to that surface, these terms, "flat" and "curved," are, perhaps, not permissible, at least, not necessary, since the metrical properties of the surface can be discovered without them.

A 2-dimensional curved surface can be *visualized* in three dimensions, but to *visualize* a 3-dimensional curved surface is impossible. Nevertheless, by the extension which Riemann made of Gauss' generalization and principles, it would be possible for a theoretical inhabitant of this space also to ascertain, without leaving it, its character, and

---

[36] *Vide*, for much of the material of this account, Bolton, L., *Introd. to the Theory of Relativity*, Chaps. XVI–XVIII, *passim*.

likewise for a 4-, a 5-, an n-dimensional space, indeed, *for an n-dimensional manifold.* For a 3-space it is found that it would be necessary to determine six g's, for a 4-space, ten g's.[37]

It is not necessary to my purpose to present this matter in any further detail. We are discussing "theoretical metricity," and to this discussion the details just presented are germane. The point is that the "geometry" of an n-dimensional manifold can be determined *theoretically,* giving a range of possibilities, either logically or metrically as I have defined and used these terms. Whether or not *there are instances of these possibilities,* and, if there are, which possibilities are instanced or realized, and which not, is a matter for empirical investigation to decide. It thus becomes evident that, if we return to the matter of "cuts," the result of a "cut" depends not alone on the "direction" of the "cut" (frame of reference), but also on the character of the manifold that is "cut." If this manifold is curved, the result of the "cutting" will be different from what it would be if the manifold is not curved.

The foregoing discussion has been concerned chiefly with two-dimensional surfaces. These, it has been found, can be so defined theoretically, in two ways, logically and metrically, as to determine the character of isotropic surfaces of three kinds, namely, one flat and two curved. But such theoretical determination is not limited to two-dimensional surfaces; it may be *extended* to 3, to 4, to any finite number of spatial dimensions, or to *any n-dimensional manifold, whether spatial or not.* This means that it is possible, theoretically, so to define three kinds of isotropic n-dimensional manifolds, without regard to whether they

[37] d'Abro, A., *opus cit.,* Chap VII, especially p. 96.

are instanced or not, and, if instanced, without regard to what they are instanced by, as to "give" *the intrinsically differing structures* that may be called "flat," negatively curved, and positively curved, or, respectively, Euclidean, Lobatschewskian, and Riemannian. A hypothetical inhabitant of any of these manifolds could, theoretically, "from within" the manifold itself, ascertain the peculiar *metricity* of the manifold in which he lived. None of these manifolds need be *instanced or exemplified;* or, some of them might be, as "a matter of fact," and others not; or all might be, but not by the same manifold, but by different manifolds. However, the evidence is, that *some*, at least, *are exemplified.* Thus, *e.g.*, a 4-dimensional Euclidean *manifold* is exemplified by the instance, which can be defined logically, of a 4-dimensional (Euclidean) *space*, but likewise, a 4-dimensional space can be so defined, in two other ways, as to exemplify, respectively, a Lobatschewskian and a Riemannian 4-dimensional manifold. But also, any of these three 4-dimensional *continua* might be instanced *by other than spatial manifolds, e.g.*, by temporal manifolds.

Of especial interest, however, is the fact that the Theory of Relativity is identical, in part, with the acceptance of *space-time* as instancing, in the Special Theory, *a semi-Euclidean,* and, in the General Theory, *a Riemannian 4-dimensional manifold*, which means, in the second case, that *space-time is a continuum of positive curvature.* This "selection," this "instancing," however, comes, not from above, but "from below." It is "decided" quite empirically. Thus, with it found, in the development of the Special Theory, quite empirically, that measurements of space (three dimensions) and of time vary from one frame of reference to another "according to a rule" (the Einstein-Lorentz transformations),[38] it is also found, *as springing from this source*, that an invariant quantity or magnitude which will allow for these variations can be found only in that 4-dimensional manifold which *is space-time*, and which is an instance of a 4-dimensional semi-Euclidean manifold.[39] That is, only in this specific manifold can there be that specific invariant magnitude which is called the *interval*, and which is symbolized by the expression, $ds = \sqrt{dx^2 + dy^2 + dz^2 - c^2\, dt^2}$ To obtain the invariancy, with time, as measured, one of the variables, *the negative sign is necessary*, but, with this the case, the manifold must be semi-Euclidean. Thus the solution is not arbitrary, but forced.[40] The observed facts choose, as it were, for themselves, the specific manifold. The mind of the physicist, "starting" with these facts, but "follows their lead," and therefore accepts space-time as a 4-dimensional semi-Euclidean manifold of point-events between which there are invariant quantities called intervals.

But empirical data include not only distances (lengths) and times as measured in or from frames of reference in uniform rectilinear motion in relation to one another, but also bodies that move with changing velocity, *i.e.*, *accelerated motion*. Such changes in velocity have been tradi-

---

[38] *Cf.* Einstein, *opus cit.*, Chapter XXVI.

[39] Einstein, *ibid.*, p. 110, says that the space-time of the Special Theory is Euclidean; d'Abro, *opus cit.*, p. 190, and Bolton, *Introduction to the Theory of Relativity*, p. 147, say that it is semi-Euclidean.

[40] *Cf.* Bolton, *opus cit.*, pp. 91–92. "The use of the Lorentz transformation is not a matter of choice or convenience. It is a necessity if the statements of differently circumstanced observers are to be correlated, and therefore this fourth dimension is forced upon the physicist." . . . "He is obliged to realize that lengths and times as manifested to him are not absolute properties of bodies existing independently of him, but relations between himself and some fundamental entity in which time plays the part of a dimension."

tionally regarded as due to gravitational forces. These forces have been held to produce either a change in velocity only, or a change in direction, as, *e.g.*, in the case of the motion of the moon around the earth, or both at the same time. These data have led the physicist to the General Theory of Relativity in which *a specific substitute* is found for the *unsatisfactory force of gravitation* of Newton. This force was unsatisfactory for a number of reasons: (1) No mechanism for, and, in this sense, no rational explanation of, the force could be found, even with it assumed that there was a universal ether in which all bodies moved. (2) It was a force that was supposed to "travel" instantaneously, *i.e.*, with infinite velocity. (3) It was a force that varied inversely as the square of the distance (d^2), but the distance was a distance *now, instantaneous*, with no lapse of time. Such a distance, (a) cannot be measured, since (actual) measurement requires time, and (b), is ambiguous, since, as Einstein showed, that which, as measured, is *simultaneous* to one observer is a *time-duration* to another.

It is, therefore, due to Einstein's insight that these unsatisfactory features of the classical theory can be avoided. This is done by taking the position, not only that there is no ether [41] whose "machinery" might explain gravitation, but also that there is no force of gravitation. In place of this force, Einstein "offers" a four-dimensional curved continuum of space-time, and the equivalence of gravitational forces with the *geometrical* properties of the fields or regions in which these forces occur. This second principle is the well-known *Principle of Equivalence*, that

[41] The results of the Michelson-Morley experiment showed that there is no ether.

"a gravitational field of force is exactly equivalent to a field of force introduced by a transformation of the coördinates of reference, so that by no possible experiment can we distinguish them." [42] Such a transformation may be due to the acceleration of the system. The outcome is, that when the four-dimensional curved manifold is "cut" or "split" or "separated" by an observer or recording instrument, there result a curved space and a curved time,[43] strange as this latter, especially, may be. Accordingly, physical agencies—bodies and light—conform to the characteristics of the space in which they move, to its geometry, and to the time "required" for their motion.

The curvature of space-time as "demanded" by the General Theory, or, better, by the data or "facts" with which it starts, is not, as in the Special Theory, semi-Euclidean, but Riemannian, *i.e.*, it is *a positive curvature*, "like" that of a sphere. The intrinsic geometry of this manifold is given by the *g*'s, the potentials,[44] and only in a space-time that has this specific geometry can a quantity be found that will be invariant "when" other quantities— distances, times, forces, masses, velocities—as measured, vary. Such an invariant quantity is not dependent on the frame of reference "in which" or "from which" distances, times, forces, and masses are measured, nor on any particular motion, whether uniform or accelerated, of such a frame, so that it is, in this respect, *an objective fact*.

But again, it is not my purpose to present a detailed discussion of Relativity. We have been led to some of the important points in this Theory as we have followed the

[42] *Cf.* Einstein, *opus cit.*, pp. 62–64, and Eddington, *Report on the Relativity Theory of Gravitation*, pp. 19, 43, and *Space Time and Gravitation*, p. 76.
[43] See d'Abro, *opus cit.*, Chap. XXXI.
[44] *Ibid.*, p. 96.

line of possibilities from (Simple) Serial Order through Dimensionality in general to "theoretical" instances of this property, such as 3-, 4-, and *n-dimensional manifolds in general*, and in turn to instances of these manifolds, such as 4-dimensional space and space-time. Each of these more specific manifolds is in turn capable of further specification as regards its geometry. Thus, 4-dimensional space may be, if it is isotropic, either Euclidean, Lobatschewskian, or Riemannian, and space-time may be either semi-Euclidean or Riemannian. But *the whole range of data* to be considered, viz., those data "used" in the General Theory as well as in the Special Theory, "select," as it were, the Riemannian geometry for space-time rather than the semi-Euclidean. One may say, then, that space-time is, *on the whole*, a four-dimensional positively curved manifold of point-events, "between which" there are intervals, world-lines, geodesics, that are invariant.

This fact, that the selection of a space-time that is Riemannian rather than semi-Euclidean, is *empirical*, is of philosophical importance. It means that a "start" is made with data that *cannot originally be deduced from anything more general*. They are data that are *just found*. This statement "holds good" equally well for the data of the Special Theory and for the data of the General Theory. These data *are* in both cases merely *what they are; they are not necessitated by anything, nor is their opposite impossible; in brief, they are contingent,—quite a matter of chance*.

But, given these data, they "fit into" one scheme of things, one specific possibility (Riemannian space-time) and not another. And what are these data? They are what we "ordinarily" meet with in the common-sense world and the world of physics; they are *bodies,—material bodies,*—separate from one another, unequally distributed in space, moving differently in many ways as to direction, speed, constancy of speed, etc. Let us call all this "*Matter.*" And among these material bodies are *special ones* called *physicists* who use *other special bodies* called, some *measuring-*, and, others, perhaps, *recording-instruments*. And these bodies, both physicists and instruments, are on another body from which they cannot escape, namely, the Earth, although they can escape from, or be removed from, any body that is moving with reference to the Earth, *e.g.*, from a house, or a laboratory, or a train, or an airplane. The results of all their measurements are found to be relative to the frame of reference, "from which" or "in which" the measurements are made, whatever it be, whatever its "state of motion" may be.

But the *matter is found;* it is found empirically, and not deduced; and it is also found to be *unequally distributed. No transformation of coördinates of any kind* so "disturbs" this unequal distribution as to make it *equal*, whether matter be identified with its crude common-sense definition, or with its scientific definition as, *e.g.*, that it is that which produces a change of velocity, *i.e.*, an acceleration.

Now from this *purely and very empirical source* there springs a "demand" on space-time. "*By and large,*" space-time can be of constant positive curvature, but, here and there, there must be variations in curvature. These *variations* are "demanded" by the *irregularities* in the *distribution* of matter in space (3-dimensional); the "by and large" constant positive curvature as a whole is "required" *by the whole, the totality of matter*. In other words, if material bodies *were* empirically discovered to be uniformly distributed throughout space, as to sizes and densities and distances, then space-time would have an absolutely constant positive curvature. It does not, however, have this constancy, "the reason" being that material bodies are not uniformly distributed. This is an empirical fact that cannot be explained away.

Material objects might, then, *not* be unevenly distributed. They are, however, as a matter of fact, so distributed. But, also, there might be no material bodies at all, and so, also, *no physicists, no "measuring bodies," no recording instruments*. None of these is necessitated by anything else; their absence is quite as possible as their presence; neither absence nor presence is impossible; each is entirely contingent. All that can be said is: There *are* material bodies, these bodies *move*, and there *are* physicists who measure these bodies and their motions by the use of "measuring bodies," and, sometimes, of recording bodies, and who, on the basis of these measurements, inspect and analyze, compute and calculate, predict and confirm, but no part of this state of affairs is necessitated. It all merely happens to be the case.

But, if there were no material bodies of any kind, there would be no Space (3-dimensional) and no Time, and also, of course, no motions, no accelerations, no momenta, no forces, etc., but there would still be *the possibility* of these, and *that possibility is, in part, space-time*, with a constant positive curvature, if it is the possibility for a material world of "even distribution," but with a varying curvature, if for a world, in space *and* time, such as ours is found actually to be. Thus, as pure possibilities, there would be two distinct kinds of space-time, the one characterized by *constant positive curvature*, the other by *varying positive curvature*. But each *could* remain a pure possibility, and nothing more. But there *are* unevenly distributed material bodies (and their motions, uniform and accelerated, either rectilinearly or rotationally), and there *are*, therefore, different frames of reference; there *are*, also, on these different frames of reference, physicists with "natural," or physical, measuring and recording instruments, and there *are the records*. The result is that space-time of varying curvature is "split up," separated, "sectioned," "cut," into *space and time*,[45] but a space and a time both of which are curved. This curvature of space and of time "represents" nothing "but a mere relationship between the intrinsic condition of space-time and the observer's motion or frame of reference." [46]

Now, into the details of this mysterious subject-matter I do not wish to enter to any great extent. Only certain outstanding features of it will be considered, and, at that, briefly.

First, it may be asked, What can possibly be meant by the *curvature of time?* Or, How can *time be curved?* In answer,[47] it may be said that there is an actual *"slowing down" of time* as a material body, such as, *e.g.*, the sun, is approached. This in turn means that, *e.g.*, in the case of the periodic phenomena of "perfect clocks" such as atoms, in a nebula, the periodicity is slowed up. This slowing up is due to the curvature of time, and is not the same as the relativity of time as this is found in the Special Theory. It means that there are *different rates of aging in different parts of space*. This effect is known as the "Einstein shift-

---

[45] d'Albro, *opus cit.*, p. 301.
[46] *Ibid.*, p. 293.
[47] I take this account essentially from d'Abro, *opus cit.*, Chapter XXXI: The Separation of Space-Time into Space and Time.

effect." It implies that hypothetical twins, first living together, but then separating and residing in different parts of space, would not age at the same rate, and that, if they could subsequently be conscious of their respective ages, they would agree that their ages were different.

On the basis of this effect the prediction could be made that, *e.g.*, atoms of sodium in the sun's atmosphere would "beat" more slowly and therefore appear to us redder than would atoms of sodium examined in our own laboratories. This is due to the fact that the gravitational field of the earth is much smaller than that of the sun. This prediction was made by Einstein, and has been confirmed, especially in the case of the enormously dense companion of Sirius.[48] To this curvature of time is due, also, the bending of a ray of light by the amount of "0.87 as it grazes the sun's limb.[49]

The "uneven" curvature of space (3-dimensional) as it results from the "cutting" of an unevenly positively curved space-time is much more readily comprehensible than is the curvature of time.

Briefly stated, space—the space in which we live—is Riemannian. This means that space is of positive, though, "here and there," of varying curvature. The "effects" of this curvature are, as is well known, two-fold. First, it is due to this curvature that there is a precessional advance of the perihelion of Mercury and of other planets. The advance is greatest in the case of Mercury, "0.43 per century. Secondly, there is the effect on a ray of light, and on bodies moving with velocities approximating the velocity of light, 180,243 miles per second. This effect is, that a ray of light, and, also, such bodies, "travel" or

[48] d'Albro, *opus cit.*, footnote, p. 298.   [49] *Ibid.*, p. 294.

move, not in a straight line, but in a curve that is, approximately, an arc of a great circle, which means that, "given time enough," they move in a great circle. This accounts for the "bending" of the ray of light by $''0.88$,[50] in addition to the "bending" by $''0.87$ that is due to the curvature of time, making a total of $''1.75$ as observed in the eclipse expedition of 1919 to Sobral. Einstein's prediction was that the ray would be bent by $''1.74$.[51] "Given time enough," namely, a thousand million years, a ray of light would travel around the physical universe, and return to its "starting place."[52]   The path along which a ray of light moves is a geodesic, but a particular kind of geodesic, namely, a "null-line" or a minimal geodesic.[53]   In thus moving, the ray but *conforms to the structure of space*, as does also anything else that moves, whether the velocity approach that of light or not. It is for this reason that, in the Theory of Relativity, there is no room for a force of gravitation, acting across great distances instantaneously, and having no mechanism, but only for a space and a time *with a metrical structure (curved), so that bodies, when they move, conform to this structure.* Sometimes they move *as if* they attracted, and sometimes *as if* they repelled one another, but there is really no attraction and no repulsion. There is only a "going toward" or a "going away from" one another, as each body, in moving, conforms to the structure of space and of time.

In the long, foregoing account, we have proceeded from relations, serial order, types of serial order, including dimensionality in general, n-demensional manifolds, to the

[50] *Ibid.*, p. 292.
[51] Eddington, *Space, Time and Gravitation*, p. 109.
[52] Russell, B., *A B C of Relativity*, p. 169.
[53] d'Abro, *opus cit.*, p. 303.

theoretical geometry of these manifolds, and, finally, to instances of some of these manifolds. Thus we came to space-time as a 4-dimensional, positively, yet variably, curved Riemannian manifold, as "demanded" by both the Special and General Theories of Relativity. It is only because we have in this sense been led to Relativity that it has been presented. No effort has been made to present the Theory in *all* of its more important aspects.

From relations, serial order, and types of serial order, "down" to space-time, the "descent" has been made by discovering instances of properties that are, in turn instanced, until we came to space-time. This is one instance of 4-dimensional order, but there are other instances, *e.g.*, 4-dimensional space; but 4-dimensional order is in turn an instance of a "higher" property, *n*-dimensional order. It is thus found that there is the *same general scheme of structure* that has been presented in previous chapters. Functions or properties are specific possibilities-of-being-instanced, -exemplified or -realized, but the instances cannot be deduced from the possibility in any case, but must always be found empirically. The instances, being neither necessary nor impossible, are, in every case, then, quite contingent.

Space-time is no exception to this principle. *It merely is,* but it need not be. And so, likewise, is *matter,—the totality of material objects.* By this I mean that *matter,* or that material objects, both separately and in their totality, *cannot be deduced from space-time.* In fact, *matter is not an instance of space-time, rather, it is that which, on the one hand, "cuts" space-time into space and time, and matter and motion, and, on the other hand, results from such "cuts."* Matter thus appears in a two-fold rôle. It is both that which "cuts" space-time, and that which results from this "cut." The physicist and his measuring and recording instruments, and the material objects which "determine" his specific frame of reference, have the effect of "cutting" space-time into other material objects, which might well be *other physicists*, on other frames of reference, with other, distinct, measuring and recording instruments, and the relation is reciprocal.

Thus, in distinction from the relation between a property and an instance of that property, the relations between space-time and matter is *circular*. There must be a space-time of such a character that, when "cut," it "gives" *space, time, matter, and motion*, yet to have this "cut," *there must be matter and motion existing in space and time*. Space-time may thus be defined as *the specific possibility*, (a), of being so "cut" as to give space, time, matter, and motion, but, (b), *of also being of such a character* that, with the results of the measurements of space and time varying from one frame of reference to another, and with gravitational forces found (experimentally) to be equivalent to inertial forces produced by constant rectilinear acceleration, an *invariant magnitude, the interval*, subsists between these variables. Space-time is related, then, to space, time, matter, and motion, *not as is a property to its instances*, but as a realm in which there are invariant magnitudes in relation to which other magnitudes, both those which "cut," and those which result from the "cutting" of, space-time, are variable.

Given different specific sets of quantities as identical with sets of numerical values of these variables as determined by measurement, there is, for each of these varying sets, an invariant quantity, the interval, or geodesic, or world-line between point-events. This interval is of such a metrical character that it may be said to be positively curved in a four-dimensional manifold, and to approach uniform curvature in a small or infinitesimal "region." [54]

At last, then, we have reached *matter, motion, space, and time—the existent world of objects and processes.* In this world there is also radiant energy, electro-magnetic in character. This energy is not, as such, in space-time. Shortly, we shall consider the existent world, as regards certain of its important aspects.

The existent world, of material objects, has been found to be the result of a "cutting" or "sectioning" of space-time, and space-time, as a four-dimensional manifold with a specific geometry, has been found to be an instance of a more general four-dimensional manifold, and so on back to such properties as Relatedness, Necessity, and, finally, Functionality, Ultimacy, Possibility of the First Order, and Contingency. Each "step" downward is identical with the finding of instances of a "preceding" property, this property itself being a specific possibility-of-instances. But these instances can in no case be deduced from their possibility; they must in every case be found empirically, and thus they are at each step contingent. Contingency is, therefore, found "all the way down," for there *is* "a way down" consisting in the fact that an actual instance of any property is in turn a specific possibility-of-instances the next step down, until, starting with Contingency, Functionality, Ultimacy, and Possibility, we come to space-time. Then, as both "cutting" space-time and as resulting from "cuts," *there occur matter, motion, space, and time*, but the relation is not that of instance and property, but of "cutting"

[54] For the elaboration of this point, see d'Abro, *opus cit.*, p. 263.

and of that which is "cut." Are there any further, specific aspects of these realities that are also contingent? To the consideration of this question later chapters will be directed.

EXPLANATION

The material on Relativity for this chapter has been derived from various sources, and is, of course, not original. That for which I am responsible is the synthesis of this with other material, such as that which concerns Relations, Order, Number, and Dimensionality. Among the sources from which I have drawn, there are the following:—

d'Abro, A.	*The Evolution of Scientific Thought*
Barnes, E. W.	*Scientific Theory and Religion*
Bavink, B.	*The Anatomy of Modern Science* (translated by H. S. Hatfield)
Bolton, L.	*Introduction to the Theory of Relativity*
Bridgman, P. W.	*The Logic of Modern Physics*
Eddington, A. S.	*Report on the Relativity Theory of Gravitation*
	Space, Time, and Gravitation
	The Nature of the Physical World
Einstein, A.	*Relativity, The Special and The General Theory*
Freundlich, E.	*The Foundations of Einstein's Theory of Gravitation*
Russell, B.	*The A B C of Relativity*
Silberstein, L.	*The Theory of Relativity*
Swann, W. F. G.	*The Architecture of the Universe*
Thirring, J. H.	*The Ideas of Einstein's Theory* (translated by R. H. B. Russell)
Weyl, H.	*Space, Time, Matter* (translated by H. Brose)

VII

THE EXISTENT WORLD—NATURE;
MATTER, QUALITY AND QUANTITY

In the preceding chapter we at last "reached" matter, both as a totality and as distributed into distinct bodies "determining" distinct frames of reference. Matter thus appeared as both that which "cuts," and as that which results from "the cutting" of, space-time. Thus it is not an instance of space-time, as space-time *is* an instance of 4-dimensionality. Matter is just found; it is not deduced; it is quite contingent, yet its relation to space-time is determinable.

But matter as thus found, quite empirically, along with space, time, and motion, is "in the crude." Light, or radiant energy (electro-magnetic), is also "just found" in this same way. Its speed is measured, and found to be constant (186,243 miles per second), thus to furnish a basis for synchronizing clocks.[1] In the existent world these five realities, space, time, radiant energy, matter, and motion, are not identical, but, rather, *qualitatively different*. This difference does not preclude certain similarities, whatever these may be, but, if there are differences between these five realities, these differences are irreducible. Just as difference is itself not identity or similarity, and conversely, so, also, is space not time, time not matter, and matter not radiant energy.[2]

[1] *Vide* Thirring, J. H., *The Ideas of Einstein's Theory*, Chap. IV.
[2] *Cf.* later chapters, especially VIII, and IX, on organization. Even if "Matter" "consisted" of radiant energy, it could be qualitatively *more*, or *other*, than radiant energy.

We are "speaking" of "things" "on the surface" or "in the rough"—of "crude matter," "crude motion," and "crude" radiant energy—light, perhaps. Scientific analysis may penetrate beneath this surface of "crudities" to entities more "refined," but the general thesis which I shall maintain is, that this *analysis does not displace the reality with which it starts, but only results in finding "deeper" levels that are in correlation with higher ones.* It is, now, to some of the details of this scientific analysis of matter, motion, radiant energy, and, perhaps also, of space and time that I turn in these later chapters, or, to some of the more important "principles" of these details, such as Quantity, Atomicity, Causality, and Creativity or Emergence, for it is not my purpose to present in detail a Mechanics, a Physics, a Chemistry, or a Biology. The subject-matter of these sciences is, in general, presupposed in the discussion that follows. It will be my purpose, then, to show that Nature— the existent world—*instances*, or is the aggregate of instances of, a group of specific *properties*, which, like all other properties, are but the specific possibilities-of-being-instanced or realized, without this "instancing" or "realization" being in the least necessitated. In carrying out this program both Common Sense and Scientific Realism will be assumed and not argued. This Realism means that at least some (and, perhaps, all) of the entities or objects of both our common sense and our scientific experience are, as "presented" or "known" in that experience, quite independent of it. Related, of course, to that experience, these entities are not created by, influenced by, or modified by it.[3]

---

[3] The Realistic Theory has been briefly "defended" in the Introduction. For a longer argument for Realism, see the writer's *The New Rationalism*, *passim*. I have not changed my position in any essential respects since that volume was written.

The several properties which we shall consider are: Qualitativeness and Quantitativeness, Atomicity or Discontinuity in Nature, Continuity (in Nature), Causality, Creativity or Emergence, Freedom, and Value. These properties are related, perhaps in many ways, so that it is difficult to find among them any one "logical" order by which to determine the order of discussion. However, there are certain reasons, which will appear as we progress, for beginning with the first three, so that it is to the discussion of these that we now turn.

QUALITY, QUANTITY, AND ATOMICITY [4]

Qualitativeness (or Propertiness) is a property or function of which everything that is irreducibly different from something else is an instance. All instances of this property are qualities. Qualitativeness is itself a quality, different from Quantitativeness, which is another quality or property or function. Some qualities are quantities—under certain conditions—and other qualities are not. For example, "particular" material bodies (*e.g.*, a 2-meter rod), times (*e.g.*, a period of three seconds), velocities, wave-lengths (of light), etc., etc., are, as measured, quantities, but such qualities or properties as Possibility, Necessity, Contingency, Negativity, Transitivity, are not. These cannot be measured, yet they are irreducibly different from one another, and so are *qualities*. They are certainly not substances, nor events, nor relations, although they may occur in relational situations.

However, it is not in qualities of this "abstract" type, but, rather, in those qualities that, in part, *are* the irreduci-

---

[4] Certain "aspects" of atomicity are discussed in this chapter; other aspects in Chapters VIII, IX, and X.

ble differences of the existent world (Nature), that I am at present interested. These qualities, on the common-sense level, need hardly be mentioned. They are familiar to all. They are the particular colors, sounds, odors, tastes, motions, hardnesses, softnesses, etc., etc., of common sense. These qualities are classified and arranged. But there are also the qualities that are especially recognized and referred to in Science. Such qualities include mass, velocity, acceleration, momentum, electricity, magnetism, inheritance, potential, force, etc., etc. The entities for which these scientific terms stand are either different from one another or not different, but, if they are different, then they are qualitatively and not quantitatively different. This holds whether any entity is complex or simple, and also whether or not, in addition to *the quality*, there is something else to "support" the quality, or *of which* the quality is a quality, or *in which* it inheres. That there is, indeed, that there *must* be, this "something," and that it *is substance*, is the *traditional* view, but it is just this view that is challenged in the paragraphs and chapters that follow. The thesis will be advanced and defended that anything which may be regarded as *a substance,—e.g.*, the *matter* of a material object as distinct from the property, mass, or the property, impenetrability, is, *as distinct, qualitatively distinct from other qualities, and is, therefore, an instance of qualitativeness.* In short, it will be maintained that, if there are substances, these are really, as distinct from what are usually called qualities, themselves qualities, and that accordingly they are instances of the more general quality or property or function, *Substantiality.* That there is this possibility, and that it might be found by empirical investigation to be realized, will be granted. But, that "actually" this possibility *is* found, by such investigation, to be realized, will be denied. In brief, it will be maintained that no substances whatsoever are found empirically in Nature, but only events, relations, and qualities, *that are distinct qualitatively*.

Some qualities, however, are also *quantities*, and others are not. Those that are, are *measurable;* those that are not, are *not measurable*, although they may have an order, perhaps the order of a "simple series," whether continuous, compact, or discontinuous. Thus, *e.g.*, one might "arrange" a group of aesthetic objects, such as a group of paintings, in an order *from less to more beautiful*, and still find no means of measuring these, on which basis to assert that one picture is *twice* or *three times* as beautiful as another. Measurement may presuppose order, even linear order, but order does not involve or imply measurement. Qualities—some qualities—may, then, have an order, but not be measurable; other qualities may be measurable, and, therefore, as measured, "give," or, be, quantities, but still have no order, although the quantities of any particular quality have an order. Thus, *e.g.*, there is no order to the qualitatively different entities, mass, velocity, magnetic intensity, but each of these is measurable. Each, as measured, "gives" quantities, "expressed numerically," and these quantities have an order, in fact a serial order.

MEASUREMENT

Actual measurement is a contingent fact, neither necessary, nor impossible. The actuality of measurement presupposes its possibility, *measurability*. Any actual measurement is an instance of this property. Measurability is a relational property between something to be measured and a means of measuring. Anything measurable is a magnitude. Conversely, only magnitudes are measurable. But, anything is measurable only provided there is a unit of measure. A *unit* of measure presupposes a correspondence, a one-one correlation, between a specific quality as a unit and *two numbers*, either o and 1 or −1 and o. The unit is, then, the stretch of some quality from o to 1 or from −1 to o, *i.e.*, if the quality is of such a character that there is a stretch with two "ends," one in correlation with o, the other with 1, or with −1 and o [and the other parts of the stretch are in correlation with certain fractions, positive or negative, rational or (and) irrational]. Length is an example of a quality of such a character, instanced by such arbitrary units as a foot, a yard, a meter. Thus actual measurement presupposes measurability; measurability involves magnitude; magnitude demands a unit of measurement; and this last presupposes *number*. This means that only that which can be put into one-one correspondence, by means of measurement, with integral numbers, and also with the rational fractions, is measurable. Actual measurement is but a means of setting up, or of ascertaining, this correspondence. It is the bridge which connects the quality which is measured with the numbers, but the two ends of the bridge are not for this reason identical. A quality may, as measured, be a magnitude, and, in relation to a unit, be a quantity, and as a quantity be in correspondence with specific numbers, *but it is not for these reasons identical with these numbers.*[5]

Measurability is, then, the possibility, (a), of something measurable, *i.e.*, of magnitudes, (b), of a unit of measure, (c), of quantities, as the specific correlations of certain

[5] This view is directly opposed, I think, to that of Eddington, *The Nature of the Physical World*, in Chapter XII, on Pointer Readings.

qualities with numbers, and, (d), of establishing these correlations. This last possibility, as realized, is, in any particular instance, a process of measuring. Actual or existential measurement is the totality of measurements.

Actual measurement or measuring, as such a totality, is itself a part of the existent world, perhaps in more ways than one.

First, no measurement would be possible if there were not material or solid bodies. Without such bodies there might, *perhaps*, be space, and time, and space might have certain metrical properties, *e.g.*, it might be Euclidean, but, whether it had, or had not, these properties, could not be established. Indeed, I venture the assertion, of which, however, I am not sure, that even a space "filled" with radiant energy and not "matter," if such a thing were possible, would give a world in which measurement would be *impossible*.

Secondly, I maintain that all measurement reduces to, or is identical with, *either* the selection and use of some spatial unit, either (1) a length, or (2) an angle, or (3) the correlation, through its "effects," of that which is to be measured, with a length or an angle—in both cases, however, with a *spatial quantity* as itself measured by a *material body*. Thus, to illustrate, a length is measured by *a length* (unit = foot, yard, etc., arbitrarily chosen), or by *an angle* (in triangulating these bodies), and an ordinary temperature is measured by its effect, in the case of a thermometer, in raising or lowering (length) a column of mercury up and down a scale (length). Even the measurement of time is dependent, finally, on the length (the arc of a circle) of a material body or of material bodies. For example, if the measurement of time be *standardized* by a clock with a pendulum (and it is), then it is the time of the motion of this material object from one position, to be specified by reference to another material body, to another position, similarly specified, and back again, that is selected as *the unit of time*, whatever this unit may be called.[6]

Thirdly, the selection of the unit of measurement, whether it be for length, for temperature, for time, or for weight, or, indirectly, for other qualities, is, of course, quite arbitrary. The unit of length may be the yard *or* the meter, or any of their subdivisions; the unit of temperature that of a Centigrade or a Fahrenheit scale. This is obvious. But it is likewise quite as obvious, or should be, if it is not, that any specific quantity, *e.g.*, the mean distance from the earth to the sun, namely, 93,000,000 miles is *large or small* only in relation to the unit selected. Largeness and Smallness have, of course, long been recognized as purely relative long before Relativity ever came on the scene. But, a unit having been once selected, two possibilities regarding it must be recognized:—As "used" in the actual process of measurement, (1), it may remain "rigid;" (2), it may not. If it does not, then it may either contract or expand, perhaps, according to law, perhaps, not,—whatever these terms may mean.

There is, obviously, no way experimentally, by direct measurement, of showing that any one of these three possibilities either is or is not the case. For either contraction, or expansion (non-rigidity), or "rigidity" could be "shown" experimentally, by measurement, only by the use of a smaller unit that *remained rigid*, in which case the possibly expanding or contracting or "rigid" "unit" would not be *the unit*, but the smaller one would be, and it is precisely as

[6] The situation is not different if the periodic motion of the earth on its axis, or around the sun, or the periodic change of any other "natural clock" is taken.

to the "behavior" of this "final unit," that the question arises. And the question is answered. For this smallest unit (and fractional parts of it only presuppose it), whether it be an inch of length, or a second of time, or something much smaller than either of these units, *there is no way experimentally of showing either "rigidity" or its absence.* Theoretically, there are, then, three possibilities. A yardstick may, during a process of measurement ("taking time"), remain constant, it may contract, or, it may expand; the beats of a pendulum are not necessarily equal in duration; they may be this, but, also, they may not. Operationally, it is impossible to determine which is the case. Operationally, then, science must proceed, especially if distance and time measurements are fundamental, *positivistically, i.e.,* all that can be established by actual measurement is that a specific quality which, as measurable, is a magnitude, and as measured, is a quantity, is *that quantity only as measured. In other words, the quantitative character of any measurable quality has a meaning only in relation to the actual measurement of that quality.* One can say only, *e.g.,* that this extension as measured *now* contains this unit of length this number of times, and is, therefore, *now this quantity. Tomorrow,* results might not be the same; actual measurement might give a different quantity. And likewise with the measurement of time itself. On the operational basis, then, *we take what we find,* and make our definitions, and build up our science accordingly. For example, on this basis, we will define the shortest distance between two points as that distance which contains our unit of measure the least number of times, saying nothing, and being able to discover nothing, about the behavior of that unit during the process of measuring; also (as an example), we shall be prepared to find either that the speed of light is constant or that it is not, or constant under certain circumstances (*in vacuo*), and not under others (gravitational field); further, that a mass as it moves remains constant, or decreases, or increases (it is now "said" to increase with increase of velocity); in brief, we shall be ready to accept any results whatsover of our measuring.

Obviously, this "operational," positivistic method of proceeding is quite oblivious as to the three possibilities in the "behavior" of any unit of measure. Operationally, this behavior cannot itself be ascertained by measurement; operationally, then, it is a matter of complete indifference to the physicist whether the units remain politely rigid, or misbehave by swelling or shrinking. They could do any of these things only in relation to a theoretical, smaller unit that remained rigid, but in such a unit the "operationist" is not interested, since *operationally it cannot be found*. Indeed, even if "units" did swell or contract, as measured by a unit that did not, the effect of this on the results of measurement might well be compensated for by a correlative swelling or contracting of the quality to be measured, so that, even theoretically, the results of (theoretical) measurement would not differ from the results obtained by measurement of a "rigid" quality or "body," with a rigid unit.

The results of a series of measurements in showing that a specific quantity, *e.g.*, the speed of light *in vacuo*, the charge on the electron, "Planck's constant," h, is constant, are quite consistent with either one of three theoretical possibilities, viz., (1) that both unit and quality measured remain rigid, (2) that both contract in the same ratio, (3) that both expand. Actual measurement cannot "decide" between these. For this process (actual measurement), then, these alternatives are unimportant; for it, they have no meaning. Actual measurement is "thrown back," then, on the *purely operational and empirical method of measuring* a quality, and, thereby, a magnitude, which may or may not change while measured, by a unit which also may or may not change while used. All that is required is a *relative constancy of results* as regards any particular quantity, *e.g.*, the speed of light. Only if the unit changed, and the "thing" measured did not, or conversely, would this constancy be endangered, and any "derivation" of laws on its basis be difficult, if not impossible. *That laws are derived from measurement, and that predictions are made from these laws and confirmed,* may be inductive evidence that this supposition is *not* realized in Nature, but there is nothing which makes its realization impossible any more than there is anything which makes its opposite necessary.

Fourthly: Actual measurement, as Eddington has pointed out, is itself a physical process, involving physical and material instruments scaled to some unit, and therefore is subject to the same general conditions existing in Nature as are the qualities or magnitudes that are measured.

One of these conditions is Time,—Time not as measured more or less accurately by an instrument, but as lived. In this respect, it may be said, paradoxically, perhaps, that Time (as lived—unmeasured) is required in order to measure Time, even by the most accurate and delicately constructed pendulum clock; and Time, either as lived, or as measured, or both, is certainly required in all other processes of measuring. In short, *measuring is itself a temporal process* consisting of the use of physical or material instruments by a measurer and observer who is, among other things, a material body. No actual measurement is instantaneous, at least not to all observers even from the standpoint of the Special Theory of Relativity. Since all actual measuring is temporal, the suppositions of the preceding paragraphs as to possible changes in both unit of measure and in "thing" measured are not impossible.

But at this point other possibilities with reference to the conditions of actual measurement are to be discussed. Measurement is a temporal process, but it is this because it is a physical process, involving physical and material instruments and units and a measurer. What is involved in this fact? What are the possibilities?

I do not wish, at least at this point, to stress the advantages which the method of measuring has over other methods of "dealing with" Nature, but some of these advantages may be briefly mentioned:

It is well known that the Greeks in their philosophy and science interpreted Nature in accordance with "preconceived" intellectual or rational patterns whose norms were at least internal consistency and the presence of (at least) some relations of implication. Thus, *e.g.*, Aristotle, as is well known, "made" the paths of the planets conform to the "rational pattern" of "the perfect circle." Briefly, for the Greek, that was true, and that was fact, which stood the test of reason.

In contrast with this, the Middle Ages, under the domination of the Church, set up, as the criterion of truth and of fact, a complex pattern of reason, authority, and revelation, with "a circular relation" between these three. Reason depended on authority (ecclesiastical), authority on revelation from God, but this revelation was in turn supported by this very reason when "working" in accordance with "truths" derived from authority and revelation. A "vicious circle," but an obstinate one to those not within the bounds of its "divinity."

Then came Galileo, admittedly successor of Archimedes, but nevertheless originator, in many ways, of the principles of Scientific Method in the natural sciences. Not to reason unaided, as with the Greeks, also, not to reason as supported by faith in Church, Revelation, and God, as with the men of the Middle Ages, did Galileo appeal, in order to find fact and truth, but to reason as buttressed by *the method of putting questions to Nature through the means of controlled experiment and measurement, and of "getting Nature's reply."* It is this method, in its refinements, that is the dominant characteristic of Modern Natural Science, especially of Astronomy, Physics, and Chemistry. The principles that "underly" this method are as follows:

(1) An experiment is accompanied, if possible, by measurement. Thus Galileo, as is well known, experimented on "falling bodies" by letting balls roll down an inclined plane. Distance was measured by equal notches (units) on the plane, Time, by equal volumes of water syphoned out of a receptacle—by a clepsydra.

(2) An experiment, whether accompanied by measurement or not, but especially *if* thus accompanied, *eliminates, to the highest degree practically possible, the influence of temperament, tradition, personal bias, and emotion.* Thus, *e.g.,* Galileo found, by his experiment and measurements, that, contrary to tradition, the motion of a falling body is accelerated, and not uniform. An experiment accompanied by measurement is, therefore, the *most impersonal method* that there is, of "getting at fact" at least at certain kinds of facts, namely, quantities—*which are always quantities*

of qualities. As a corollary of this characteristic, an experiment, especially if it is accompanied by measurement, can be repeated by other individuals, who will either confirm or not confirm, within a certain range of error, the results of the measurements of other individuals. *Thus science becomes social.*

(3) The results of measurement—repeated, of course, and averages taken, and average errors determined—is to assign, *upon the basis of the units chosen,* whole numbers to the different qualities measured, whereby these qualities become, also, quantities. Thus, *e.g.,* Galileo measured time and distance, and then, in his experiment, the distance travelled in different times. Thus he found, *e.g.,* that if a ball rolled down an inclined plane one unit of distance in one unit of time, in two units of time, it would roll four units of distance, in three units of time, nine units of distance, etc. On the basis of temporal and spatial measurement, he thus measures motion as to, (a), its velocity and, (b), the rate of change of this velocity, *i.e.,* acceleration. He thus discovers certain variables, and the way in which these variables are related to (correlated with) one another, *i.e.,* he finds that, as the numerical "values" of one variable change, there are specific correlated changes in the "values" of certain other variables, *e.g.,* the times, 1, 2, 3, 4, are correlated, (a), with the distances 1, 4, 9, 16, (b), with the velocities, 1, 2, 3, 4, and, (c), with an increase in velocity of 1, 1, 1. These four variables are found to form *a closed set,* if no question is asked as to the cause of the acceleration, and so to be *independent of other qualities* (variables) such as temperature and color. It is thus found that certain qualities *may be related and yet be independent* in the sense, at least, that changes in one quality, *e.g.,* tem-

perature, do not involve changes in another quality, *e.g.*, velocity.

We thus have an instance of an important principle, namely, that, although certain qualities are present to other qualities, *e.g.*, temperature to velocity, and cannot be *experimentally* eliminated, nevertheless the process of measurement *virtually eliminates* them, since it shows that changes in their values are not correlated with changes in the values of other variables, *e.g.*, changes in temperature with changes in velocity. This is the method of "analysis *in situ.*" [7] Various properties must be left together, since they cannot be experimentally removed or eliminated; but, by the process of measurement, some of these properties are found to be so related that changes in one property involve changes in another or in others, but *no changes in still others*. What properties are correlated in this way and what not, cannot be known prior to the measurement, for it is the measurement itself that discloses either the presence of the correlations or their absence. Prior to measurement one might "entertain" the possibility that all properties that are measurable are correlated, so that changes in any one property would involve changes in *all* others; but, also, one might entertain the two alternative possibilities, (a), that no properties are thus related, and, (b), that some are, and some not. Empirical investigation would seem to show that the last possibility, (b), is the one that is realized in Nature, and it is only actual measurement that will discern which specific qualities *are* correlated, and which *not*.

(4) On the basis of finding correlations, "expressed numerically," between two qualities, *e.g.*, distance travelled

[7] *Cf.* the writer's *The New Rationalism*, pp. 27 ff., 207 ff.

and time periods, and of being able to interpolate between the numerical values found for each quality by using fractions, or smaller units of measurement, recognition is made of the fact that these numerical values have a specific numerical relation to each other, *whatever* the specific values may be, so that it becomes possible to discover *a law*. Thus, *e.g.*, in Galileo's experiment, from the values 1, 4, 9, 16 for distance, and 1, 2, 3, 4 for time period, it is "clear" that the distance travelled varies directly with the time squared, $d = t^2$. This law is really a (complex) property that is instanced by *any* falling body, and is of such a character that, if *any* specific numerical value of one variable is assumed or found, the numerical value of the other variable can be inferred. This means that each specific value of one variable is correlated *with one and only one* value of the other variable. Accordingly, the law may be used for the purpose of prediction, either by interpolation or extrapolation, in terms of specific numerical values. Given or assumed the value of one variable, *e.g.*, in Galileo's experiment, $t = 5$ *units*, then the value of the other variable can be deduced (predicted), viz., $d = 25$.

This is the type of any exact scientific law. An exact scientific law is based on measurement, and is a complex property, involving two or more constituent properties or qualities, that is of such a character that, if there are n constituent properties, and $n-1$ of them are instanced by specific numerical values, the value of the other property can be deduced. Thus, *e.g.*, a gas has three properties, pressure, volume, and temperature. The well-known Law of Gases is $pv = RT$ (R = a constant, T = absolute temperature scale, with absolute zero = $-273°$ C); given the specific values of any two of these, the other value can be deduced. So, also, the "attracting force" of two specific masses, *e.g.*, the Sun and the Earth, is, according to Newton's Law of Gravitation, deducible from specific values of the two masses and of their distance apart, according to the well-known formula, $f = \dfrac{mm'}{d^2}$. Here we have three constituents, four variables, but *one (complex) property*, of which any two *existing* (particular) masses-attracting-each-other-at-a-distance are an instance.

(5) The "aim" of an experiment, whether accompanied by measurement or not, is to eliminate entirely, prior to the experiment, the observations, the measurements, and the "derivation" of laws, the attitude of mind that certain specific properties, specific values, and laws of a specific type must be found. "At best" this attitude may take the form only of a working hypothesis that, if such and such is the case, then something else must also be the case. *This* attitude is justifiable. But "back" of it is the purely empirical, positivistic attitude—identical with the completely "open mind"—that *anything whatsoever may be found to be the case*. This is that attitude that, in the last analysis, *and* "ultimately," there is *no necessity for anything, not even for this fact itself*, and that the correct attitude of mind of the (physical) scientist is that he will endeavor, by experiment and measurement, to find merely *what is*, whatever it may prove to be. This means that nothing that the scientist finds is of such a character that its opposite is impossible; therefore, that nothing that is found is necessary;[8] but that everything is *ultimately* contingent.

[8] Of course, the scientist finds instances of what is called "causal necessity," *i.e.*, of the "principle" that, if A (cause) occurs, then B (effect) *must* occur. But this "must," on analysis, disappears, for, on the one hand, it

It was this attitude of mind that, *e.g.*, characterized (1), Galileo, when he found, contrary to tradition, that the natural condition of a body is to move, rather than to be at rest; (2), Kepler, when he discovered that the planets move in elliptical orbits, and not in circles; (3), the Curies, when they discovered that atoms disintegrate, and (4), Planck, when he discovered that the flow of energy from a "heat enclosure" is not continuous, but discontinuous or discrete. It is also this same attitude that recently has led, *e.g.*, Einstein and Heisenberg, regarding the very process of measurement itself, to look critically at certain presuppositions that were made tacitly by Galileo and by Newton, and thus to recognize that the opposite of these presuppositions is not impossible.

Galileo, as is well known, revived the Archimedean principle of experiment and measurement, and he tacitly assumed, as did also his predecessor, that measurement, although itself a physical process, had no effect on that which is measured. He also assumed, as did Newton, the *perfect rigidity* of his units of measurement, by which is meant that, *e.g.*, (1) a unit of length remains the same whether in motion or at rest, and whatever its position in space, and also, (2) that a unit of time remains that unit whatever its "position" in the time series. These last two assumptions were incorporated in Newton's *Mechanics* and became orthodox, so much so that their opposite was regarded as inconceivable and so impossible. Yet it was

is found to mean merely this, that it is not the case, or not the fact, that A occurs and B does not occur (analogous to "material implication"). This means that it would not be impossible for A to occur and then C, rather than B. But, secondly, also, it means that, even if "causal musts" in some sense be granted, as "connecting" cause and effect, within a limited "frame" as it were, then this situation itself is *merely the case*, the fact, and is not necessitated.

just this "impossibility" that was converted, first, psychologically, and then logically, into a possibility by such radical empiricists as Lobatschewsky and Riemann in Geometry, and by Mach, Lorentz, Fitzgerald, and, finally, Einstein, in Physics and then found to be a possibility that was realized ("a fact").

This meant, "among other things," that, if the physicist takes a thoroughly positivistic and empirical attitude toward his own measurements, he will find that the results of the measurement of distances and times on different frames of reference *do not agree*, and that this disagreement is due, not to "the ordinary inaccuracies" of measurement, but to the relative motion, either uniform or not uniform, of frames of reference in relation to each other. The results of the measurements of time, of space, and of mass, made by two or more observers in one frame of reference who will agree with one another, will not be agreed to by observers in other frames moving relative to that frame, for the very simple reason that, even with the most accurate measurements, the same results are not obtained. We are thus thrown back upon the position—the positivistic attitude of mind—that, contrary to the tradition, and, accordingly, to that which came to be regarded as *necessary*, there is no *one* (*cosmic*) *time* (with a uniform flow) and no "single" space in which, *e.g.*, a circle is "always" a circle, a square, a square, but that there are as many times (different "time-flows") and as many spaces (with reference to their radii of curvature) as there are different frames of reference (in motion with reference to each other) in which and from which measurements are made.

This is, of course, the "basis" for Relativity, which accordingly may be said to have resulted from the attitude of mind that there is no necessity for there being only one uniform time and only one space (geometrically), but that the contradictories of these are not impossible. Thus envisaged, these contradictories are found to be not only possible, but actual. And yet, this actual "state of affairs" is, in turn, also not necessary, so that it remains, like all other facts (ultimately), contingent.

The Special and General Theories of Relativity result from the fact that the measurement of spaces and times, and also of velocities, accelerations, masses, and forces, from different frames of reference, gives quantities that vary, and that are relative to the frame of reference "in which" or "from which" the measurement is made. The differences may or may not be great; they are, as a matter of fact, found not to be sufficiently large to be detected if two frames are moving, relatively to one another, with such speeds as, *e.g.*, those of the bodies of the solar system, but, for speeds of the order of the speed of light, and for distances measured by the "yard-stick" of "a light year," they may be, and are, detected. Pragmatically, then, for "earth-bound" purposes, we may ignore these differences; they hold only for cosmic magnitudes.

But the physicist of the present day measures not only cosmic, solar, and planetary, but also molecular, atomic, and sub-atomic distances, times, and other magnitudes, with the result that, contrary to Galileo's tacit assumption that the "process of measurement" has no effect on "the thing measured," it is now maintained not only that such an effect is not impossible, but, indeed, that it is actual. The "implications" of the fact of this effect—if it is a fact, and it is generally accepted as such—are considered to be most revolutionary as regards the traditional scientific point of view. Fact and implications constitute the now well-known (in scientific circles) Principle of Uncertainty, or, of Indeterminacy, of Heisenberg.

Again it is not requisite to my main purpose to present this Principle in great detail. It is here discussed only in so far as it is germane to the subjects of *measurement* and of *quantity*.

A clear statement of the issues involved is found in Bavink, *The Anatomy of Modern Science*,[9] and may be advantageously quoted:

". . . The task of physics . . . consists in measuring as exactly as possible the phenomena observed. The method of measurement consists in continual approximations, in which we try to eliminate unavoidable errors by taking their supposed value into account in a given case from other results of measurement. If, for example, a temperature is to be measured, the use of the thermometer . . . causes a small change in the temperature . . . to be measured. . . . But this amount can be taken into account beforehand by using the known data of the thermometer with the aid of the material constants concerned (specific heat of glass and mercury, etc.) and thus the error can be corrected more or less perfectly. *This example shows that every measurement necessarily changes a little that which is to be measured.*[10]

"It has hitherto been classically assumed, that by means of this kind of correction of measurements . . . *every existing degree of accuracy for any measurement may still be superseded by greater accuracy.* . . . But Heisenberg's Theory leads to the consequence . . . that this belief in the convergence of accuracy of measurement to absolute certainty was an error, and that, on the contrary, a finite, though very small, lower limit to accuracy of measurement is *fixed by Nature itself*. According to the 'Uncertainty Principle,' action can never be determined more accurately than to the order of magnitude of the Planck Quantum.[11] The consequence of this is, that in the region of the extremely small, the accuracy of the measurement of distance can only finally be increased at the cost of the accuracy of measurement of impulse, and that of the measurement of time only at the cost of the accuracy of the energy measurement."

Now, with reference to this Principle, there are found, in the literature, two interpretations, the one, represented by Planck,[12] that the Principle has a bearing only on *method*,— *on knowing by means of measurement*, one might say; the other, represented by Eddington,[13] that the Principle has implications not only as to method, but also as to the basic *ontological status or structure of the physical or material world*. And it may be that, if there are the latter, there must also be the former implications.

We shall first consider, briefly, the methodological implications.

The Principle of Indeterminacy is, as is well known, the result of the development of discoveries and theories in the field of atomic structure. The atom is now known to be a complex, a system. One of its parts is the electron, and this is found to have two "sets" of characteristics, the one set indicating that the electron is a "particle," the other, that it is a group of electro-magnetic waves. This may mean that a group of waves may be of such a character under certain circumstances that it acts as a particle, so that it will be found, as Eddington says,[14] that "the equations for the motion of a wave-group with given frequency and potential frequency are the same as the classical equations of motion of a particle with the corresponding energy and potential

[11] $h = 6.55 \times 10^{-27}$ erg-seconds. *Cf.* Chapter VIII, *passim*.
[12] Planck, *The Universe in the Light of Modern Physics*, pp. 51–58.
[13] See later quotations, this chapter.
[14] Eddington, A. S., *The Nature of the Physical World*, p. 213.

energy." But this still means that the electron is a "particle" in certain respects, and (a group of) waves in other respects. It has, as it were, *both "external" relations*, and an *internal structure*.

Now the methodological interpretation of the Principle of Indeterminacy has to do with the impossibility of simultaneously measuring, and so of determining, *e.g.*, both the position and the velocity (momentum) of an electron. If the one is determined accurately, the other is *simultaneously* completely indeterminable, so that there is a reciprocal limitation. Or, more generally, as Lenzen says,[15] "if Δq is the uncertainty in q (the coördinate), and Δp is the uncertainty in p, then $\Delta p \Delta q \geqq h$, *i.e.*, the combined uncertainty is of the order of h, and cannot be smaller than h."

The reason for this uncertainty, either "shared," or ideally "located" in one *or* the other quantity, may be made clear by the example of an ideal or hypothetical observation as stated by Eddington:[16]

"Suppose that (ideally) an electron is observed under a powerful microscope in order to determine its position with great accuracy. For it to be seen at all it must be illuminated and scatter light to reach the eye. The least it can scatter is one quantum. In scattering this it receives from the light a kick of unpredictable amount; we can only state the respective probabilities of kicks of different amounts. Thus the condition of our ascertaining the position is that we disturb the electron in an incalculable way which will prevent our subsequently ascertaining how much momentum it had. However, we shall be able to ascertain the momentum with an uncertainty represented by the kick, and if the probable kick is small the probable error will be small. To keep the kick small we must use a quantum of small energy, that is to say, light of long wave-length. But to use long

[15] Lenzen, Victor F., *Physical Theory*, p. 266.
[16] *Opus cit.*, pp. 223–224.

wave-length reduces the accuracy of our microscope. The longer the waves, the larger the diffraction images. And it must be remembered that it takes a great many quanta to outline the diffraction image; our one scattered quantum can only stimulate one atom in the retina of the eye, at some haphazard point within the theoretical diffraction image. Thus there will be an uncertainty in our determination of position of the electron proportional to the size of the diffraction image. We are in a dilemma. We can improve the determination of the position with the microscope by using light of shorter wave-length, but that gives the electron a greater kick and spoils the subsequent determination of momentum.

"A picturesque illustration of the same dilemma is afforded if we imagine ourselves trying to see one of the electrons in an atom. For such finicking work it is no use employing ordinary light to see with; it is far too gross, its wave-length being greater than the whole atom. We must use fine-grained illumination and train our eyes to see with radiation of short wave-length— with X-rays in fact. It is well to remember that X-rays have a rather disastrous effect on atoms, so we had better use them sparingly. The least amount we can use is one quantum. Now, if we are ready, will you watch, whilst I flash one quantum of X-rays on to the atom? I may not hit the electron the first time; in that case, of course, you will not see it. Try again; this time my quantum has hit the electron. Look sharp, and notice where it is. Isn't it there? Bother! I must have blown the electron out of the atom."

Eddington continues: [17] "Other examples of the reciprocal uncertainty have been given, and there seems to be no doubt that it is entirely general. The suggestion is that an association of exact position with exact momentum can never be discovered . . . *because there is no such thing in Nature.*"

Here Eddington passes from a *methodological* to an *ontological* or objective interpretation, and many physi-

[17] *Opus cit.*, p. 225. Italics are mine.

cists agree with him in this. This interpretation means that there is *an objective indeterminacy* in Nature, a "lifting" of causation. Let us see just what *this* is held to mean.

Eddington, in "explaining" this objective indeterminacy appeals [18] to Schrödinger's model of the particle (the electron) as a *wave-group*. What is this "model"? Not to go into too much detail, it is found to be described as follows: [19]

"Imagine a sub-aether whose surface is covered with ripples. The oscillations of the ripples are a million times faster than those of visible light. . . . Individual ripples are beyond our ken; what we can appreciate is a combined effort—where by convergence and coalescence the waves . . . create a disturbed area of extent large compared with individual ripples, but small from our own Brobdingnagian point of view. Such a disturbed area is recognized as a particle; in particular . . . an electron. . . . To this we now add that the frequency (number of oscillations per second) of the waves constituting this disturbance is recognized by us as the energy of the particle."

"We have considered a stormy area, of so small an extent that its position is as definite as that of a classical particle, but we may also consider an area of wider extent." "If we try to interpret an extended wave-group in classical language we say that it is a particle which is not at any definite point of space, but is loosely associated with a wide region." "The spreading is not a spreading of density; it is an indeterminacy of position, or a wider distribution of the probability that the particle lies within particular limits of position." "Thus, if we come across Schrödinger's waves uniformly filling a vessel, the interpretation is—that the vessel contains one particle *which is equally likely to be anywhere.*"

"It is an advantage . . . to follow the course of events in the sub-atom a little farther." "Suppose that two sets of waves are present. If the difference of frequency is not very great the two systems of waves will produce 'beats.' A boundary to the group is provided by interference of waves of slightly different

[18] *Ibid.*, p. 228.   [19] *Ibid.*, pp. 211–218.

length, so that while reinforcing one another at the center they cancel one another at the boundary. Roughly speaking, if the group has a diameter of 1000 wave-lengths there must be a range of wave-length of 0.1 per cent, so that 1000 of the longest waves and 1001 of the shortest occupy the same distance. If we take a more concentrated stormy area of diameter 10 wave-lengths the range is increased to 10 per cent; 10 of the longest and 11 of the shortest must extend the same distance. In seeking to make the *position* of the particle more *definite* by reducing the area, we make its *energy* more *vague* by dispersing the frequencies of the waves. So our particle can never *have* simultaneously a perfectly definite position and a perfectly definite energy."

"What precisely is the entity which we suppose to be oscillating when we speak of the waves in the sub-atom? It is denoted by ψ. . . . It seems possible to interpret it (ψ) as a *probability*." [20]

What, now, is the nature of *this probability?* In answer, Eddington says: [21]

"We commonly deal with probabilities which arise through ignorance. With fuller knowledge we should sweep away the references to probability and substitute the exact facts. But it appears to be a fundamental point in Schrödinger's Theory that his probability is not to be replaced in that way . . . by exact knowledge." "ψ itself acts as the source of light emitted from the atom, the period of light being the beats of ψ. I think this means that the spread of ψ is not a symbol for uncertainty arising through lack of information; it is a symbol for *causal failure—an indeterminacy of behavior which is part of the character of the atom.*"

I have indulged myself in these long quotations because they show that Eddington (recognized as an authority) very definitely accepts not only a methodological, but also an ontological, interpretation of Indeterminacy. In con-

---

[20] *Ibid.*, p. 216. Not, of course, the "ψ" of the earlier part of this book.
[21] *Ibid.*, pp. 305–306.

firmation of this I find his formulation [22] of the Principle: "A particle may *have* a position or it may *have* velocity, but it cannot have both." To try to find both is to try to find "*something which does not exist.*" [23]

Let us now ask just what this *ontological* interpretation means, and again I will let Eddington answer. This author says: [24] "We have two chief ways of learning about *the interior of an atom.* We can observe electrons entering or leaving. Bohr has assumed a structure connected by *strictly causal law* with the first phenomenon, Heisenberg and his followers with the second. If the two *structures* were identifiable, then the atom would involve a complete causal connection of the two types of phenomena. But apparently *no such causal linkage exists.* Therefore we have to be content with a *correlation* in which the entities of the one model represent probabilities in the second model."

Analysis of this statement would seem to show, then, that it means, (1) that there are two "structures" that are *not causally connected*, so that the "whole" that is made up of these two structures cannot be treated as are those wholes with which classical mechanics (Newton) deals. Such wholes are of the character that is illustrated by a planet going around the Sun. "In terms of the position and velocity of the planet at some instant we can calculate the subsequent course of the planet." "The laws which 'control' the planet are such as to determine one and only one velocity for the planet when in a given position, provided that the appropriate things about the planet, position, velocity, etc., have been specified at some previous instant." [25]

---

[22] *Ibid.*, p. 220. Italics are mine.   [23] *Ibid.*, p. 221. Italics are mine.
[24] *Opus cit.*, p. 306.
[25] Swann, W. F. G., *The Architecture of the Universe*, p. 108.

It is in terms of *this* "space and time description" that the concept of strict causal determination has taken form, and it is this causal description that, it is held, does not apply to the electron, since it is "at once" both particle and wave-group. But this does not prevent there being *two* structures, the one of "a space and time causal character," the other of "a wave-probability character." As Eddington says,[26] "The stormy areas (if small enough)"— the particles—"move under precisely the same laws that govern the motions of particles in classical mechanics." But the areas themselves are not, internally, as we have seen, of this character. *Yet they have a structure*, depicted, *e.g.*, by Eddington,[27] as a "sub-aether," *its* "oscillations," *their* wave-length or frequency, *their* difference of frequency with the consequent *production* [28] of "beats," the formation of "stormy areas" large or small, and the consequent possibility of asserting only "the probability of the electron being within a given region." This is, for me, however, a *causal* description, although in different terms from the causal description of classical mechanics. It is *a description of a structure with a kind of causation within it that is different from the space and time causation of classical mechanics, but that is nevertheless causation.* It is thus a structure that is *internally determined.*

What we have, then, is, seemingly, two systems or structures each of which is *determined according to specifically different laws;* the one system is that of *the particle as a particle;* this "follows" the laws of classical mechanics; the other system is that of *the internal structure of the particle;* this follows the laws of wave-mechanics. But "between" these two structures or systems and their laws

[26] *Opus cit.*, p. 213.   [27] *Ibid.*, p. 216.   [28] Is this (not) *causation?*

there is *no law*, either of classical mechanics, or of wave-mechanics, or of any other kind, so that the two do *not* in this respect form *a larger causal system* or whole. *The two systems are, then, indeterministically related.* In agreement with this interpretation are Eddington's own [29] acceptance of a *"microscopic structure"* (p. 228), a *"Relation Structure"* (p. 230), and *"two structures"* (p. 306); also Planck's statements: [30] "The disintegration of wave-groups is no evidence in favor of indeterminism, since it is equally possible for a wave-group to conglomerate: in both the wave theory and the corpuscular theory the *direction* of the process is immaterial." "A given wave-group generally, of course, exists only at two selected instants: in the intervening period, as well as before and after the process, the different elementary waves will exist separately. But whether they are described as material waves or as waves of probability, in either case they will be *completely determined.*"

I cannot, however, see that this *indeterminism between two systems* is (logically) different from what I have stressed in previous chapters as *Contingency.* In brief, I maintain that this Indeterminism is but an instance of Contingency, a special one, of course, although in this case the Contingency may be "one-sided" or asymmetrical.

We have *two systems, two structures:* the particle as such is a "member" of one, which is a classical mechanical system; but internally the particle *is* waves, but it is merely *found*, empirically, to be this. Accordingly, this wave-structure is on the one hand not necessitated, nor, on the other hand, impossible; it is, thus, merely *contingent.* Yet,

---

[29] *Opus cit.;* italics are mine.
[30] Planck, *The Universe in the Light of Modern Physics*, p. 57.

with it found empirically, or perhaps deduced, *as a matter of theory*, that there are *waves* of a sub-aether, or of ψ, etc., it may (also) be *deducible* that there are *wave-groups*, "stormy areas" of greater or lesser extent, so that this fact is not contingent. Still *the groups as groups* or as wholes, *could have certain characteristics that are not deducible*, and if they *do* have, then these characteristics would be *contingent*. But that there are such characteristics is found to be the case.

Given the two systems, or structures then, *contingently related* and thus forming a whole which is not, *as a whole, causal*, there may well be a "principle," if not a law, "connecting the two." That principle is not only that position and velocity, time and energy, cannot simultaneously be *determined (measured)*, but also, that, as a "reason" for this *methodological* impossibility, there is the *ontological* impossibility, that the two members of each of these pairs *should co-exist*.[31]

One further point may be added to this discussion of Indeterminancy, and that concerns the tendency of certain writers to *generalize* from its methodological aspect, and thus to assert that all Knowledge, *all observation, all awareness*, is of the same type as the "observation" we have been considering, and therefore "disturbs," "alters," or modifies that which is to be observed, or is at least limited in its accuracy. If this is the case, it follows that nothing can be observed as it really is, or was.[32]

Now I wish to point out that this generalization cannot be made, and for very simple reasons. For example, if, in accordance with the methodological aspect of the Prin-

[31] Eddington, *opus cit.*, pp. 217, 220–221; also, *idem, Aristotelian Society*, Sup. Vol. X, 1931, p. 176.
[32] Dewey, J., *The Quest for Certainty*, pp. 201–221.

ciple of Indeterminacy, observation of a certain type (in the case of the ideal experiment quoted in a preceding paragraph) *disturbs* that which is to be observed, then this (complex) fact itself is in turn "*the observed*" *to another observation*, which must in turn either "disturb" or not disturb, and so on, indefinitely. The outcome is, that "sooner or later" there is an observation, of some "order" or type, *which does not disturb that which is observed. Observation of this type is presupposed as the condition of "knowing" that there is real disturbance in any other case or kind of observation.* The principle involved is quite clearly another instance of the Theory of Types.[33]

As other examples of observing, or of "knowing," or of "being aware," that do not "disturb" that which is observed, or known, there are: (1) *the observation* that, if a particle has position, it *cannot* simultaneously have velocity;[34] (2) the knowledge of *any fact that is not part of nature*, therefore, of any fact in "the general scheme of things, down to Nature," as this scheme has been developed in preceding chapters.

[33] See Chapters II and III.
[34] Here, *an impossibility* is observed,—but not by a microscope and light; also, this is not "a measuring instrument."

VIII

ATOMICITY AND ORGANIZATION

The discussion just preceding leads naturally to the consideration of Atomicity. We have been using the terms "corpuscle," "electron," "atom." Each of these is a name for entities which are in the general sense of the term *atomic*. Such atomic entities are discrete; they are separate from one another; discontinuous with one another. But there are many other such entities either recognized in science today, or regarded by the science of the past, as existing in Nature. The list includes atoms, protons, electrons, positrons, neutrons, the ultimate electric charge, e, Planck's constant, h,—the unit of action, and the quantum of energy, $\epsilon = h\nu$ (all units of energy *equal* for the same wave-length,—of "radiant" energy).[1]

Again, it is not my purpose in discussing Atomicity, and particularly the instances of this property or function that are found in Nature, either to present a history of the Atomic Theory, or a detailed account of the "atomic side" of the Physics and Chemistry of the present day. I shall, rather, be concerned with the "principle," or, rather, *the property of Atomicity* as this is exemplified in Nature, and with certain other principles or properties which are closely connected with this property and its realization in Nature. Among such properties there are:

[1] ν = frequency; $h = 6.55 \times 10^{-27}$ erg-secs.

Discontinuity [2] and Continuity, Qualitativeness, and Quantitativeness, Causality and Creativity or Emergence, Probability, Contingency, and Freedom. What the connection of these properties, as they are realized in Nature, is, it is the purpose of the immediately subsequent discussion to show,—at least in part, for the subject is an extensive one.

Nature is *found* to be atomic, discontinuous, in many ways or in many respects, but there is no necessity for this "atomic structure." As a well-known scientist, Professor G. P. Thomson, says: ". . . Atomicity. There is no apparent reason why the world should have been constructed [3] in this way, and the fact that it has been so constructed is perhaps the supreme discovery of science. Not only is the existence of small equal units important when these units can, in fact, be isolated, but it is the explanation of another large group of laws. These are the laws called 'statistical.' They depend on the curious fact that the most irregular chaos that can be conceived has by its very irregularity an order of its own." [4] In other words, the atomic structure of Nature is recognized by Professor Thomson, in agreement with the main thesis of this volume, to be entirely *contingent*.

But Nature could be atomic in more than one way. What some of *the different kinds of Atomicity are*, as specific possibilities-of-realization, I shall presently discuss, and I shall then show that that specific possibility which empirical evidence shows is realized, is one that carries with it, as Professor Thomson suggests, the realization also of

[2] As previously noted and explained (Chapters V and VI), I use the terms Discontinuity and Discreteness as synonymous.

[3] I should use the present tense, to avoid, possibly, the suggestion of a *Constructor*.

[4] Thomson, G. P., *The Atom*, pp. 226–227.

certain other specific possibilities. Thus I shall endeavor to show that, if Nature's Atomicity is of one specific type, then there is also the exemplification or realization of Causality and Emergence, of Probability, and of Contingency (perhaps of a subordinate type) and of Freedom, whereas, if Nature's Atomicity were of a different type, these properties, at least some of them, not only would not, but could not be realized, in short, that their realization would be impossible. This is, doubtless, a difficult task, but it will be attempted.

So much, then, by way of introduction. Let us now attack our problem.

I am primarily concerned with Atomicity as it is actually found *in Nature*, since in the two preceding chapters we "finally reached matter." Yet, in accordance with the main "principles of procedure" that run through this book, I must ask, Is Atomicity itself an instance of a function or property "still further back," and, if it is, of *what* function?

I answer, Atomicity—*in its most general sense*—is either an instance of the "higher" property, Discreteness or Discontinuity, or it is identical with this property. I shall consider it to be identical. A manifold is discrete or discontinuous (identifying the two) if it is in one-one correlation with the integers, the whole numbers,[5] but manifolds that are thus correlated may either be ordered, according to the property of "Simple Serial Order," or not so ordered. In the first case, a manifold could be at once atomic *and* serial; in the second case, it could be atomic and not serial. The Quantum Theory of the "flow of energy" from, *e.g.*, "a heat enclosure," illustrates the first case; a *group* of

[5] *Cf.* Chapter VI.

atoms (of any element) free to move in any direction [6] (unorganized motion), the second.

Now, each of these two kinds of Atomicity has an extensive "application." Each "applies" to, or is realized by, (1), instances that are *quantities*, *i.e.*, qualities that are *measurable*, and, (2) instances that are *not measurable*, and, therefore, *in no sense quantitative*.

To illustrate this, and, in so doing, to go back to previous chapters: The sub-properties of any property, *e.g.*, Necessity, Contingency, and Impossibility as instances of Possibility of the First Order, are *discontinuous or atomic qualitatively*, but they have no order, whereas, *Negativity as a necessity and Necessity as a possibility* are not only qualitatively distinct (atomic and discontinuous), but they also have *a serial order*. *But none of these "abstract" properties are quantities*. In contrast with these properties, there are qualities which *are* quantities, and these quantities are in some cases only atomic (and not serial) and, in other cases, both atomic and serial. As illustrating the first case there is the *totality* of the atoms of any chemical element, or of the "atoms" designated by *e*, *h*, and "*the electron*"; the totality in each of these cases is one of "atoms" that are quantitative, but that have *no order* in relation to one another. Exemplifying the second case is the *series* of elements of The Periodic Table according to their "atomic number" as this is determined by the number of "satellite-electrons" ("atoms") in "the planetary atom" (of the Bohr Theory). From the Hydrogen atom with one such electron, and the Helium with two such electrons, to Uranium with ninety-two, the number

[6] In accordance with the "Kinetic Theory" of gases, liquids, and solids.

of electrons (and, accordingly, the elements) which are quantities, form, as is well known, a series which is in one-one correspondence with the whole numbers from 1 to 92.

Atomicity may, then, be "combined" with *quantity*, or not, with *Serial Order*, or not. The "atoms" of Nature are atomistically distinct *qualities* (*e.g.*, *h*, *e*, and *the electron*) that are also *quantities*, and that are "repeated," or that exist, in each case, in enormous numbers. Each "atom" is distinct from every other, *e.g.*, electron A is distinct from B, so that there is *discontinuity* of individual quantities. Some of these quantities seem to "stand for" a combination of this specific kind of Atomicity with *Substantiality* (substance), others, for a combination of Atomicity and Eventness (action, process). For example, the *proton* would seem to be *an atomic substance*, but *h* is a *unit* of action ($h = ET$) (T = energy, E frequency), of "value" (quantity), 6.55×10^{-27} erg-seconds. What about the electron? Is it "substance," or is it process, or both, or neither? I think the answer is not clear.

There are, then, *atomic substances* and *atomic events*, in Nature. These are, as *substances* and *events*, qualitatively discontinuous with one another. But, in turn, there are, or may be, a number of qualitatively distinct atomic substances *and* atomic events. All of these are quantities if measured either directly or indirectly, and each kind may exist in enormous numbers.

This is the kind of atomicity that seems to be realized or found in Nature. *Nature is a plurality of qualitatively discontinuous quantities of both substances and "events," with each distinct kind existing in enormous numbers of (discontinuous) units.* This is the picture that is given by "a world" of protons, electrons, positrons, neutrons, units of action, h's, and units of energy, $\frac{h}{\nu}$'s. Such an Atomicity is, as it were, n-dimensional.

Now, it is the realization, in Nature, of this kind of Atomicity that allows, I find, also the realization of a number of other properties or possibilities, notably, as already mentioned, Causality, Creativity or Emergence, Freedom, and, perhaps, Contingency and Probability.

Let us consider, then, a radically different type of Atomicity,—one which, of course, does not seem to be found empirically, but which nevertheless can be "entertained" *as* a possibility. To "develop" this specific possibility, let us make the following assumptions:

I.—All "atoms" are "just exactly" *qualitatively alike* in respect to one or more qualities. For example, there might be *only* electrons, of the same mass and the same charge $(-)$, or *only* positrons, or *only* "cosmic rays," or *only* "material corpuscles," as the crude materialism of the past maintained, or only "neutral entities."

Since we are dealing, in this chapter, with "the material world," let us assume that

II.—These atoms are "spatially separated," at different distances from one another. Comment: I purposely overlook the *qualitative difference* between the *space* assumed and the *atoms* that, by assumption, occupy it.

III.—These atoms persist in time. Comment: Of course, if they did not persist, they would change. Such change could not, by Postulate I, be a qualitative change; it could not, at best, then, be anything more than *a change of degree (continuous)*,—of the *same quality* or qualities.

IV.—The qualitatively similar atoms (varying, perhaps,

in the degree of quality or qualities) *move* (since, by assumption, they are spatially separate) and form different
groups or combinations, these groups differing as to the
number and the distance apart of the atoms in them.
Comment: No assumption is necessary as to *why* they
move, but it might be assumed either (1), that they are
self-moving, or (2), that they all attract, or all repel, one
another, in either of which cases they could still all be alike.
Further, as they persist in time, move, and form groups or
combinations, both they as individuals, with reference to
one another, *and* the groups as groups, might show certain
tendencies as to *distribution;* such a tendency might be
from less to more uniform distribution, or from more to
less, or there might be a periodicity of such distributions.

Now, the thesis which I submit is, that an Atomicity of
this type absolutely precludes or renders impossible the
appearance "in the course of time," whether longer—
Evolution—or shorter—Development,[7] *of anything new*—
of anything that is "at best" anything more than *a greater
quantity* (in some unit volume), or *a different degree, or
both, of the "original" quality* or qualities of the atoms
themselves. Briefly, such a scheme precludes the realization of Creativity, defined as the appearance, in a temporal series or as the result of combination, of *new qualities.*
And likewise, as I shall endeavor to show, it precludes
Freedom as I shall later define it. Such a scheme, further,
either limits Causality to the assumed "reasons" either
for the forming or for the disintegrating of combinations,
or "makes no use" of this Principle or Property whatsoever, in which case we have complete Contingency as to
the formation and disintegration of the combinations of

[7] These terms are here used very generally.

atoms. In either of these cases, however, the principle of Probability would be "applicable," but on a purely empirical or "frequency" basis.

The foregoing set of assumptions presents a possibility which has been, as a matter of fact, held to be realized. There has been, as is well known, in both Science and Philosophy, a tendency, on the part both of some scientists and of some philosophers, to "derive" everything (at least, everything in Nature) from *one kind of "brick,"* whatever this might be regarded as being.[8]

Now the "thesis" toward which I am tending, in this discussion, is in direct opposition to this tendency. It is the thesis that only that kind of Atomicity is found empirically to be realized or exemplified in and by Nature, which permits of greater opportunity (whatever this may mean) for the appearance of *a greater diversity of qualities* than does the kind of Atomicity just considered.

One might go even further, in the direction of "simplicity," by envisaging the possibility of *no atomicity at all in a qualitatively single something* "extending" throughout space and persisting in time. What this "something" might be, is difficult to conceive, but in any case *the whole of it would be a "lump"—one lump*—with no parts, even as any ultimate unit, *e.g.,* a proton, or a positive charge, *e*, is a *"lump."* It could not be even a "jelly," since a "jelly" has parts, and these parts move. In such a whole there would and could be *no change, no causation, no creativity, no freedom, no probability.*

Reversing our direction, then, it will be contended that

[8] The "atoms" of Democritus; the Hydrogen of the Chemistry of the nineteenth century, according to Prout's Hypothesis—before the day of electrons, x-rays, etc.; the "monads" of Liebnitz; the "Realen" of Herbart, are historical examples, each of them, of qualitatively similar "bricks."

the qualitative diversity (of quantities) which is empirically
found in Nature "fits into" only Atomicity, and, further,
only into *that kind of Atomicity which is combined with
Organization or Structure.* This kind of Atomicity does
allow of Causality, Creativity and Emergence, Freedom,
and Probability.

In this connection the question may be raised whether,
in accordance with the kind of Atomicity first considered—
an Atomicity of qualitatively similar atoms free to move,
form combinations, and disintegrate,—there is *organization*
or not. I am willing to say that there is, but that it is the
very minimum of organization. A group of qualitatively
similar atoms is a group of entities that have some spatial
configuration at any one instant, and that are related by
Similarity. But whether this be accepted as organization
or not, I would lay down the following "principles" regarding Organization and Atomicity:

I.—Organization or Structure involves both terms (*"re-
lata"*—Eddington [9]) and relations. The ultimate terms
which we are here considering are "atoms," defined as
units (qualitative) that have (tautologously) no parts
(smaller units). The minimum of organization in this
respect would be *two terms in one relation*.

II.—A relation is organizing if, (a), negatively, it is not
the *conjunctive relation* (*and*) nor the relation of (bare)
difference [10] (perhaps, ∼, *i.e.*, "not"), and, (b), positively,
if the relational complex as a whole is *qualitatively different
from any of the constituent terms or parts*. Otherwise stated,
if organizing relations, one or more, subsist between two
or more terms, then the whole has or is a group of qualities

[9] Eddington, *opus cit.*, p. 230.
[10] *If* difference *is* a relation. *Cf.* Chapter VI.

different from the qualities of the terms, and, conversely, if there is such a whole, then its parts are organized.

Comment: (1) Even the two wholes, *x and y* $(R = .)$ and xRy $(R = \sim)$, might be regarded, according to this definition, as organized wholes. I am willing to grant the point, but, if I do, then *all relational wholes are organized.*

Comment: (2) Space and Time, according to this definition (II), are organized wholes of a specific kind, as has been seen in a preceding chapter (VI). But, no "atom" is, by definition, such a whole.

III.—Organization is of different types. These types may, perhaps, be classified as Spatial, Temporal, and Logical. One and the same organized whole in Nature may be "at once" spatially, temporally, and logically organized; it is the last, if it is the first two, but the *logical organization* is not exhausted by the spatial and temporal.

IV.—An organization or structure of any one type may vary as to complexity, *i.e.*, it may be less or more complex according to the number of organizing relations present in it. The different degrees of complexity are the "values" of the function or *property*, Complexity.

V.—Each specific "degree" of complexity of each type of organization or structure is a specific, invariant, set of relations, perhaps themselves related, in which the terms as variables may have different values.

Thus, to give a very simple example, in Chemistry, if "the graphic symbol," $<$, represents a specific structure, we may have $O\!\!<^H_H$, or $O\!\!<^{Na}_{Na}$, or $O\!\!<^K_K$, in which the structure is invariant, but the terms "vary."

VI.—As Chemistry illustrates (see the preceding example), and empirically shows, and assuming II, then, (1) according as the structure or organization is less or more complex, and, (2), according as, in the same structure, the number of qualitatively different terms which can "take their place" in the structure, is small or large, the less or the more extensive is the resulting diversity among the qualities of the wholes which result—as the "outcome" of the organization.

Postulate VI (together with I–V) defines one specific type of Atomicity (and Organization).

In contrast with this, we may "envisage" four other possible types, as follows:

(1) "Atoms" *all qualitatively alike*, and either no organization, or a minimum,—whatever this minimum might be. This has been discussed.

(2) "Atoms" *all of different kinds*, and a total absence of, or a minimum of, organization. In the first case there "would have to be" as many kinds of atoms as there is variety of qualities experienced in Nature; in the second case, more qualitatively different atoms than science at present finds.

(3) "Atoms" all alike, but a maximum of organization,—whatever this might be,—and what it would be, I do not know.

(4) No two "atoms" alike, and no organization at all; at most, only the relations of, (a), similarity as regards Atomicity, (b), of "and," and, (c), of "difference." This defines a perfect chaos.[11]

(5) In contrast with these (see VI above) a few "atoms"

---

[11] One might, perhaps, object that, if a *chaos* can be *defined*, then it is not a chaos. I am not sure but that the objection is legitimate.

qualitatively different, and, if not a maximum, then at least "a high degree," of organization.

Given the same degree of organization of any type, the greater diversity of qualities results from the greater number of qualitatively different terms (atoms); given the same number of terms, the diversity varies with the complexity of organization.

With five types of Atomicity and Structure before us, as "perfectly good possibilities," the question arises as to which of these is shown by empirical evidence to be the one that is realized in Nature. Perhaps it is impossible to obtain agreement with the answer given to this inquiry, but, to the writer, it would seem to be Possibility (5). There is no reason why this should be the case. The other possibilities, both as to the realization of Atomicity in one form or another and its total absence, are equally good. Nature might conform, or have conformed, to any one of these five types. That it conforms to one type (5) is quite contingent, since no possibility ever gives rise to its own realization. Physical science of the present day finds a number of qualitatively irreducible atomic quantities (atoms). They are: the electron, the positron, the proton, the neutron (?), the unit electrical charge, e, and Planck's constant, h. Having found these "atoms," Physics is concerned with the *structures of varying types, and of varying degrees of complexity*, into which these "atoms" enter, and with the qualities (also quantities, as measured) which result from these organizations. The complexity varies, (a), with the number of relations present, (b), with the number of qualitatively different terms which "take their place" in the structures.

Physics is also concerned with "what happens" when,

(1), not atomic quantities, but "first degree" complexes arise as organized wholes, and these wholes in turn take their place as terms in "second degree" structures. We thus have the possibility, starting with a finite number (small) of atoms, *none of which is a structure, of having a discontinuous series of structures and qualities.*

In this series of structures there appears the following principle, or, stated differently, this series is an instance of the following property:—

VII.—An organized whole is, "at one and the same time" *both a complex, and a unit* in its relation to or "action toward" other coördinate units. These coördinate units are, in some cases, similar to, in other cases, different from, this unit as regards structure, or constituents, or both.[12]

Coördinate units act toward one another as wholes or units in respect to certain characteristics or qualities which are the *"non-additive"* result of organization, and which, therefore, are not, in any case, also qualities of the constituent parts. *Such new qualities are emergent;* they are not in any way necessitated by the qualities of the constituents of the whole, so that they not only cannot, but could not, be deduced; they can only be found empirically. Thus they are quite *contingent.* Once found, however, and measured, these qualities are *correlated,* according to some formula, with the measured qualities (quantities) of the parts, and thus an empirical law of the relation of the two "levels" is arrived at. Such a law is itself, then, entirely contingent. It is merely a specific, though complex, function or property

---

[12] In essential agreement with the analysis and account of "organization" which I have given is the article by Dr. Y. H. Krikorian, with the title, *The Concept of Organization,* in the Jour. of Philosophy, XXXII, 5, pp. 119–126.

of which the varying correlated quantities (as measured) of the qualities of both whole and parts are values.

In succeeding chapters the further (material) "implications" of this "situation" will be developed, and a number of examples given.

IX

CREATIVITY AND CAUSALITY, FREEDOM AND DETERMINISM, TELEOLOGY

We shall now proceed to "make use" of the principle just stated, at the end of the preceding chapter, in order to consider Creativity, Causality, Freedom, Determinism, and Teleology. Each of these is a *property;* each might or might not be exemplified or realized in Nature, but each is, as a matter of fact, thus realized. Each, as realized, is found to be at least "associated" (a loose term) with the other four.

As a preliminary to the discussion of these five properties, each may be defined, at least tentatively, as follows:

(1) Causality is (the Property or Function of) Productivity [1] or Efficacy. Of it there are, as possibilities, two sub-types, the one "combining" Productivity and Necessity, the other, Productivity and Contingency, and of each of these, in turn, there are the two sub-types, namely, Continuous and Discontinuous. Causal Laws are, in turn, instances of one or the other of these four types, and Nature might exemplify any of these (specific) Causal Laws. Nature is found, however, quite empirically, to exemplify the Contingent Type of Causality, either continuous or discontinuous: *i.e.*, in any case in which *a* is (actually) found to produce *b*, whether *a* and *b* are found to be *de facto* con-

[1] *Cf.* University of California Publications, *Causality*, 1932, Mackay, "Causality and Effectuality," pp. 129–144.

tinuous or not, it is not impossible that a should not produce b, but that it should produce something else, c. A may be said to produce b just in so far and within such limits as it is actually found to produce b, and no further.

(2) Creativity or Emergence. Creativity is the property which a situation or "state of affairs" may possess or present, as a result of organization. This property is realized if, as a result of organization, there is a whole which is more, quantitatively, or other, qualitatively, than the parts. If Productivity (Causality) is purely empirical and contingent, then Creativity may be realized; conversely, if Creativity is realized, Productivity must be contingent: there is no necessity in the cause producing the kind of effect that it is found, empirically, to produce.

Creativity may be temporal or non-temporal; in Nature, it is temporal; in the realm of organized wholes that are "outside" of Nature, it is non-temporal. "Where" there is Creativity, there is Emergence; and there is Emergence "where" there is *organization* of parts.[2]

(3) Determinacy (or Determinism). This property is both logical and causal. Logical Determinacy characterizes a situation or whole in which the parts *necessitate* one another in the sense that "given" one or more parts, *any other* part or parts than those which are actually found, are impossible, *i.e.*, given certain parts, the other parts *must be*. Such wholes are circumscribed or limited systems, *internally deterministic*. Causal Determinacy characterizes a situation or whole if, up to certain points, or within certain limits, certain specific causes are found, quite empirically (*the opposite not impossible*), to produce certain effects. Such a

---

[2] In my *New Rationalism*, 1918, I stressed in various places this general principle of Creativity or Emergence by the use of the term "Creative Synthesis."

whole, or system, as it may also be called, may be said to be internally determined; it is a system of specific properties related productively, *i.e.*, causally, but in no case is the opposite of any specific productivity impossible. This Determinism is purely "matter of fact." Such wholes are illustrated by, (a), biological processes, (b), molecular wholes (in Chemistry) as opposed to atomic.

We are here concerned with this second kind of Determinacy, and not with the first kind (logical).

(4) Freedom. Freedom is not opposed to Determinacy, of either kind, nor is it identical with Contingency. Freedom characterizes a situation or a whole, "when" there is Internal Determination within certain limits, and up to certain points, *i.e.*, when there is either logical or causal *self-sufficiency* or *autonomy;* but, "when" there is this autonomy, there is *freedom from external determination.* Freedom, then, is "always" "freedom from," and it is quite consistent with, indeed, it is identical with, a specific circumscribed internal Determination.

As examples: Euclidean Geometry, as a logical system, is at once both *free from* external compulsion *and internally determined.* Likewise Biology as a whole, and special biological sciences, *e.g.*, Genetics, are, as sciences, autonomous; they are self-sufficient *accounts*, in terms of a limited group of properties, of specific (causal) processes. They do not need to go outside themselves.

(5) Teleology (Purposiveness). This property is present "when" and "where" there is Freedom. There is Purpose (of some specific kind) present, then, if there is both Freedom, and Internal Determinism. But Internal Determinism is of different types. One such type may be found, *e.g.*, in the case of an individual organism that regenerates a

new part, a new organ, or that heals a wound. The whole so controls this process, that that part is produced which "fits into" and serves the whole.[3] Another type is found in the case of well-recognized purposeful actions on the part of human beings. These actions are not indeterminate; they are instances of very specific Determinisms, so that there is an autonomous situation. For example, the ability to select or accept a specific, desired, future end, and to adopt a means to that end, is at once, (1), a freedom from habit, (2), a determination by an end, and, (3), a teleological process.

Teleology, then, "rests on" Freedom, and *Freedom on a Discontinuity of Specific Determinisms* (each autonomous). But such Discontinuity in turn is an instance of Contingency. There could be, then, no Freedom and no Teleology, if there were no Contingency, *and* instances of this, but there could be Contingency and yet no Freedom and no Teleology, for there need be no internally determined, autonomous systems, either logical or causal. Such systems are themselves quite contingent, and so also, then, are Freedom (as defined) and Teleology. The "world"—Nature—might have *no determination of any kind whatsoever in it*, but, also, it might have this; there is no necessity for either possibility being realized, although, as a matter of fact, the second is found to be the case. There is, in Nature, some Determinism, and some Indeterminism, some Freedom, and some absence of this, some Purpose and some Purposelessness.

Having defined the five Properties I am here especially considering, I may now proceed to present in further detail an account of Nature in terms of these properties. For it

[3] *Cf., e.g.*, Thomson, J. A., *The System of Animate Nature*, Vol. I, Lectures II–IV.

would seem that empirical investigation shows that each of these properties is realized *in* and *by* any number of specific instances in Nature. In giving this more detailed account, I shall make use of the conclusions of the preceding chapter as to, (1), the specific kind of Atomicity that is realized in Nature, and, (2), "the principles" of Organization and Atomicity stated at the end of that chapter. However, it is not my purpose to present more scientific details than is necessary. *Principles*, chiefly, will be stressed.

I shall not enter into territory in which there is much uncertainty as to certain details, namely, that territory which concerns the question as to just what are the several *constituents of the atom* (the list includes the electron, the positron, the neutron, the proton) but I shall start with that which is at the present time accepted as fact, namely, that *the atom has constituents*. There is an *atomic* level and a *sub-atomic* level. There then come, "after" the atom, as is well known, the *molecular*, the *corpuscular* or, perhaps in some cases, the *crystalline* and the *colloidal*. I mention this last because the *cells* of living organisms are regarded as being organizations of *a number* (usually, if not always) of colloidal solutions. So there are the cellular levels, (a), of one-celled organisms, (b), of many-celled, and in these last we have specific organizations of cells into *organs*, which in turn are organized into *the organism as a whole*. This organization varies in complexity according as two factors, (a), the structure, and, (b), the terms, vary, the former in complexity, the latter in kind or quality.

Now the several "levels" of this list cover the subject-matter of the sciences of Physics, of Chemistry, of Biology, and perhaps of one kind of Psychology, namely, Behaviorism; and accordingly one may ask: Just what is actually done in each one of these sciences as the special field of inquiry of each science is pursued? In answer, I find this to be the fact: The *physicist* pursues his special study of the *constituents of atoms* and of the structures (dynamic) into which these constituents "fit" without regard to the qualities of the atoms themselves as atoms (the 92 of the Periodic Table), but in turn these atoms can be and are studied *as atoms*, yet, again, with no reference to the specific qualities of the several millions of *molecules* of which these atoms are the constituents. A similar procedure is repeated as regards molecules *and* particles, particles *and* colloidal solutions (a solution is a *solvent* and a *solute*), colloidal solutions *and* the protoplasm of a cell, cells *and* organs, etc.

What is there, now, "in" this whole situation that makes this specific procedure of isolated or independent inquiry possible? To be specific, and take a very simple example, Why is it possible to study, *e.g.*, the "action" of molecules of water (or of steam or of ice) and not be forced also to study Organisms, since all organisms contain water; also, to study water (at the molecular level) and not be compelled to study *the atoms* of Hydrogen and of Oxygen (and, in turn, their constituents) of which water is composed? I answer, that it is because it is found to be *a fact* (even as Galileo found it to be a fact that some quantities did not depend on, or vary with, others) that the phenomena of the molecular level (to continue our example) are *independent* of those of both the atomic (below) and the organic levels (above) in the precise sense that, *as molecular phenomena or qualities*, they are, as a matter of fact, *measured*, "*related causally*," and their peculiar *laws* obtained at this (molecular) level without going outside of this level either to that below or that above. One *may* thus go "outside," and then proceed at each of these other levels as one has proceeded at the molecular level. The procedure is *methodological,* of course, but it has an *ontological* justification. Once, however, three such levels have been "studied," each in this independent, autonomous manner, the question may well arise, and be put to Nature in order to get an answer,— *by measuring,* if possible: Just *how* are any two levels, A and B, or B and C, and, therefore, indirectly, A and C, *through* B, related or perhaps *correlated?* This question is asked, and is answered even though it is not possible to *deduce* and so to predict the phenomena of one "subsequent" level from those either of the immediately preceding level or of indirectly preceding levels. The relations or correlations of the specific phenomena of any two levels, *once these phenomena are empirically discovered,* can themselves be empirically ascertained, but such relations or correlations do not do away either with the *specificity* of the higher level, or with the *independence* of the lower level as regards the higher, or, stated more generally, with the *discontinuity, both qualitatively and quantitatively* [4] *between the two.* The evidence is, (1), that the phenomena of any higher, or subsequent, level are *the discontinuous causal product* of the phenomena of the immediately preceding, lower level, and, indirectly, of still lower levels, *in serial order;* (2), that, in any case of two levels, the phenomena of the next higher level, are quite *contingent* as regards those of the (next) lower level, as well as of still lower levels; (3), that *each level consists of certain qualities (some) peculiar to that level* which can either, (a), be measured, and so be found to form a set of correlated variables (*e.g.,* the pressure, volume, and temperature of a

---

[4] There is a quantitative discontinuity because *a quantity is always a specific quality as measured.*

gas), or, (b), be related by "purely descriptive causality" (as is the case, *e.g.*, in the greater part of Biology, Psychology, and the Social Sciences), but, in either case, forming a "closed system;" (4) that the phenomena of any two distinct levels can be found to be so related, or so correlated, either merely descriptively, or quantitatively, that purely empirical laws "expressing" these relations or correlations, are obtained, with the results that two "remote" levels may be correlated through the mediation of one or more intermediate levels.

This means that two kinds of causal laws can be discovered, namely, (1) laws for *one level;* (2) laws "connecting," quite empirically, *two or more levels.* As an example of the first, there are the Laws of the "Kinetic Theory of Gases" (Clausius, O. E. Meyer, Maxwell, and others); *these are laws of the molecular level* without regard either to the atomic and chemical constitution of the molecules (the next lower level) or to any "higher" level or levels. Another example of the first kind of Law is the Mendelian Law of Heredity in its original form (unit characters and chromosomes) or its more recent form (genes). *This is a law of distinctly biological phenomena.* As an example of the second kind of law, there is the Law of the Correlation of the "position" of each chemical in the Periodic Table, as regards its "family" qualities and its chemical activity, with the number of electrons (from 1 for Hydrogen to 92 for Uranium) in "the outer ring," according to the Bohr Theory of the Atom. As is well known, the elements form an "array" consisting of, (a), Periods (horizontal) and, (b), Groups (vertical), in which each Period (there are six from Helium to Uranium) is a *discontinuous series* "determined" by the relation "less chemical activity—more chemical activity" (*e.g.*, Helium to Uranium in the First Period), and each Group is a *discontinuous series* "determined" by, (a), a similarity of chemical properties, but an increase of atomic weight. The whole Table is both a *series* of Periods and a *series* of Groups.[5]

Such correlations—and, between levels, it is *only correlations* that science can obtain—do not in any sense "explain" the higher level by the lower. The properties of the higher level must be *first discovered*, quite empirically and as a matter of fact, in order to have *something subsequently to correlate with a lower level*, and these properties continue to "stand on their own feet" as just those specific properties even if they are subsequently found to be correlated with the specific properties of a lower or of lower levels. The correlation does not show the identity of the two levels, nor make it possible to deduce the properties of the higher level from that of the lower. This deduction is not possible for the very simple reason that the former are not necessitated by the latter; they are new and quite contingent properties that result from *organization;* their "occurrence" cannot be predicted, but must be "experienced"; once experienced, however, they may be correlated with the properties of lower levels, one or (sometimes) more.

Now in such situations, of which there are many instances, there are Causality, Contingency, Creativity, Freedom, Determinism, and Teleology.

I.—There is Causality, in the sense of Productivity, of two kinds, (a), vertical, (b), horizontal. The former, (a), is between levels, from lower to higher, and, as I shall also later maintain, *from higher to lower;* the latter, (b), is *at some one level*—whatever this may be—molecular, atomic, sub-

[5] *Cf.* Chapter VI, the first part.

atomic, organic, psychological, or social. Each kind of Causality, *i.e.*, as regards the instances of it that are found, is purely empirical; specific cause and specific effect are what they are found to be, and nothing more; some other specific effect (of any specific cause) than the one actually found is not impossible.

The properties of a "higher" level (*e.g.*, the Molecular in relation to the Atomic) are the causal result of the organization of, and are (in many instances) qualitatively different from, the parts and properties of the next lower level, so that, as qualitatively different and new, they are *emergent*. They form a level of phenomena that is, within itself, causally determined. Each level is, in this respect, *autonomous*. The molecular and the biological levels are each an example of this. In the one case, there are *molecular causes for molecular effects;* in the other case, *biological causes, e.g.,* genes, for *biological effects, e.g., "unit-characters"* in the mature organism.

For these reasons, there is a *two-fold* Freedom. The lower level is more *limited* than the next higher; the higher is more *specific*, or richer in qualities than the next lower. The lower level is, then, *free from the specificity of the next higher,—e.g.,* molecular phenomena take place whether there are biological present or not,—and *the higher level is free from the limitations of the next lower level by virtue of those properties in respect to which it is more than this level;* being more, it is free to "act" in accordance with these properties, which constitute its own peculiar nature. *In respect to these properties, it is self-determining* or *autonomous. The ground for this Freedom is the contingency of these properties in relation to the properties of the next lower level.* This is limited contingency, however, since these properties are

*Free Will = the ability to choose be-
tween alternatives.*

superposed on, and coexist with, the properties of the lower level. For example, an organism *is* chemical *and* physical, *and* mechanical, spatial, temporal, and mathematical,—it is all of these, *but it is more than any one of these, or all of these together; it is an organism, a collection of distinctive and irreducible "vital" properties.*

*Not quan-
titatively*

In respect to these distinctive properties, by virtue of which it is autonomous, the organism—to continue our example—is a self-determining *agency or spontaneity* that is not only free from that specific type of external compulsion which "comes from" the lower level, with its limitations, but that is also active in producing effects, or, shall I say, in "directing" processes, in at least some of the lower levels. For example, *what* molecules do in an organism may be, and in some respects *is*, the result of the *organism as a whole,—* in other words, *the organism is a self-regulating whole*—but the molecules may still, no matter *what* they do, act as molecules in relation to one another. Such self-regulation is shown, *e.g.*, (a) in the transformation of chemical materials taken in as food by an organism into those specific materials that are required by the organism in its own organic processes; (b), in processes of regeneration.[6]

No

Such regulation discloses the effects of structure, of organization. The organism is not merely parts—cells, colloidal solutions, molecules, atoms, etc.—but it is also *a structure, an organization*, of subordinate structures and organizations, dynamic, to be sure, and not static, and it is

[6] In general agreement with the position stated in this and other paragraphs are, I think, such writers as Haldane, J. S., in *The Philosophical Basis of Biology;* Morgan, L., *Emergent Evolution;* Russell, E. S., *The Interpretation of Development and Heredity;* Smuts, General J. C., *Holism and Evolution;* and Woodger, J. H., *Biological Principles.* All of these are relatively recent books, and they are typical of a very strong current tendency in Biology, or in the Philosophy of Biology.

in respect to this primary structure that the organism as a whole may be said to "reach down," as it were, to substructures and their "terms," to *control* what these wholes do, all to a single end, namely, that of the organism itself, in respect to its own peculiar, emergent, vital properties.

All of this is, of course, Teleology; but it is not the kind of Teleology that necessitates a *conscious* agent adopting a means to a consciously desired end. Yet it is consistent with such a specific Teleology, since, with a sufficient degree, or with a specific kind, of organization, or both, just this specific kind of regulation *might* well emerge. And, indeed, the evidence is that it does, *e.g.*, (1) in the case of human beings in their self-regulation with reference to the future, thus freeing themselves from servitude to the past, or, (2), in their self-regulation with reference to "the *logic* of a situation" by which they free themselves from *habit*.

In general agreement with the main thesis of this chapter is the position that is taken by Professor George Birkhoff of Harvard University in an article contained in the volume, *Science for a New World*, 1934, edited by J. A. Thomson. Professor Birkhoff says:

"Now when we survey the varied fields of scientific knowledge we are led almost inevitably to divide knowledge into five categories or 'levels,' characterized respectively as mathematical, physical, biological, psychological, and social. Here it is not the number of divisions which is to be regarded as especially significant, for there are intermediate domains. The important general truths involved are the following: (1) Each level is a natural one in the sense that it possesses its own especial fundamental intuitive language which is largely if not completely independent of that used in the other levels. (2) Every specific fact may be analyzed from any one of these levels taken as fundamental. For example, a child tosses a ball to another. The mathematician thinks of a sphere in space and time; the physicist, of a material body moving under the action of certain forces; the biologist perceives a biological significance in the act of play; the psychologist is interested only in the psychic accompaniament of the act; and the sociologist sees an instance of an important kind of social interaction. (3) According as we take one or the other of these levels as the most fundamental or 'real,' we are led to a corresponding systematic philosophic point of view.

"These levels, together with the corresponding systems of philosophy and fundamental terms, may be catalogued as follows:

>Mathematical, Absolute Realism:
>>Class, Relation, Inference, Abstraction.
>
>Physical, Materialism:
>>Space-Time, Matter, Electricity, Uniformity.
>
>Biological, Detailed Naturalism:
>>Organism, Stimulus, Function, Evolution.
>
>Psychological, Positivism:
>>Sensation, Memory, Will, Idea.
>
>Social, Ethical Idealism:
>>Personality, Freedom, Value, Ideal.

"It may also be remarked that these levels form a kind of hierarchy in which the earlier levels are objective in the sense that they involve no explicit reference to personality, while the later levels are subjective, since they involve necessary reference to personality. The whole range involved may be termed the 'nature-mind spectrum of knowledge.'

"It seems to be probable that those who take a particular one of these levels as the most real are merely those who insist on starting in their thought from this particular level; for instance, I, as a mathematician, would naturally consider physical, biological, psychological, and social knowledge in so far as it is embodied in abstract form. If this is indeed the case, the only rational point of view is to regard all of these levels as having co-ordinate reality."

X

EVOLUTION AND PROGRESS; VALUES AND THE VALUELESS

Since the preceding chapter brought us to the verge of Evolution, it is to the examination of this subject that we now turn. Having "reached matter" or Nature, Quality and Quantity, Atomicity, Causality, and certain other Properties or Functions have been examined, but our account would be incomplete were Evolution not included. Again, it is my intention to present "principles" and not details.

I shall include, in my discussion of Evolution, three generally accepted "kinds" of Evolution, and add a fourth, not so widely accepted as *differing* from the other three. Cosmic or Inorganic, Organic, and Psychological or Mental, are the three that are hardly disputed. In some respects these three must be different, else the distinction is not justified. On the other hand, if it is justified, then, by the same token, I shall maintain that a fourth kind of Evolution must be accepted. This I shall call Social. What the many differences are between the Social *and* the Psychological will appear in the later discussion. Suffice it to say at this point that, even as the position will be taken that, just as there are certain phenomena, *e.g.*, learning by trial and error (well recognized in Psychology), which cannot be reduced to (identified with) physiological phenomena, and certain properties, called vital or physiological, that

are qualitatively *more than*, or *other than*, inorganic properties, so there are also certain properties, as the qualities
of certain specific situations or structures or organizations,
that are so *novel* in contrast with psychological, organic,
and inorganic phenomena, that they must be granted to
be qualitatively discontinuous with these three, and therefore to form an autonomous realm of their own.   This
realm I call the social.   This is, of course, the realm that
is constituted by human beings and by the *relations* of
human beings (the *structure* or *organization*) to one another.
It is "in" this situation that language and communication, art, science, religion, conduct (both individual and
group), and politics have their being.   These are all realities, but they are realities that are not found in such situations, *e.g.*, as (1) that of a rat learning to get out of a maze
(psychological), or (2) that of a fertilized egg segmenting
and developing (organic), or (3) that of two atoms of Hydrogen combining with one atom of Oxygen to form ordinary
water (inorganic).   These occurrences are real, too, but
none of them presents the peculiar, novel properties that
"society" presents.   I shall maintain, then, that, if Evolution is to be envisaged as a universal (or nearly so) process
in Nature, then, if it includes the inorganic, the organic,
and the psychological realms, as qualitatively different
from one another, it must also include the social realm as
likewise *sui generis* in certain respects.

This statement indicates that the general principles
concerning Causation, Creativity, Autonomy, Freedom,
etc., which were presented in the last chapter as "applying"
to what may be called "short-time" processes and situations, are also here regarded as "applying" as well to that
"long-time" process in Nature which is Evolution.   This

means, of course, that I find that the Evolutionary Series as a whole is of such a character that in it there are realized, by particulars in space and time, Causality, both discontinuous and Continuous, Creativity or Emergence, Self-Determination or Autonomy,—of qualitatively distinct realms or levels,—Freedom,—Freedom both from limitations and from "Specificities," and Teleology or Self-Regulation. This last brings us to "the realm of ends" and therefore to *values* (the problem of Goodness and Beauty and their opposites), so that a discussion of "ends" or of values will be included in this chapter. Such an Evolution is, as is well known, called Creative or Emergent; it is an Evolution that is *qualitatively discontinuous* at certain points, be these few or many; as such, it is an Evolution that is opposed to a Theory of Continuity. However, both a Theory of Continuous and a Theory of Discontinuous Evolution can each be stated "logically" as possibilities. It remains for empirical evidence to "decide" which is realized in Nature, in Existence, *i.e.*, which is *true*. I shall maintain that the evidence is very much in favor of the Discontinuous Theory.

However, both theories have much in common; thus, *each is a Theory of Evolution that includes, I maintain, four realms*, the inorganic, the organic, the psychological, and the social. What, then, are the common properties or characteristics of Evolution *in general?* They are as follows:

I.—Evolution is change, process, in time. But it is a special kind of temporal change. It is not Development, which is change, in time, in an individual, *e.g.*, in an organism. It is also not change of position (motion), or of velocity, or of qualities, as, *e.g.*, the colors of a fading fabric. It is *irreversible change* (universal), but, even more than this, it is *a specific irreversible change*.

Irreversible change in Nature is an instance, as regards *both* the qualitative content of the change *and* the time, of some type of Serial Order, either continuous or discontinuous, either with no beginning and no end, or with a beginning and no end, etc., as presented in an earlier chapter.[1] It is a change in which the terms are related by a relation that is irreflexive, connected, transitive, and asymmetrical.[2] Now there is one well-known and widely recognized type of irreversible, universal temporal change in Nature that is not only distinct from, but that is also, perhaps, "just the opposite" of Evolution—whatever this phrase may mean. The law of this change is the well-known *Generalized Second Law of Thermodynamics, or, The Principle of Entropy*. This Law, or this Principle, is stated in different forms. One statement is to the effect that all the energy of the universe tends to get into the condition of *a dead-level* of "potential" or "intensity," so that "nothing more could happen" (Ostwald).[3] Another statement (Eddington) is that all events in Nature proceed from greater organization to less, therewith approaching *a minimum*.[4] Still a third is (Jeans)[5] that all matter tends to be transformed into radiant energy, and that then this energy tends to become of longer and longer wave-length ("heat-death").

It is not, however, germane to my purpose to present further details regarding this law or principle, or to criticize

[1] Chapter VI, also IV.
[2] See Chapter VI.
[3] Lehrbuch d. Allgem, Chemie, 1892, *passim*. Ostwald was the leader of "the Energetiker."
[4] *The Nature of the Physical World*, Chap. IV.
[5] Jeans, J. H., *The Universe Around Us*, Chap. VI, especially pp. 309–310.

it in any way. The matter is mentioned only because it concerns *a specific irreversibility* in Nature that is not identical with the irreversibility of the Evolutionary Series.

What, then, is the specific irreversibility of this series (Evolution)? Several answers, none of which, perhaps, is incompatible with the others, are given. These answers are as follows:

1. The Evolutionary Series is characterized by the fact that there is *an ever-increasing complexity* as regards the "individuals" that occur in it. To illustrate this simply,— Electrons and protons become atoms; atoms, molecules; molecules, particles; particles (some of them, viz., colloidal), cells; cells, complex organisms; organisms, in some cases, groups,—non-social and (some) social. At each "stage" there is more and more complexity.

2. The Evolutionary Series is one of ever-increasing Divergence as regards Diversity of structure, form, and organization, and of resulting qualities. This is especially well illustrated, as is widely known, in organic evolution.

Corollaries: As further characteristics, accompanying those stated in (1) and (2), there are an ever-increasing integration and self-regulation of individuals, *as a result of which qualities*, *individuals act more and more as* "*units*."

3. The Evolutionary Series is irreversible in the sense that there is *a definite order* to the four chief divisions of the Series. This order is: Inorganic, Vital, Psychological, Social. These four realms must be either different *in kind* or different *in degree* (*of the same kind* of "fundamental" entity), but, *in either case*, the "position" of each in the Series is *fixed*, and the Series is irreversible.

II.—The Evolutionary Series is *autonomous* as regards

causation, *i.e.*, the specific causes that operate to produce effects *are all within the series itself.* The series is *as a whole, then, free,—free from* external compulsion,—and so, *self-determining* as regards its own specific properties, *e.g.*, its irreversibility.[6]

The foregoing are *the common properties* of the Evolutionary Series, whether this be continuous or discontinuous. But there are also the two *distinct, further possibilities:*

I.—Continuous Evolution. If Evolution is continuous, then the type of irreversibility is the type of a continuous series as this has been defined in Chapter VI. Accordingly all change in complexity, integration, etc., is continuous, as are, also, all diversities. The seemingly diverse is "really" not diverse, *but the same.* This means that there is change and diversity as regards only the *degree* of some basic quality or qualities. There are, then, in turn, two sub-theories, according as one "interprets" Evolution from "below" upward, or from "the top" downward. According to the first sub-theory, if "the start" be made with, *e.g.*, protons and electrons, or, crudely stated, with "matter," then everything that later appears is merely *more* of these same realities and of their characteristics. According to the second position, if the start be made "at the top," with social characteristics, *e.g.*, with morality (whatever this may be), then there must be granted to be present, in some small degree, at least, this same property, no matter "how far back" one goes. Morality, logical thinking, memory, life, would each have to exist in some degree even in the electron and the proton side by side with the material aspects, unless—another version—these material aspects are themselves interpreted to be lesser degrees

[6] No external agent of any kind is needed.

of the higher or highest properties (mind, morality, etc.) and nothing more. According to this "version" matter vanishes; it is only an appearance—of something else.[7]

Empirical evidence does not, in my opinion, confirm any one of these three theories of Continuous Evolution. On the contrary, it shows that life is characterized by *some properties* that are not found *in any degree whatsoever*, even the slightest, in the inorganic realm; that psychological phenomena are qualities distinct from purely biological; and that social phenomena are, in turn, entirely absent from the three preceding realms. It may be "*theory*," but it is not the "empirical fact," that, *e.g.*, *logical thinking is* a sub-vocal laryngeal muscular action, or *learning* a mere biological process, or the *development* (of a cell) a mere chemico-physical series of events. Logical thinking, learning, and development are each just what they are found to be by empirical investigation; each "stands on its own feet" as just "the kind of thing" that it is; each is "what is done" or "what happens" at a specific level of phenomena. Each rests, to be sure, on "a lower story" *but it is not that story*. Social, psychological, and organic phenomena simply are not found to be *merely* material or inorganic, however much they may be correlated with these. *This is stark Realism*, to be sure, but it is what "the facts" show. And certainly, as concerns the other theories of Continuous Evolution, it would seem to be the rankest nonsense to assert that empirically even the slightest degree of religion, morality, scientific thinking, or art—all social phenomena—is found in the electron and proton, as the theory implies these should be found. This

[7] The position, in a sense, of the Idealism (ontological) of Berkeley, of Leibnitz, and of the modern Objective Idealists.

extrapolation may be made "in theory," but it receives no confirmation whatsoever from empirical research.

If we stick to the facts, then, or to the results of empirical investigation, we must grant that it is a Theory of Discontinuous Evolution, and not one of Continuous, that is *true*. What is this Theory? I answer: It is essentially that Theory of Emergence, etc., *applied to Evolution*, which was presented in the preceding chapter. In it, then, the *general* factors of Evolution must be *combined* with those more *specific* characteristics that distinguish a theory of discontinuity from one of continuity (as regards Evolution).

The *general* factors are: (1) Irreversible change in time, with this irreversibility identical with, (a), increasing complexity, (b), increasing diversity, (c), increasing integration; (2), internal causation, *i.e.*, causal autonomy.

The *specific* factors are as follows:

I.—In addition to the three "phases" of *irreversibility* just mentioned, there is the fourth phase, (d), of an irreversibility *of kind and not of mere degree*, as given, *e.g.*, by the order, *inorganic, organic or vital, psychological, social*. Within each of these, in turn, there may be *further differences of kind*.

II.—In addition to an internal causation, as a general factor, causes may be different in kind, as well as "alike." Those of one level are alike as belonging to that level; those of different levels are unlike.

III.—Especially from level to level, *e.g.*, from inorganic to vital, from vital to psychological, and from psychological to social, there are Contingency and Creativity. Something new arises, at a "critical point," as a result of organization (both increasing complexity of relations *and* kinds of terms).

This is Creativity. But *the specificity* of the newness is not necessitated. It is, then, contingent.

IV.—Each level, *e.g.*, the vital, and the psychological, is autonomous in the sense that it is a "closed set" of causes and effects, each definable in terms of the other. In this respect each level is internally determined. For example, in Genetics, "genes" are defined as *causes* of specific *mature* characters (eye-color, hair, horns, etc., etc.) as *effects*, *i.e.*, a *biological cause* is "correlated" (descriptively) with a *biological effect*.

V.—As concerns any two levels, there is a two-fold Freedom. (1) The "higher" level is *free from the limitations* of the "lower" in that it is *qualitatively* distinct from, or more than, the lower level, and acts or "behaves" in accordance with this specific "newness" and "moreness." (2) The lower level is *free from the specificity* of the higher level in that, whether the higher level is superposed or not, the lower acts or "behaves" in accordance with its own specific laws—discovered quite empirically. For example, the physical and chemical processes that take place in the synthesis of H_2O and CO_2 to form carbohydrates in plants are no less physical and chemical because of the fact that this synthesis would not take place ("normally,") except as "plant structure" is present.

VI. As a result of more and more organization, accompanying more and more complexity, there is more and more Integration, Self-Regulation, and Freedom. Accordingly, there is more and more Teleology in the sense that each integrated and self-regulating individual whole at a specific level *is its own end*. For example, everything that an organism does is "life preservative" either of the individual, or of the species, or of both, or of a group of species living together [8] (*e.g.*, insects fertilizing flowers and flowers furnishing the food for insects, etc.). There is more and more Freedom—and the Freedom "goes by jumps," because, with the discontinuous causal production of each new level, there is *more*, as regards "preceding" levels, *from which to be free.* For example, an individual that is capable of logical thinking is more free than is an individual that is capable only of "trial and error learning," even as an individual capable of such learning is freer than an individual that cannot learn at all.

We may now ask the important question: Is such a "scheme" of Evolution one that also carries with it the characteristic of Progress, or, more generally, Does Evolution itself, whether discontinuous or continuous, mean Progress? To the answering of this question we now turn: In giving my answer, I shall keep to what seem to me to be the "empirical facts," in the broad sense of this term (empirical).

Whether one accepts a Continuous or a Discontinuous Evolution, it is the empirical fact that there *is* Human Society, the collective name for the social level with its distinctive phenomena, *i.e.*, there is no denying the fact, in some sense, that there are and have been human beings between whom and among whom, both as individuals and as groups, there are found the phenomena of language and communication, of relatively unreflective and uncritical religion, art, politics, and conduct, and, more reflective, and critical, of ethics, rational theology, aesthetics, political theory, science (logic, mathematics, and the natural sciences) and philosophy. These phenomena are to be admitted, whether they are different in kind, or only in

---

[8] The subject-matter of Ecology.

degree, from the "stages" in the evolutionary process that preceded their appearance.

Now, out of this group of phenomena I select for special examination, as germane to the inquiry, Is Evolution Progress, three, namely, Ethics, Science, and Philosophy. I am not especially concerned with the question as to what are the lines of demarcation between these three, but, rather, with the fact that each of these is a social phenomenon that is the result of, or that is characterized by, *rational inquiry*. Science is, broadly speaking, of two kinds, natural and logical; in natural science there are sense-perception (observation), experiment, and measurement, but there is also reasoning; in the logical sciences, there are postulates and the theorems deduced from these; in ethics there is rational examination and criticism of customs and codes, standards and systems of conduct. Common to all three, however, is *rational inquiry*. Now the point which I wish to stress is, that, once rational inquiry starts (as history shows), there is no "heading it off." It may be directed to anything whatsoever. Natural science investigates on the basis of, or through, sense-perception, measurement, generalization and reasoning, but these methods of investigation may be and are, in fact, themselves investigated. Logical situations are studied, and Logic and Mathematics are developed, but these are in turn studied logically. Likewise ethical customs (tribal), conduct (individual), standards, and systems (*e.g.*, Hedonism) are investigated,— rationally, however, and not ethically. Ethical conduct is not ethics, nor is ethics, as a rational system, ethical conduct. And finally, *e.g.*, such a question as that of the relation (synthesis, or priority) of these several realms to one another may become the object of research, to give—Philosophy.

These examples are sufficient to give a basis for the generalization that, with the coming, in the evolutionary process, of the social realm or level, with its distinguishing characteristics, there is, *negatively*, as it were, more Freedom than "before," since there is more to be "free from," and, *positively*, that this Freedom reaches a high-point of development (I hesitate to say the highest, although this may be the case) in *rational inquiry*. This means, of course, that Natural Science, Logic, and Mathematics, Ethics, Aesthetics, the Philosophy of Politics, of Religion, and of Science, are themselves products of the evolutionary process in the social realm. These "bodies of knowledge" are the results of rational inquiry, which is itself an "evolutionary product." This inquiry ultimately is *logical inquiry*, by the use of *propositions* that are logically connected, and once this inquiry has issued in conclusions, these conclusions are themselves meanings or *propositions*. And, it is by virtue of meanings or propositions that there is, as has been seen in Chapter I, the possibility of communication between minds. The "above" bodies of knowledge are, then, as regards their method as well as their results, both logical and social phenomena.

But, rational inquiry, once begun, is difficult, as has been seen, to stop or limit. *With its method logical, and its subject-matter anything*, it is *free from* custom, tradition, authority, respect, fear, habit, consequences, and from the subject-matter of any specific field. Indeed, so free is this method, in both of these respects, that it may be directed to the investigation of both *Freedom* and *Investigation* themselves.

Quite obviously, then, the question, Is Evolution Progress? may be rationally investigated, and this investigation may take different courses. There is freedom in this respect, too. Accordingly, I propose to adopt one of these (perhaps) many possible courses of investigation.

That course which I shall adopt begins with the recognition, which I should say is quite rational, that my question involves what in one current field of rational inquiry is called a *"value-term."* Progress is such a term. Is Evolution Progress? means, *Is Evolution Betterment?* and Betterment is advance in respect to some quality that is *good*, and, therefore, *an instance* of Goodness.

Goodness is *a Value*, but not the only one, for there are also Beauty, and perhaps, as distinct from each of these, Aesthetic Value,[9] but it is not, at least to any extent, with these last two values that I shall be concerned, but, rather, with the first, Goodness.

Goodness is itself an instance (a subordinate property) of Value: in other words, if there is Goodness, there is Value, but, if there is Value, there need be no Goodness. There might be only Beauty and Aesthetic Value, but no Goodness; in fact, there might be any one of these without the other two, or, indeed, none of the three. For here, as elsewhere, a property is merely *the possibility-of-instances*, so that one must admit that, while Goodness and Beauty and Aesthetic Value are *de facto* found and experienced as instances of Value, and are *realities* of some kind, nevertheless each is an entirely contingent fact in the universe.

Indeed, in the "structure" of "things," as that structure has thus far been traced in this volume, *no value* of any kind has thus far been found, unless it be *the value of the whole in relation to the part and parts in a self-regulating system*, as this was presented in the preceding chapter, and to this we

[9] See *The Philosophy of Art*, by C. J. Ducasse, especially Chaps. I, VIII, and XI–XIV. I should interpret Ducasse as accepting this distinct value.

shall return shortly. But, aside from this one possibility, neither *value* itself, nor any of its instances have thus far been encountered. What of goodness or beauty or aesthetic value, to use the *instances*, is to be discovered, *e.g.*, in Necessity, or in Impossibility, or in Negation, or in Implication, or in Irreversibility, or in Space-Time, or in an atom or a molecule, or a colloidal solution, etc., etc.? I answer, frankly, *Nothing*. Accordingly, it seems to me, that I must admit, as a result of rational inquiry, that most, if, indeed, not all of the realities that have been examined thus far, "participate in," or are instances of, a common property, *Valuelessness*, if I may use this term. Indeed, I cannot discover that Evolution itself is "any exception to this rule." What is there, I ask frankly, of Goodness, or Beauty, or of Aesthetic Value, one or all, in a universal process, "in Nature" (or that *is* Nature), that is temporal, and internally causal, and irreversible as regards an increasing (either continuously or discontinuously) complexity and organization and integration? What is there, of any of these values, in Creativity, and Autonomy, and more and more Freedom, even to the point, at the social level, of rational inquiry? I mean, What is there, of any of these three values, in an Evolutionary Process as a whole, that instances, either as a whole, or, in part, "here and there," these properties? I again answer, Nothing.

And yet Value and Values—*Goodness, Beauty, and Aesthetic Value and their instances*—are experienced. *Value and Values are, in some sense, facts. There is a realm of values, as well as of the Valueless.* What is this realm? What is its structure? In what respect are values facts? How are they experienced?

To attempt to answer these questions at all adequately

would require not one, but many volumes. I shall, of course, not attempt this task. The questions are asked only because they are germane to my major question, Is Evolution Progress?, and only as they relate to this question shall I attempt to answer them.

The first thing that I discover is, that I can answer this question *affirmatively* (this admission itself being perhaps to the liking of some of my readers), but only on certain conditions or with certain *provisos*. For example, I find that I can admit that evolution is progressive, with it admitted (1), that it is a process of ever-increasing complexity, organization, diversity, self-regulation, or freedom— of any specific kind, *provided*, (2), *that more of any one of these properties or characteristics is better than less.* For *progress is betterment*, and *betterment* is a *property*, to be instanced or not. Betterment is realized, then, (1) *if any one characteristic, e.g., complexity, is good*, and, (2) if Evolution is—among other things—an *increase* of that characteristic, and a similar statement can be made as regards each of the other characteristics mentioned. Evolution is betterment, then, and, therefore, progress, *provided* (1) that such a characteristic as organization, or diversity, or self-regulation, or freedom, *is* (*a*) *good*, and (2) that Evolution is a process which, by "its very nature," *is* more and more of any one, or two, or three, or of all of these properties (for they are not incompatible).

And the "situation" is not different if, instead of these specific characteristics, each of which in the evolutionary series might be strung along a line of *continuity*, we accept Evolution as being discontinuous, and so creative of such novelties, *in a definite order*, as, following the inorganic, *the organic*, then *the psychological*, and, finally, *the social*, with this last realm characterized by the highest degree of freedom that exists, namely, the freedom of rational inquiry itself. Is Evolution Progress because it is a *creative* process in this way? And again I answer, "*Yes, provided rational inquiry is better than its absence; learning (to take an example) better than 'just acting physiologically;' and life better than just an inorganic condition.*" [10]

I thus find that, recognizing the *proviso* in each case, any affirmative answer to the question whether Evolution is to be regarded as *ipso facto* Progress, is an answer that is *conditioned*. It is conditioned either, (1), by a prior acceptance of some characteristic, *e.g.*, complexity, as an instance of *goodness*, in which case an *increase* of this "means" betterment, and so, progress; or, (2), by the prior *assumption* that something, *e.g.*, life, is good, and that accordingly its *presence* is *better than* its absence, in which case the same conclusion follows. I thus find not only that the question itself, Is Evolution Progress?, can be asked, but also that it can be answered *only at a certain "level*," namely, at that level in which questions are asked, rational inquiries are made in order to answer questions, and the method of these very inquiries is itself made a subject of rational investigation. *This level is the social.* In other words, I find that the evolutionary process *itself, as a whole,* does not ask the question that is being discussed, but that only a specific product of that process raises the problem, namely, that product which *is* rational inquiry, in the general field of values, *by* human beings, *in* a society. To say that the Evolutionary Process itself, as a whole, asks the question, or that to itself, as a whole, it answers it, is meaningless,

[10] One may *assume* this order, but, accordingly, it may be challenged. It was challenged, as is well known, by Schopenhauer.

but that the process as a whole should be, or seem to be, Progress, *to a specific part of itself*, and, at that, to a part that is produced by preceding parts of the process, is not meaningless. Indeed, this is what actually happens. The Evolutionary Process may be said itself to produce, at a certain stage, a situation in which not only is the process itself known or disclosed, but also in which the question is asked, as it were, "Am I Progress?" The question is asked, of course, by human beings, by "thinking" individuals. And the answer is given, by some who make the inquiry, "Yes"; by others, "No," but by still others, who are, perhaps, more versed in the methods of rational inquiry, "That all depends."

To some it is clearly seen at a certain stage in the development of rational inquiry, that, whether Evolution is regarded as *progressive* or not, depends entirely on what is accepted as the *standard* or "Ideal," and that this depends, in turn, on what is accepted as an instance of Goodness. That is, to some, the decision as to the question, whether Evolution is Progress or, conversely, a universal "going to the dogs,"—a sort of Principle of "Value-Entropy," is regarded, perhaps, unlike the Priniciple of Entropy in Physics, as a matter that is wholly dependent on the standard that is arbitrarily set up, or postulated. Whether or not this relativistic position is correct or not, is itself a question for further inquiry, so that it is to this problem that I shall next turn.

There are, undoubtedly, Goodness and Beauty "in the world," in some sense, and, as perhaps distinct from these two, also Aesthetic Value.[11] This, I would say, is an empirical fact that is involved in the experience of certain "things"

[11] *Vide, e.g.*, Ducasse, *opus cit.*

as good, or as beautiful, or as having aesthetic value. The "things" thus experienced are, at least tacitly, therewith regarded as *instances* of some one or other (perhaps of all) of the three sub-types of Value. But,—and here I think that rational inquiry shows that there is Relativity in the situation—there would seem to be no way of showing that what is regarded as an instance by one person is also regarded as being this by another. For example, Complexity, Organization, Freedom, Consciousness as over against mere Life, may each be accepted as *a good* (*an instance*) by one person and not by another, with no way of definitely showing what are the facts in the case, thus to settle the issue.

Now I have no doubt that there is the *fact* of Value, and that there are also the instances of this, namely, Goodness and Beauty—to omit from further consideration Aesthetic Value. This is Realism. But I do find that it is very difficult, if not, indeed, impossible, to determine, with any degree of certainty, *what are the instances of these two values.* The most that I can discover in this situation, by way of fact, is, (1), *the fact of the freedom to assume or to postulate* that "such and such" a property, *e.g.*, Organization, or Freedom, or Life as against death (or non-living), is *a good*, but, to proceed in this way, is, (2), freely to *select* some one fact, *e.g.*, Life, and, then, (3), to *regard* it as being *an instance* of another fact (goodness).

The seemingly *complete arbitrariness* of this procedure is illustrated perhaps even more clearly in that special field of rational inquiry which is Ethics. Here we have, first, *the question, What is the Good*, in Life, in Conduct, Individual and Social?, *and then the several answers* that have been given to the question in the course of the development of Ethics. Candidates for *the* Ethical Good have been, as is well known, *e.g.*, Pleasure (either sensuous or intellectual, or both), Excellence or Perfection, Christian Love, the Good-Will (of Kant), Biological Adjustment (Spencer), Social Welfare, etc., and "arguments," to the extent, in some cases, of "forming" philosophical systems, have been advanced to demonstrate the superiority, if not the exclusive right, of the claims of each of these candidates against the others. But, which has established this claim beyond any doubt?

Now, it is not my purpose in this volume to enter upon a discussion of Ethics at any length. Brief appeal to this field of inquiry is being made only because, as with our question concerning Evolution, Ethics takes us into *values*, —those, namely, that are *instances of Goodness*. And in the Ethical realm, or, rather, in Ethics, I find a situation that exactly parallels that which has been found in considering the answers that are given to the question, Is Evolution Progress? Pleasure, Excellence, the Good-Will, Social Welfare, etc., have each been *assumed* to be *a good*, indeed not only *a good*, but *the highest good, the Summum Bonum*. The same may be said of the several characteristics of Evolution, such as Complexity, Diversity, Integration, Self-Regulation, etc. *Each* of these may be *assumed* to be *a good*, and *one* of them to be better than *all* the others, and so *the best*, from either one of which assumptions it follows, of course, that Evolution is Progress, provided that, in this process, there is more and more of that one of these properties which is selected as the standard, or, that there is a "tendency" toward the attainment of such a standard.

I find, then, as common to both of the two fields of inquiry that concern *values*, namely, Ethics, and, in this discussion, Evolution, *two factors.* The first is that, for the generic yet specific *value,* Goodness (specific, as an instance of Value; generic, as itself having instances), the *instances* are, in every case, merely *assumed and not proved,* and the second is, that these instances may be and are (by some, at least) *arranged in a certain order,* namely, the order of *good, better, and best,*[12] the last being the *Summum Bonum.* For example, one might say that the order of Ethical "goods" is, from "least good," to "better," to still better, and, finally, to "best," (1) Sensuous Pleasure, (2) Intellectual Pleasure, (3) Perfection, (4) Good-Will, (5) Social Welfare, or, of Evolutionary characteristics, (1) Life, (2) Habit, (3) Reason.

Now what I wish to show is that, not only is the regarding, or the selecting, of anything (Pleasure, Social Welfare, or, for Evolution, Life) as *a good,* merely a matter of *assumption,* but also, that the *order assigned to the specific "entities" that are selected as goods is equally arbitrary.* Both the selection and the order assigned are *entirely relative*—relative to "interests," which in turn may be relative to, or conditioned by, temperament, social position (generally speaking), culture, culture-period, etc., etc. In other words, there is no objective basis whatsoever, by way of either empirical evidence, logical proof, or the method of finding presuppositions,[13] on which one selection

---

[12] This order is not the order of *betterment.* Betterment, or its opposite, is the property of a temporal series, Evolution, Development, Living, Social Change, in relation to, or as conditioned by, that specific instance of Goodness which is selected as the standard, or the *Summum Bonum.*

Rather, the order under consideration is that which concerns the rational inquiry as to *which* of a number of goods *is the standard, the highest, the Summum Bonum.* Obviously, there is here a special instance of Serial Order and of the relations which it involves. This instance is *special* by virtue of its terms, which are not points, or numbers, *but specific instances of Goodness.*

[13] *Cf.* the Introduction and Chapter I.

can be shown to be correct or true as against others as incorrect or as false.

The further considerations which show this conclusion to be justified are as follows:

Before several instances of Goodness can be arranged in the order of *good, better, still better, and, possibly, best,* there must be the *instances.* Now the property, Goodness, does not itself give any clue at all as to what these instances are, neither does that which is regarded as *the best,* since this last will vary with the order assigned, and is itself an instance of the Good. The instances must, then, either be found empirically, or be "derived" logically by the method of presupposition, or, if these methods *fail*—and they do—be *merely assumed.* I find that they are merely assumed.

Once assumed, however, the instances are to be *ordered,* in accordance with the relation, *"better than."* [14] But this relation must have a "content." It must be the relation of "better than" *in respect to some specific property* which all of "the goods" that are ordered not only possess as a "common factor," but also possess *in varying degrees.* Only by virtue of *such a property* could one say, *e.g.,* that *such a good* as "Social Welfare," is a "higher" or "better" *good* than the "Good-Will," and this last "higher" or "better" than Individual Pleasure. If now, *to continue our example,* these last three are themselves *standards,* (and each has been so regarded in the development of Ethical Theory) and if, in order to arrange them *serially,* in the order of good, better, still better, and perhaps best, *a specific property must be found in which all share, but*

[14] Professor A. P. Brogan has, in a number of articles, made use of this specific "ordering relation" in discussing special problems. *Vide, e.g., Ethics as Method,* Int. J. of Ethics, XXXVI, 2, pp. 263–270, and *Objective Pluralism in the Theory of Value, ibid.,* XLI, 2, pp. 287–295.

unequally, then this property may be called "a standard of standards."

I ask, now, can such *a standard of standards* be found? In answer, I would say that this standard cannot itself be one of the subordinate standards which *by it* are to be arranged or ordered. To make it any one of these is to beg the question at issue. Also, it cannot be Goodness itself, for the (generic) property is "always" indifferent to its instances—both as to what they are *and* as to their number.[15] Accordingly this standard of standards, if there is such a thing, or if it can be found, must be another instance of Goodness, yet an instance that is quite "outside" the group of those other instances which, *by virtue of (being, regarded as) possessing this specific Goodness in varying degrees, have an order.*

Can, now, such a standard of standards be found in any field whatsoever that concerns *values*, especially the value which we are especially considering, namely, Goodness, *and its instances?* For example, and to be "specific," Is there *a standard of standards* as between the Civilization of the East and that of the West, between Protestantism and Catholicism, between Christianity and other religions, between Capitalism and opposed social, political, and economic philosophies, between the rational life and brute dumbness, between Hedonism, Perfectionism, and the Formalism of Kant, etc., etc., by which the issue can definitely be decided as to which is *best* in the latter case, *the better* in the former cases? Each of these is regarded not only as *a good*, but also as the better of two, or as the best of three, by its adherents, but this does not settle the issue. The question is, Can it be settled, by finding a

[15] *Cf.* Chapter IV.

standard to settle it? I find that *no such standard can be discovered*, but that argument in these several fields always proceeds on the basis of the tacit assumption that *one of the standards which is to be compared with others so as to obtain an order is itself the basis or the standard for the comparison.* Thus to proceed is, of course, but to beg the question at issue, and perhaps also, in accordance with the situations which have been discussed under the caption of the Theory of Types, to make one and the same *specific good both a standard of standards and not such a standard.*[16]

But, the fact that such a standard (with content) is not found, does not mean that there is no such standard. There may be, and there may not. However, if there is such a standard, then it must be, in order to avoid the contradiction of "being both a standard and not a standard," *other than* any one of those standards which are to be arranged by means of it. It must really be *a standard of standards*. And, further, admitting that there may be such a standard, *what* it is, cannot be deduced from its possibility. Rather, the "content" for it must be found either empirically, or by the method of presupposition, *or* by assumption, and, if by this last method, then on the basis of the *purely gratuitous postulate, that this specific content is an instance of the good.*

I conclude, then, that, as concerns the two more special fields of inquiry which we have been examining, namely, Ethics and the question as to whether Evolution is Progress or not, both of which raise problems about Values, there is only to be found what may broadly be called a Theory of the Relativity of all Values. And in this I include the Values, Beauty and Aesthetic Value, and their instances,

[16] *Vide* Chapters III and IV.

as well as Goodness and its instances. This means that nothing is good, or beautiful, or of aesthetic value, except *relatively and by assumption*—*relatively* to those influences that lead to the selection of certain qualities or properties *as* instances of some one (or more) of these three values,— by *assumption* in that assumptions spring tacitly from interests.[17] Such a position does not deny, however, that values are experienced and are *facts*, any more than in the Theory of Relativity in Physics, the relativity of the results of measurement to the "position" of the observer, denies the *factuality* of these differing results. *The facts are as experienced*, but further consideration of them shows that they are relative. The results are factual, but there is *the fact, also, of their relativity*.

Similarly in the field of values. There is something irreducible and undeniable in the experience by any individual of any particular object, event, property, etc., as good, or as beautiful, or as aesthetically satisfying, but it is also quite as much an irreducible and undeniable fact that this experience is shown by rational inquiry to be *relative* to the interests, etc., of the individual. In Physics, however, one goes beyond the relative to "the absolute,"—beyond that which varies from individual to individual to that which is *invariant*. This procedure, as we have seen,[18] takes the physicist, *e.g.*, to Space-Time. Space-Time, as "cut" by different measures on different "frames of reference," "results" in varying spaces and times, masses, motions, velocities, etc.

Is there not a similar situation in the field of Values?

---

[17] There is, in the case of the Value we are considering,—Goodness, the selection,— (1) of the instances that are to be ordered; (2) of that instance *in respect to which* an order is "found;" and (3), as resulting from this order, the selection of the Highest Good, with this varying, of course with that which is selected as *the principle of order*.

[18] Chapter VI.

Could one not assert, with justification, that Goodness is, as it were, the "Ethical Space-Time," to be "cut" by different individuals, according to their interests, into varying Standards, such as Individual Pleasure, Excellence, and Social Welfare? I think not. And the reasons for my so thinking? The answer:—The two situations are different. "Spaces" and "times" are, as we have seen, not instances of Space-Time, but the results of "cuts" by measurement. Measurement "makes" *quantities* of qualities. But, to get our *standards*, in the field of Ethics, we do not "cut" Goodness by measurement, but we *assume* that something is an instance of that quality. We then get other instances, and endeavor to *order* these instances. Submitting this order to criticism, we endeavor to find *an objective basis* for it, a standard of standards, but with no result. We are left, then, in the realm of values, (1), with only *assumed instances*, (2), with only an *assumed standard of standards*, (3), with only an *assumed order*, and, therefore, (4), with only an *assumed Summum Bonum*, the assumption in each case being relative to, and conditioned by, the interest of the "assumer," perhaps undeniably experienced by him, and so, in this sense, factual, but quite as undeniably not experienced by another.

In the realm of values, then, that cannot be done which is done in Physics. *One cannot get from the relative to the absolute, from the varying to the invariant.* In Physics one does this by, and on the basis of, measurement supplemented by Mathematics, but, in the realm of Values, there is no measurement and no Mathematics. There is at best only *ordering*. And this proves to be an entirely relative matter.

I conclude, then, that, in the field of Values, one cannot escape Relativity. Yet this does not deny Values. Values may be as factual, even if they are relative, as they would be, if they were not. This is simply to assert the factuality of their being experienced, the fact of their being *what* they are experienced *as*, and the fact of the irreducible relativity of these experiences, as disclosed by rational inquiry. Equally factual is *the valueless,*—as disclosed also by rational inquiry,—the property (negative though it be) of being neither good, beautiful, or aesthetically satisfying, nor the opposite of these. This property characterizes many of the entities (and their relations) that have been considered and examined in this volume—*e.g.*, Necessity, Contingency, Necessities, dimensions of various kinds and orders, spaces, times, and, I am now willing to say, *Evolution itself. Any of these* is good, *or* beautiful, *or* aesthetically satisfying "at best" *only by the most gratuitous assumption*, but by assumption only by that part of reality which is free to make assumptions and which does make them, namely, human beings in a society *some* of whose members are capable of rational inquiry to the extent that they discover that all that can be done in certain circumstances or situations *is to make assumptions*.

This is the irony of the situation. Is Evolution Progress? Yes, but only to those who, themselves "produced" in the evolutionary process itself, make those assumptions, either tacitly or explicitly, that imply this conclusion. *But to the evolutionary process itself, as a whole, neither "Yes" nor "No."* To it, it is a matter of supreme indifference whether such assumptions are made as will enable one of its own products to show that it is Progress or not. The Evolutionary Process, *as a whole*, does not value; it has no interests; it does not make selections as to what shall be regarded as *instances* of the good; it does not attempt to order these "goods" so as to find a *Summum Bonum;* it does not assume *one* of these values to be something that is *both a standard and not a standard*.

I conclude, then, not that Value and the instances of this, Goodness, Beauty, and Aesthetic Value, are dependent on human beings—indeed I maintain the opposite—but only that *the selecting* and *the ordering* is "human."

The possibility of one final appeal from this conclusion remains. May not the very fact *that there are human beings* who are capable of rational inquiry in the field of Values, who are free to *assume*, first, *goods*, and then some specific good, *e.g.*, Pleasure, as a standard, who may even recognize the arbitrariness of this procedure, but who may nevertheless act in accordance with the standard assumed,—may not this complex situation itself be, not a relative, but *an absolute, objective good*, with the result that the Evolutionary Process itself, as producing this situation, must be acknowledged to have produced not only a good, but also *something better than something else*, and therefore to be progressive.

I answer: This situation is a fact. Human beings *do* select or postulate various standards, and, after inquiry, some one of these which they regard, by some standard of standards, as highest—whether this be Pleasure, or Perfection, or Duty, or Social Welfare, or something else; and they may then act in accordance with this Ideal, this Highest Good, thus to control what they do. As acting in this way, a human being is not only self-regulating, but self-regulating to a much greater extent than is, *e.g.*, a being that is merely alive, but can neither learn, reason, nor act in accordance with an ideal. There is a greater freedom.

Is not *this* realized possibility an irreducible good, objective, and not subjective, absolute and not relative, "a sure mark" of progress?

To this question I confess that I find that I must again give the answer that was given previously, namely, "No!" Such self-regulation is (1) *a good, i.e.,* an instance of Goodness, and (2) as *a good,* is *better than* something else, *e.g.,* mere habit or custom, *only by assumption* in the manner that has been presented. And there is no way of establishing the correctness of this assumption over against contrary and opposed assumptions.

This final, possible appeal, then, does not succeed, and with its failure we are left with the conclusion, previously reached, that (1) as concerns *the specific content* (the instances) which is given to the Good, the Beautiful, and the Aesthetically Satisfying, this is only by assumption; (2), that, as concerns the ordering of these instances, so as to find, if possible, an order, and, perhaps, in the case of *Goods, a highest Good, this order varies* with the standard, the common quality, by virtue of which other Goods are ordered, so that the specific value, *e.g.,* Pleasure, which is the *Summum Bonum* for one, is not this for another; and that, (3), as concerns this "standard of standards," on the one hand, no content can be found for it as distinct from that which is to be ordered by it, so that, on the other hand, its only content is really obtained by assumption—namely, by the assumption that it is some one of those specific values which by (2) are to be "arranged" in a certain order. It thus appears that first, the selection of the *instances* of the Good, secondly, the *order* that is "assigned" these instances on the basis of some (hoped for) standard of standards, thirdly, the finding in this way of a *Summum Bonum*, which is in turn (illegitimately) made the Standard of Standards, is, in each case, *a matter of pure assumption,* either tacit or explicit. Such assumption is, if tacit, conditioned by such influences as (1) the culture, and the period of that culture, into which one is born, and in which one lives (*e.g.*, European culture in the twentieth century— each an instance of two variables); (2) the nation and the race to which one belongs (*e.g.*, German, Aryan), (3) the religion and theology to which one is a convert (*e.g.*, Protestant Christianity), (4) the economic, political, and social class of which one is a "member" (the examples are obvious), (5) the individual temperament and the individual experiences (leading to "suppressions" and thus to "escape-mechanisms" and the like).   On the other hand, if such assumptions are completely explicit—*i.e.*, if they are really made quite freely, with no concealed (perhaps subconscious) influences, and assuming that it is possible to do this—then there are (by assumption) no influences. *But, in either case, there are assumptions or postulates, and only these.* In either case, then, and, therefore, in both cases, it is impossible to get beyond a complete and thorough Relativity. This "holds good" for the *instances* that are selected, for the *order* that is given these instances, for the finding of the *Summum Bonum*, and for the selection of the *standard* by which this order and this *Summum Bonum* are found (this always being a circular process).

This is the situation, as I find it, in the realm of that specific instance of Value which is *The Good*. And a similar situation holds for the other two specific instances of Value, namely, The Beautiful, and The Aesthetic.[19]   In the case of no one of these three instances is it possible, I maintain, to get beyond a thorough-going Theory of Relativity.

[19] This is a mere statement, but it is based on analyses and investigations which I have not included in this book.

XI

STRUCTURE AND MIND

In the preceding chapter we have found that the Evolutionary Process in producing something that has interests, is capable of rational inquiry, selects and assumes and orders specific values, etc., turns around, as it were, on itself, to estimate or assess itself in terms of value. Also it was found that even this procedure itself can be identified with *a good*, and, possibly, with a good that is better than all other goods, and, therefore, *highest, only* as a matter of assumption. However, the analysis of this situation, and the method by which this conclusion has been reached, are not themselves instances of "valueing," [1] but stand, as it were, quite outside of this. In other words, to find that specific values, *e.g.*, those that are selected as instances of the good, *are relative to interests*, is itself a discovery, as the result of an inquiry, that is not relative to any interest unless it be the interest in the truth, or in the facts, whatever these may be found to be. Such a "disinterested interest" would be quite as "willing," *e.g.*, to accept it as a fact, should this be "established" by investigation, that the Evolutionary Process is one that is ever-productive of more and more evil, as to accept it as a fact that the opposite is the case. [2]

The Evolutionary Process, then, produces, as part of

[1] See Chapter V for a footnote as to the various predicaments.
[2] According to Chapter X either of these positions is really only a matter of assumption.

itself, not only a valuation of itself, positive or negative, in terms of the values, goodness and, perhaps, beauty, but also an *assessment* of this valuation. That process may, then, be "pictured" as turning around on itself, not only to value itself, but also *to know itself*. It can thus turn around on itself, however, only by producing, as a very specific *part of itself*, something which is *free* in the sense that, in its "functioning," it is *not limited to that part which is itself*, but can "extend" far beyond this. This very peculiar part, this very special "function," is *rational inquiry. Its realm is the Realm of Mind*. Mind, then, may be defined, not as a psychical substance, or as a stream of consciousness, or as an association or integration of ideas,[3] and the like, but as the *fact, or "occurrence," of rational inquiry in the world*— rational inquiry into anything whatsoever, for there seem to be no limits,—which does not mean that limits may not be discovered, *by* rational inquiry, *i.e.*, limits in the way of surds, or "irrationals," or things which cannot be rationally explained, but must be accepted as "just being." What further characteristics Mind has, as thus defined, we shall see shortly, for *Mind is what it does*, and its "nature" will be sought in its doing.

Mind does not evolve in the sense that there is a *continuous* evolution of Mind, *e.g.*, from the electron to the most rational human being. Rather, mind appears, "where before" it did not exist. Mind is an emergent, a novelty, but even at that, a novelty among novelties.

Mind has its conditions,—I may also say, its "causes." It appears as a result of organization, but of that special organization which *is the social realm*. This realm is itself an organization of human beings who are themselves highly

[3] Each a "traditional" definition, as is well known.

organized psychologically, physiologically, and chemico-physically. It is in this social realm that rational inquiry appears. This is inquiry by means of propositions (and their logical relations to one another) which are formulated by language-symbols, and thus form the basis of, or sole condition for, genuine communication between minds, as we have seen in Chapter I. Mind is, then, a social quality or property; it is *a new quality of a new whole*, the product of a very specific organization. It is that quality, in this whole, by virtue of which, through propositions, there is rational inquiry and communication, or, if defined, as to its nature, in terms of its "doing," it is that quality, in this whole, which is *identical with* rational inquiry and communication.

But wholes, as organized, and as "manifesting" new properties, are, as we have seen, *free*,—freedom always being, on the one hand, a "freedom from" something, and, on the other hand, a self-determination and self-regulation. And, from the evolutionary point of view, we have seen that there is "more and more" freedom, in that, with each successive level, there is more and more from which to be free. *Mind, then, I define as identical in part with the highest degree of freedom*, which means that it is identical with rational inquiry, for rational inquiry may be directed to anything, even itself. It knows no external limitations whatsoever, it is free from all external limitations, and so is completely self-regulative and autonomous. That is, it subscribes to no dictation, conforms to no laws, other than itself.

Now, what does this mean? It means negatively, that Mind or Rational Inquiry does not conform to Custom, Tradition, Authority, Habit, Fear, Love, or Expediency; positively, that it is, or that it practices, the method of thinking logically, of formulating logic, of criticizing logic, of postulating and assuming, of entertaining alternative possibilities (concerning anything), and of examining this method. It is Freedom itself, in these respects.

Rational inquiry leads to results on rational grounds only. It leads to the result, concerning any "situation," that "such and such" *is the case,* such and such the fact or "state of affairs," *because* something else is the case or the fact.[4] This means that "such and such" is *disclosed* to be the case, the fact, or the "state of affairs" as the result of rational inquiry.

Now, just what is this *disclosure?* I am willing to call it Knowledge, but only on certain conditions. These conditions are, that it is not identified with consciousness,[5] with a psychical process, or with a substantival mind. Disclosure is none of these. *They* are only hypothetical entities (and such entities have some status, I grant) that have been advanced, in the development of philosophy, in order to have a "something,"—*an end-term—to which there is the disclosure.* But these entities are not necessary. For, whether they *are,* or *are not,* there *is* the Disclosure. This is the prior fact. All that can be established empirically (in the broad sense of this term), is that *something is disclosed.* "It is disclosed that 'such and such' is the fact or the case," is all that one can say on purely empirical grounds.

Of course this means that Disclosure is disclosed. It is disclosed that Disclosure both accompanies and results from Rational Inquiry; further, that Disclosure is not a

---

[4] In other words, because the one "state of affairs" is *implied* by the other. *Cf.* Chapter IV.

[5] The behaviorist can deny consciousness, but not disclosure. If it were found that there is no consciousness, it would be *this fact* that would be disclosed. *Vide* Chapter I.

spatial, a temporal, a physical, or a mental (psychological) entity. There is disclosure *about* these entities, but the disclosure itself is, in these instances, not the same kind of thing as that which is disclosed. Thus, *e.g.*, there is Disclosure about Logic and Mathematics and Values, but the Disclosure in each of these cases is not, respectively, logical, mathematical, or "valuational." Logic, Mathematics, and the study of Values, as rational modes of inquiry, result in Disclosure, but they are not the Disclosure that results.

If, now, it is necessary to "have" something *to which* it is disclosed that "such and such is the case," then I call this something Mind, without identifying this with Consciousness. But Mind is not, then, either the Disclosure, or *that which* is disclosed, nor is this last the Disclosure. There might be facts, "states of affairs," not disclosed. Indeed I should say that this is a fact that is itself disclosed. But, whether or not there could be Disclosure and yet no Mind, at least there could be no Disclosure were not something disclosed.[6]

The Social Realm may, then, be said to be a situation in which there are human beings who make rational inquiries into "all sorts of things" with the result that what is "the case," the "state of affairs" in any particular situation, is disclosed, then, possibly, to be communicated, by language, by one human being to another. Mind, then, is (1) that which *is* rational inquiry (by means of propositions), (2) that *to which* "something" is disclosed, and (3) that which *communicates* and is *communicated to*,—again by means of propositions.[7]

[6] *Cf.* my address given at the meeting of the American Philosophical Association, Dec. 1932, with the title, *Freedom, Necessity and Mind*, The Phil. Review, XLII, 2, pp. 156–201.
[7] *Vide* Chapter I.

The foregoing chapters of this book are the results of the effort, I am frank enough to say, to make *a rational inquiry* in a certain "field of investigation." The outcome of that inquiry, as it has proceeded from chapter to chapter, is, that a very definite "scheme of things," a very definite structure "to the universe" has been disclosed, and it is this structure, this complex "state of affairs," that I have endeavored to communicate to other minds by the propositions which the statements in this book formulate.

It would be superfluous again to state in any detail, that structure. Suffice it to say, that it is a structure which is essentially *hierarchical* in character in that, through *a series* of instances of properties that are in turn instances of properties "still further back," we are finally led to the properties, Functionality (or "Propertiness"), Ultimacy, Possibility, Contingency, and Reality.[8] Properties are specific possibilities-of-instances, but they are independent of the realization of these instances. *Actual* instances are, however, found in a great many cases, but in no case are they necessitated, neither are they impossible, so that in all cases they are *contingent*. *Contingency, then, runs all through the structure of things*, not only "down" to Nature, but also "within" Nature itself, as we have seen in examining the Evolutionary Process. Indeed, even this character of the whole, *i.e.*, its contingency, is itself contingent, for all that one can say of it is that *it is*, but that it need not be, and that it certainly is not impossible.

The structure of things, as found empirically, contains both Values and the Valueless. Value is instanced by Goodness, Beauty, and "the Aesthetic," and each of these is in turn instanced, although it is impossible to find with cer-

[8] *Vide* Chapter III, the latter part.

tainty *what* the instances are. But, again, there is no necessity for there being either Value *or* its instances. Again, all that one can say is, "There is Value, and that is the end of it." But some things, most things, perhaps, are not instances of Value at all. They have "nothing to do" either with Goodness or with Evil, with Beauty or with Ugliness, or with Aesthetic Value. All *such* things have in common the property of *Valuelessness*.

Structure, or organization, is, as has been seen, "given" by relations and their terms. Relations themselves may be related, *i.e.*, they may be the *terms* "for" other relations. For example, "father of" and "ancestor of" are two relations that are *similar* in respect to *asymmetry*. Thus we may have a *structure of relations*,—a complex structure, to a greater or less extent. Such differences of structure are always discontinuous, *i.e.*, complexity of structure varies, not continuously, but *discontinuously*.

Bare structure,—structure as such—is identical with a complex of relations only, *i.e.*, with a complex in which the only terms are *relations themselves*. Bare structure, in this sense, is independent of particular *"non-relation" terms*. This is exemplified in Physics, Chemistry, Biology, and in the Social Sciences. The relations are the invariants, the terms are the variables. One term may be substituted for another in the same "relation-structure." This substitution occurs, *e.g.*, when a new Pope or a new President takes office,—to take an illustration outside of Science.

The specific structure of things of which this volume is a defense is, in the large, a structure (1), of the relation of instances to property, (2), of the relation of instances to one another by virtue of being instances of the same property, *i.e.*, of some specific similarity, (3), of the fact, if not the relation of, *difference* between instances. In each of these cases there is the fact of the *co-reality of relatedness and independence*. For, first, a property is independent of its instances, *i.e.*, of its realization by (actual) instances. For example, Necessity is independent of necessities.[9] Secondly, any instance of a property is independent of other instances; *i.e.*, if there is one instance, there need not be two; if there are two, three are not necessary, etc. Any number of other instances of the *co-reality of relatedness and independence* have been found in this volume, and this co-reality is also exemplified, as is well known, in postulational technique.[10]

Accordingly, the proposition cannot be accepted as universally true, that *relatedness "carries with it," i.e., necessitates or implies, the dependence, in some sense, of related terms*. Rather, conversely, the proposition, that there are both relatedness *and* independence in *some* cases, is true, in the sense that *actual* instances of this *co-reality* are found.

There is, however, nothing necessary about this "state of affairs." It is simply the fact that there *are* some instances of terms that are related and yet independent. The alternative proposition, then, that the relatedness of two or more terms carries with it the mutual dependence of these terms in *all* cases, is, perhaps, a perfectly good possibility which not only may be, but is, "entertained." As a possibility that is "entertained," however, this proposition is not identical with the words that formulate it, but is distinct from these; it is an objective possibility that is disclosed, and that may be true or false.

To "select" this proposition, by way of assuming it, and

9 *Vide* Chapter IV.
10 *Cf.*, *e.g.*, Lewis and Langford, *opus cit.*, Chaps. XI and XII.

then to "put it together" with certain other propositions, gives results which constitute *a radically different structure* from that which, in this book, is held to be the real structure of things. It is *a possible structure*. As a possible structure it is one in which, by virtue of the assumption that all related terms are mutually dependent, (1) any related term is what it is by virtue of what all other terms "make" it, (2) all related terms are infinitely complex, (3) all differences of terms disappear, etc.[11] It is not requisite to my purpose to develop this alternative possibility as to structure in further detail. Its outcome is what is called the "organic," or by some, the "coherence" view of the universe.[12]

The position has, however, one difficulty which should be indicated. Its major postulate is, not a group of words, not a set of ideas or conscious processes, but a specific objective "state of affairs," *i.e.*, it is *a proposition, in intension*, that is disclosed as a *possibility*. If, now, it is asserted, as a proposition, that "where" there is disclosure, there is, or *must* be, not only *what is disclosed, but something to which there is the disclosure*, then there is, first, "the situation" of *two related terms*,—the "what" and the "something"; so that, by assumption,[13] *the "what" as disclosed is different from what it would be if it were not disclosed*. The outcome is, that nothing can be disclosed *as it really is*, but only as modified by, or, at least, dependent on, being disclosed.

[11] In *The New Rationalism*, in various places, I have given a much fuller account and criticism of this position. See especially Chaps. XXVI–XXVII and XXXV–XXXVIII.

[12] Royce, in *The World and the Individual*, Joachim, in *The Nature of Truth*, and Bosanquet, in *The Principle of Individuality and Value*, are typical examples of philosophers who accept this theory of relations.

[13] *I.e.*, the assumption (of the position under examination) that any two related terms modify, and are naturally dependent on, one another, so that each term is what it is (but *was* not) by virtue of the other.

Accordingly, not even the major postulate of the position itself, can, consistently with this outcome, be an *objective possibility. The position becomes self-refuting.*[14]

The only way to avoid this is to grant either (1) that, in Disclosure, there is that which is disclosed *and* the disclosure, *but no "something" to which* there is the disclosure, *or* (2) that a "state of affairs" can be disclosed to—*a mind,* so that there are *two terms in a very specific relation, and yet that these two terms are, though related, nevertheless independent.*[15] *The very condition* of being able to "hold" the position *alternative* to this, namely, the "organic" position just previously discussed, *limits* this "organic position," *i.e.,* this organic position can be "held" or postulated, as a proposition or a group of propositions, only on the basis of the tacit presupposition of a proposition which contradicts this organic position. This means that not everything can be *organically related.* This possibility *cannot* be *a universal* aspect of structure. *Some* structures only can be organic, but not all, and even those that are need not be organically related to one another.

There is another type of possible structure of the whole—and the whole includes, of course, Nature, values, and the entire realm of possibilities—that should be at least briefly considered, because of its historical importance, if for no other reason. For it is that possibility which has been maintained, even to the extent of dogmatic assertion, in what is called the Great Tradition,[16] to be *that possibility which alone is realized, i.e.,* which alone is true. This tradition

---

[14] As shown in various places in *The New Rationalism.* See note 10, this chapter.

[15] This is the theory of External Relations. For a discussion of this, see, *e.g., The New Rationalism,* Chaps. XXVI and XL.

[16] Urban, W. M., *The Intelligible World,* especially Chs. I, III, and V.

"runs," as is well known, from Xenophanes and Permenides, through Plato and Augustine, Spinoza and Hegel, to Bradley, Bosanquet, Royce, and Croce. It is The Great Idealistic Tradition. According to this great, traditional position, the whole—everything—"heads up" into an Absolute One. There are, accordingly, such contrasts as, the One and the Many, Reality and Appearance, "The Eternal and the Practical," the Unchanging and the Changing, The Spiritual Realm and Nature. The One is real, the Many, not-real, or, at least, less real, or even illusory; the One is Eternal, Unchanging, the highest spiritual reality—even, for some, God.

The basic structure of such a universe is the relational one that rests, ultimately, I think, in every one of its variations, on the rather complex possibility, (1) that all instances of related terms are instances of terms in which each term *is what it is, so that others are not it, i.e.,* xRy, whatever R is, is a case of $x \, R \, non\text{-}x$. This is simply to "formulate" any two related terms as *formal contradictories;* (2) but, *non-x* is *everything else* than x, so that x and *non-x* are *all-inclusive.*[17] *Non-x* must accordingly be resolved into, (a) those *non-x*'s that could co-subsist with x (*e.g.*, a series may be "at once" both *continuous* and *limited*), and into (b) those *non-x*'s that cannot co-subsist with x (*e.g.*, continuity and discontinuity cannot characterize the same series—say, the Evolutionary Series). The first kind of contradictory terms are not "significant";[18] *e.g.*, "continuity" and "limit" do not have an immediately common factor; they may be "*co-real*" in the same locus,—*e.g.*, in a series.[19] Not so, however, with the second kind of contradictory terms.

[17] Or, *seem* to be, since really, by the argument that follows, they are not.
[18] See Chapters II and III.
[19] See Chapter VI.

These *are* "significant" contradictories; they have a common factor—*series*; they cannot be co-real in the same *locus*, but only in different *loci*,—*e.g.*, *Time* may be continuous, *Matter*, discontinuous (*vide* Atomicity). Significant contradictories *exclude or force one another into different loci*—spatial, temporal, logical, etc.,—and they have a *common factor*.

This common factor "gives" *the unity* that is sought, but this is a very evasive unity; for the common factor is itself a positive something, an *x*, of a "higher" order, with, in turn, a significant contradictory, so that there must be a still higher unity. Thus *a series of ever-higher unities for immediately lower multiplicies* (x R non-x's) is "generated," "until," finally, a Highest of the High (so the argument goes) is reached. This Highest is the One, Unchanging, Spiritual Reality,[20] "incorporating" in Itself all contradictories, downward, step by step, until there is reached "at the bottom," Nature, Matter, Life, Consciousness, Society, Evil, and Sin. These have their being in the Highest, yet they are below it; It expresses itself in them, but forever remains above.

This is the argument in brief.[21] However, I am not willing to admit that it really presents even a genuine possibility, for, "by its own premises" *there can be no Highest, no last member of the Series*. This "Highest" is obtained, not by logic, but by an irrational jump, that is motivated, not by logic, but by emotive thinking. Nevertheless this is what The Great Tradition regards as *The Structure of Reality*,— regards not only as a possibility, but as an actuality. I question both. There is no such Unity of the Whole as has

[20] It is also called Self, Experience, and Purpose.
[21] For a fuller statement, see *The New Rationalism*, Chap. XXXV.

been sought in The Great Tradition; rather, emotionally disappointing though this may be, *the only unity* which can be found for the whole, that is not illogical, is the Unity of a Totality.[22] Such a unity is not higher than anything else, nor is it lower; neither is it better, nor is it worse. It is merely what it is, *the total.* All else is within it, not as a member of a class, nor as an element in a series, nor as dependent on everything else, etc., etc., but simply as "a member" of a Totality. Even the Totality itself is "within itself" in some sense, such as, *e.g., being identical with itself*, else there would be an infinite regress of "totals." For, if everything is *a totality*, and this totality is not one of the "everythings," then we have *the total* of everything *and* the totality, and so on, so that there is no total. Even as with the ultimate properties, Propertiness, Possibility, Contingency, etc., "the regress is not a regress," because each of these is both an instance of itself, and also of the others, so here, the Final Totality must include itself as well as everything else. And there is no reason why it should not do this.[23] Such a whole is a *non-rational* whole: within it one *cannot* proceed from *any part to any other* by discovering implications (strict), either immediate or mediate, for such "universal" implications are not present. It is not a whole that is writ through and through with necessity (either logical or causal), but, rather, one in which there are *contingencies* here and there—parts not impossible—for they *are*, but yet not necessitated by anything else, since their alternative, in each case, is not impossible. Paradoxical as it may seem, such a non-rational universe is the most rational of all wholes, in the sense that it is the

[22] The parts of a totality need be "connected" by no stronger a "link" than "*and*."

[23] See Chapters II and III for the discussion of the Theory of Types.

most logical of—I am daring enough to say—all possible universes.[24]

Psychologically, at least, if not logically, there are still other possibilities, as the History of Philosophy shows, but it is not my purpose to discuss these in detail, for it is very doubtful if any of these can be "worked out" consistently as "accounts" of "universe-structure," *i.e.*, of that structure which will in some way include everything.

One of these possibilities goes by the name of Materialism, a philosophy that, as is well known, was first advanced by Leucippius and Democritus (460–370 B.C.), and that has appeared now and then in modified form, as science has advanced. According to this position, the structure of the universe is identical with "lines" or relations of particular causes and effects between material or physical entities, or with "functional" relations between physical variables. This means that everything conforms also to the structure of Space and of Time. Modern, extreme Behavioristic Psychology is a "branch" of this Materialism. For this Materialistic Psychology (which is really, in the last analysis, not even Physiology) there is, strictly speaking, no such thing as *rational inquiry*, or really *logical thinking*, for these "activities" are, for the behaviorist, as we have seen in Chapter I, only, sub-vocal (muscular) habits.

[24] This would seem to "mean" that *a completely rational universe is self-contradictory*, and therefore non-rational, and this proves to be the case. For a *completely rational universe*, as based on rational or logical "grounds," would be a universe in which these grounds would in turn have to be based on logical grounds, and so on, *ad infinitum*, so that, since this series is never complete, the universe is *not* completely rational. Conversely, then, if we do not look for the logical grounds *of* logical grounds, but simply accept these last as facts,—ungrounded,—non-rational,—then the contradiction above developed as to a completely rational universe is avoided, and we have the paradox that *a non-rational universe is the most rational of all universes.* "Most rational," however, is not the equivalent of "completely rational."

Another scheme of structure is Naturalism, which, as it were, softens the hardness of Materialism by granting that the "terms" which "hang on" the relational structure are all *natural*, or parts of Nature, and then *Nature* is so loosely interpreted as to comprise the physical, the living, the psychological, and the social, with these terms not sharply defined.[25] But the structure of Naturalism is, in most cases at least, the same as that of Materialism. It is a structure of "lines of cause and effect," of functional relations between variables in a "matrix" or setting of Space and Time. The so-called inorganic world, the evolutionary series, the physiological phenomena of living organisms, and psychological and social processes, all conform to, are parts of or are within, this universal structure. Such a philosophy can give no satisfactory account, I would maintain, any more than can Materialism, of *rational inquiry* and *logical thinking*, of the status of the very scientific laws to which the entities of such a "world" are held to conform, or of the situation ("the knowing situation") in which such a "state of affairs" is known or disclosed.

There are, doubtless many other "types" of structure that are at least psychologically conceivable, *e.g.*, there is the structure of "God and the World," that of "the entities of a Neutral Monism" organized in various ways, and that of Kant's "four-leaf clover" world of noumenal self and phenomenal self, and of noumenal world and phenomenal world, but into the examination of these alternative possibilities I do not wish to go.[26] Psychologically, and, doubtless, also logically conceivable though these various possible

[25] This is the position, *e.g.*, of Dewey and of Edman; *vide*, *e.g.*, Dewey, *The Quest for Certainty* and *Human Nature and Conduct*.
[26] A detailed examination and criticism of these "Structures" is given in *The New Rationalism* in various places.

structures may be up to a certain point, they nevertheless fall short, at one or more points, of being *consistent accounts of the whole*.

But even with this criticism granted, the fact (historically, and, within limits, logically) of these many accounts of structure is brute evidence of the *freedom of rational inquiry* by way of "making" various sets of postulates (*i.e.*, of selecting various sets of propositions under certain conditions), in order to discover their implications. These many possible "structures" are disclosed to mind, as mind "enjoys" its freedom by envisaging, for any one specific possibility of structure, *an alternative possibility*.

My own position as presented in this book is an account of structure to which other accounts are the alternatives. There *may be* more than one quite consistent account of the structure of the whole—the totality of all things including both the *totality itself, and the accounts of the totality*,—but I think there are not. Accordingly, I venture to maintain, that that structure of which this book is an attempt to give an account, is, at least as regards its main "features," *the only type of structure of the whole that is thoroughly consistent*. This means that only that type of structure is consistent which is *pluralistic* in the sense that the Universe is not One in that there is One Substance, or One Process (*e.g.*, Evolution), or One Experience, or One Relation, or One Property, but, rather, that there are many different properties, processes, and relations, and also entities that are not processes, but something else, not relations, but something else, and not properties, but something else. There are, also, Nature, and that which is not Nature, values and that which is not-value.

The "best candidates" for occupying the high office of

being *the One of the Universe* are Possibility, Contingency, "Propertiness," and even Ultimacy, and Reality. But it has been found that these five properties are not *reducible* to one another, although each is an instance of itself, as well as of the other four.[27] The basic structure of the Universe is, then, Pluralistic and not Monistic. The only Oneness of the Universe is its Totality.

The account of the Pluralistic Universe which I have given has, perforce, been in the form of propositions which are symbolized by the words that are now printed in this book. Those propositions are either true or false. I maintain, of course, that they are true for the reasons which were presented especially in Chapter V. As I have written, these propositions have been disclosed to a mind (mine) as have also those facts which make them true. My purpose in writing is to communicate with other minds (Chapter I), yet I have, and know of, no guarantee that I shall have succeeded. But, in so far as I shall have, it will be because *to other minds there will be disclosed the same propositions or meanings that have been disclosed to (my) mind.* These propositions together are, as meanings, identical with, or form an account of, a World of Chance. They are propositions that are "made" true or false, not by Conviction, or Belief, but only by facts that are external to the propositions themselves. And that the facts are such that we must accept the World as one of Chance is the main contention of this book.

[27] Chapter III.

INDEX OF AUTHORS

INDEX OF SUBJECTS

291